CIVIC GARDEN CENTRE LIBRARY
3000977

D1238030

THE *ILLUSTRATED* BOOK OF GARDEN PESTS AND DISEASES

EDITED BY T. H. Everett

Assistant Director (Horticulture) and Curator of Education
The New York Botanical Garden

GREYSTONE PRESS • HAWTHORN BOOKS, INC.

NEW YORK

177

All inquiries should be addressed to Hawthorn Books, Inc., 70 Fifth Avenue, New York 11, N.Y. This book was manufactured in the United States of America and published simultaneously in Canada by McClelland & Stewart, Ltd., 25 Hollinger Road, Toronto 16. Library of Congress Catalogue Card No. 62-15097. Suggested Decimal Classification: 632.

First Edition, September, 1962

EDITOR'S ACKNOWLEDGMENT

The editor wishes to acknowledge a debt of gratitude to the following persons:
Mr. Frederick Drimmer, M.A., for his editorial counsel on the selection of material and preparation of the manuscript; Dr. Caroline K. Allen for her careful reading and correction of the text to assure its botanical accuracy; to Mrs. Lillian Weber for the great task she accomplished as assistant to the editor in keeping all the many details of a complex production in order; to Mr. Howard S. Swift for assistance in locating photographs; to Miss Nancy Callaghan for so carefully typing much of the manuscript; to Miss Elizabeth C. Hall, Librarian of The New York Botanical Garden, for much patient assistance and library research; to Dr. H. W. Rickett, Bibliographer of The New York Botanical Garden, for his expert assistance on especially difficult botanical matters and to Miss Hannelore Leissner of The Greystone Press for her expert handling of the many details connected with the organization of the text and illustrations in readiness for the printer.

PICTURE CREDITS

Air-Wrap Company; American Cyanamid Company; J. F. Anderson; Armstrong Nurseries; Associated Bulb Growers of Holland; George J. Ball, Inc.; Bartlett Tree Research Laboratories; John Black and Associates; Bobbink and Atkins; Buntings' Nurseries Inc.; W. Atlee Burpee Company; D. V. Burrell Seed Growers Company; California Agricultural Experiment Station; Carbide and Carbon Chemicals Company; Cornell University; English Encyclopedia; T. H. Everett; Ferry-Morse Seed Company; Germain's, Inc.; Fred C. Gloeckner and Company; Gravely Tractors, Inc.; Joseph Harris Company, Inc.; Henderson's Seedsmen; A. C. Hornberger; Huntington Botanical Gardens; Johnson Cactus Gardens; Irving Kaufman Studio; Jackson & Perkins Company; Lawn Grass Development Company; Lord and Burnham Company; Ernest E. Martin, Logee Greenhouses; Monsanto Chemical Company; The Morris Arboretum; The Morton Arboretum; New York State Agricultural Experiment Station; The New York Botanical Garden; New York Zoological Society; Oregon State College; Panogen Company; P. P. Pirone; Plasti-Plant Hood Company; Premier Peat Moss Corp.; Roses and Home Flower Arranging; Max Schling; O. M. Scott & Sons Co.; Shaw Color Studio; Shell Chemical Corporation; The Siebenthaler Company; Stark Bros. Nurseries; State College of Washington; Sutton & Sons; Swift & Company; Texas Lawn Sprinkler Company, Inc.; United States Department of Agriculture; University of Minnesota; U. S. National Arboretum; University of California, Agricultural Experiment Station; M. Van Waveren & Sons, Inc.; Whitney Seed Co., Inc.; Roy F. Wilcox & Co.; New Jersey State Experimental Station.

COLOR PHOTOGRAPHS INDEX AND CREDITS

1. Bean Aphids (Trojan Labs.)
2. Aphids on Rose (Trojan Labs.)
3. Armyworm larva (Trojan Labs.)
4. Armyworm adult (Trojan Labs.)
5. Spotted Cucumber Beetle (Trojan Labs.)
6. White grubs (Trojan Labs.)
7. Harlequin Bug (Trojan Labs.)
8. Cabbage Looper (Trojan Labs.)
9. Omnivorous Looper (Trojan Labs.)
10. Omnivorous Looper adult (Trojan Labs.)
11. Corn Earworm (Trojan Labs.)
12. Tomato Hornworm (Trojan Labs.)

Illustrations 1–12 *appear between pages* 32 and 33.

13. Eastern Tent Caterpillar (Everett)
14. Imported Currantworm (Everett)
15. Earwig (Trojan Labs.)
16. Leaf Hoppers (Trojan Labs.)
17. Leaf Miners (Everett)
18. Seed-Corn Maggot (Trojan Labs.)
19. Root-feeding Mealybugs (Trojan Labs.)
20. Long-tailed Mealybugs (Trojan Labs.)
21. Millipede (Trojan Labs.)
22. Bulb Mites (Trojan Labs.)
23. Spider Mites (Trojan Labs.)
24. Mite-damaged Spruce (Trojan Labs.)

Illustrations 13–24 *appear between pages* 48 *and* 49.

25. Root-Knot Nematodes (Trojan Labs.)
26. Bristly Rose Slug (Trojan Labs.)
27. Black Scale (Trojan Labs.)
28. Hemisphaerical Scale (Trojan Labs.)
29. Snail (Trojan Labs.)
30. Slug (Trojan Labs.)
31. Sowbugs (Trojan Labs.)
32. Springtails (Trojan Labs.)
33. Thrips (Trojan Labs.)
34. Whitefly (Trojan Labs.)
35. Botrytis (Everett)
36. Stem Rot of Geranium (Everett)

Illustrations 25–36 *appear between pages* 64 *and* 65.

37. Anthracnose (Everett)
38. Cedar-Apple Rust (Everett)
39. Leaf Spot (Everett)
40. Mildew (Everett)
41. Pachysandra Stem Rot (Everett)
42. Lawn Grass Blight (Everett)
43. Bacterial Wilt (Everett)
44. Aster Yellows (Everett)

Illustrations 37–44 *appear between pages* 96 *and* 97.

45. Winter Injury (Everett)
46. Leaf Scorch (Everett)
47. Chlorosis (Everett)
48. Gas Injury (Everett)

49. Japanese Beetle (Everett)
50. European Pine Shoot Moth (Everett)
51. Mexican Bean Beetle (Everett)
52. Leaf Galls (Everett)

Illustrations 45–52 *appear between pages* 112 *and* 113.

53. Caterpillars (Everett)
54. Wasps (Everett)
55. Mites (Everett)
56. Cooley Spruce Gall Aphid (Everett)
57. Lacebugs (Everett)
58. Black Vine Weevil (Everett)
59. Club Root Disease (Everett)
60. Club Root Disease (Everett)

Illustrations 53–60 *appear between pages* 128 *and* 129.

TABLE OF CONTENTS

How To Combat These Destructive Enemies 6
Principal Plants—Their Pests and Diseases 11
Insects and Other Small Pests 43
Larger Pests—Mammals 95
Bacterial and Fungus Diseases 100
Virus Diseases 139
Physiological Diseases 146
Insecticides and Miticides 153
Fungicides 157

PESTS AND DISEASES

How to Combat These Destructive Enemies

It is not enough for the gardener to know the best ways to grow plants. He needs just as much to have a thorough knowledge of how to keep them in good, vigorous health. Plants are subject to many pests and diseases. If you can diagnose these afflictions and take timely steps to correct them, you will keep damage to your garden at a minimum. It is the purpose of this section not only to acquaint you with the everyday pests and diseases that may bother your plants, but also to arm you with an up-to-date knowledge of the most effective methods of preventing these troubles as well as of dealing with them when they occur.

How to Use This Section. First read the paragraphs that follow, starting with the one headed What Plant Pests and Diseases Are, through the one headed Soil Sterilization. These present basic facts every gardener should know.

If a plant is affected by disease or pest, or is suspected of being so affected, and you do not recognize the cause of the trouble, consult Principal Plants—Their Pests and Diseases (page 11), for suggestions of likely enemies. If you recognize or suspect the disease or pest or the general category to which it belongs, turn to the appropriate subsection under one of the following headings: Insects and Other Small Pests (page 43), Larger Pests—Mammals (page 95), Bacterial and Fungus Diseases (page 100), Virus Diseases (page 139), Physiological Diseases (page 146). In the appropriate subsection, in alphabetical sequence, under such headings as Ants, Caterpillars, Beetles, Rots, Mildews, Leaf Spots, etc., the principal pests and diseases that affect garden plants are described and the best available control measures given.

Materials such as sprays, dusts, etc., which are used to control pests, are listed under Insecticides and Miticides (page 153); those used to control diseases, under Fungicides (page 157).

What Plant Pests and Diseases Are. Plant pests are creatures that belong to the animal world and harm cultivated crops and other desirable plants. They include many insects and other small creatures, as well as larger animals such as rabbits, chipmunks and woodchucks.

Plant diseases, as the term is usually employed, are of greatly varied origins. They may be caused by living organisms belonging to the plant world, such as fungi and bacteria, by viruses, by the absence or unavailability of a particular element in the soil such as iron, magnesium or potash, by the presence of any substance in sufficient amounts to be harmful, and by unsatisfactory environmental conditions.

In a broader sense, a disease is any interference with the normal development of a plant that is caused by continued irritation. Such irritation may result from the activities of living organisms or unfavorable environmental conditions. In this broad sense the term disease includes the effects of insects and other animal pests but, as commonly used, it excludes these. In this section, organisms belonging to the animal world are treated as pests, and diseased conditions due to other causes are treated as diseases.

Some pests and some diseases are highly selective in the plants (hosts) they attack. In certain cases a particular pest or disease will affect only one kind of host plant. Many other plant pests and diseases attack a wide variety of hosts. In some instances, as for example the Cedar-Apple rust and the Blue Spruce gall aphid, the organism causing the trouble lives on one host at one period of its existence and on another at another stage of its growth or another time of the year.

Prevention Is Better Than Cure. The control of pests and diseases is a matter of great importance, and many methods are employed to reduce damage to a minimum. Whenever practicable, prevention is better than cure.

Good cultural practices play an important part in reducing the amount of damage done by pests and diseases. These practices include attention to soil drainage, fertilization, sanitation, selection of suitable sowing and planting dates, and protection from injury by excessive cold, heat, wetness and dryness. They also include the provision of adequate spacing to permit access of light and free circulation of air, the elimination of weeds, and careful pruning.

The selection of kinds of plants adapted to local conditions and environments and of varieties resistant or immune to particular diseases and pests is important in lessening the likelihood of trouble.

Control Measures Are Needed. Although good cultural practices and careful selection of the kinds of plants grown reduce the likelihood of harm, they will not eliminate it. Every gardener must expect to take more direct control measures. These include dusting, spraying, fumigating, disinfecting, sterilizing, baiting and installing vermin-proof guards. In a few cases the complete destruction of all affected plants is necessary, there being no known cures for some pests and diseases; affected specimens are likely to act as sources of infection to healthy individuals.

Diagnosis Is Important. As with human ills, it is important to recognize the cause of the trouble before attempting a cure. This is not always easy, even for experienced gardeners; beginners are still more likely to have difficulty making correct diagnoses. Fortunately, help is readily available. If any doubt exists as to the cause or identification of an unhealthy condition, send adequate samples of the affected plant, together with as complete a description as possible of the conditions under which it grew and of the treatment it received, to a County Agricultural Agent, State Agricultural Experiment Station, botanical garden or other authoritative source of information and request a diagnosis and recommendations for treatment.

Applying rotenone dust to control Mexican Bean beetles.

Gardeners should learn to recognize many of the commoner pests and at least some of the more prevalent diseases. By doing so, valuable time is saved in making diagnoses, and treatments can begin earlier.

Pest Problems. Pests, especially those big enough to be seen by the naked eye, are usually easier to identify than diseases. Such common pests as scale insects, aphids, mealybugs,

Modern power sprayers make it easy to cover stems and foliage with a fine mist of insecticide or fungicide.

Many insect pests, such as the scales on the stems and the aphids on the under-leaf surfaces of this Euonymus, can be easily seen with the naked eye.

inchworms, caterpillars, snails, slugs, Japanese beetles and ants, to cite but a few, are clearly visible. Certain of these, such as snails and slugs, as well as borers, cutworms, leaf miners and some others, work underground, inside plant tissues, or hide during the day and come out only at night. These may be overlooked by inexperienced and careless gardeners. It is important to scrutinize plants closely and to search assiduously for suspected enemies if harm occurs for which there is no apparent, logical cause.

Pests that are minute, such as red spider mites and other mites, chinch bugs and thrips, are less easy to detect, but an experienced observer can usually see these creatures with the naked eye. However, a good hand lens should be part of the equipment of every gardener. With such a lens it is much easier to see these small creatures and their identification is made more certain.

Some pests, such as nematodes, are microscopic and cannot easily be seen or identified even with a hand lens. As with diseases, the symptoms they cause are useful in identifying these pests; however, gardeners will often have to obtain accurate diagnoses by sending samples of the affected plants to a County Agent, State Agricultural Experiment Station or other reliable source of information.

Learning to Identify Diseases. In addition to recognizing common and prevalent pests, gardeners should learn to identify those diseases that are likely to cause trouble and are easy to distinguish. Here belong such afflictions as black spot of Roses, mildews, damping-off disease, botrytis blight and some others. Some diseases are widespread, others occur in limited areas only, or are seriously troublesome only in certain sections. An example of this last group is the Azalea flower blight, which affects Azaleas in moist, humid regions in the South.

It is important, therefore, for gardeners to pay particular attention to learning to recognize those pests and diseases most likely to occur in their own localities and to be ever on the alert for symptoms of others that may appear.

Timeliness. Once a pest or disease is correctly identified, it is possible to take intelligent action against it. Usually the sooner that control measures are taken the better, but in some cases it is necessary to wait for a particular time of the year or a particular stage of the enemy's development before taking action. In any case, timeliness is important. Neglecting opportunities to eradicate or reduce pests and diseases is poor gardening.

Inexperienced and inefficient gardeners often permit pests and diseases to become too well established before doing anything to control them. They are likely to wait until the leaves of their Elm trees have been reduced to lacelike skeletons by the Elm leaf beetle; until Rose leaves are spotted and yellowed, and are dropping as a result of infection with black spot disease; until the foliage of Viburnums is curled and distorted by the sucking of aphids, and until the white, felty or powdery growth of mildew fungus covers the foliage of Phlox, Lilacs and Roses. In such cases, killing the pest or disease will not restore the foliage to a healthy condition. Irreparable harm has been done. Insecticides and fungicides can only prevent further damage, they cannot repair that already done.

Control Measures. The science and practice of plant pest and disease control are not static, nor have perfect or even adequate methods been discovered for controlling all afflictions. A tremendous amount of research has been and is being done in this field, and each year new methods and new materials are developed for

Small plants in pots can be effectively treated by dipping them in a suitable insecticide or fungicide.

When the number of plants to be dealt with is small, scale insects can be removed from stems by rubbing them with an old toothbrush dipped in diluted insecticide.

preventing, tempering and eliminating the danger of damage by pests and diseases. This does not mean that all old methods and old materials are superseded or are not effective in a great many instances, but it does emphasize that alert gardeners should do everything possible to keep abreast of the times. Much useful information can be gained by reading popularly written pamphlets and bulletins published by the Department of Agriculture of the Federal Government, the State Agricultural Experiment Stations, and the Science Service of the Department of Agriculture, Ottawa, Canada.

Insecticides, miticides and fungicides are most commonly applied as sprays and dusts and aerosols. Some are used as fumigants and disinfectants, a few as poison baits. Spraying is often preferred to dusting because it is likely to be more effective, because it does not cover the operator to the same extent or as unpleasantly, and because, in many cases, a less conspicuous deposit is left on foliage and flowers. Aerosol applications, either from bombs or mechanical mist blowers, are very convenient and effective, but with them it is often more difficult to reach all parts of a tree or other plant than with a regular-type sprayer.

When only a few pot plants need attention, as is often true with house plants, the old method known as dipping is effective. All you do is fill a pail with diluted insecticide and then carefully and individually invert each plant and lower its stems and foliage into the pail so that all parts are wetted by the solution. Another effective hand method of removing scale insects, mealybugs and similar pests is to rub the affected parts with a soft toothbrush which has been dipped in diluted insecticide and then rinse the plant with plain water.

Equipment. Whichever means of applying dusts or sprays is used, the equipment should be of good quality. Cheap, poorly constructed dusters and sprayers waste materials and make it all but impossible to give an even coating of spray

Small hand sprayers are useful and effective where the number of plants to be treated is not large.

Ready-to-use dust guns, filled with insecticide-fungicide combination dusts, are sold by dealers in garden supplies. For effective results it is important that both sides of the leaves be covered with a fine, even coating of the dust.

or dust, yet thoroughness and evenness of coverage are essential for good results.

Spray equipment should be thoroughly cleaned after each using; with dusters this is not essential, but it is advisable to use up each charge of dust within a reasonable time—not, for example, to start dusting in spring with material that has been in the duster since the previous year. It is of great importance not to use equipment for insecticides and fungicides that has previously been employed for applying weed killers such as 2,4-D.

Mixing Chemicals. When preparing insecticides, miticides and fungicides, great care must be taken to use precisely measured amounts of the various chemicals. If you do otherwise, you court disaster. If too dilute sprays are used they are likely to be ineffective; if the sprays are not dilute enough the plants may be seriously harmed. Care must be exercised not to mix chemicals that are incompatible, such as copper-containing preparations and lime-sulphur, or lime-sulphur and oil sprays.

Some preparations are harmful under certain circumstances and not under others. For instance, sulphur may burn foliage when temperatures are 80 degrees F. or higher; copper compounds are likely to do damage in spring and fall if the weather is decidedly cool or if very humid atmospheric conditions or light rain follows their application.

Plants that have soft, tender growth, such as those forced in greenhouses, may be injured by spray concentrations that would not harm the same kinds grown outdoors. See also Sprays in the main alphabetical sequence in this Encyclopedia.

Dormant and Delayed Dormant Sprays. Because deciduous (winter leaf-losing) trees and shrubs can withstand stronger (less dilute) concentrations of certain chemicals when they are leafless, and because the use of these stronger concentrations is necessary to control certain pests and diseases, it is the practice to apply them in late winter, before the leaf buds open, yet when the temperature is above 45 degrees F. In some cases a so-called delayed dormant spray application is made; this means a spray given in spring between the time the leaf buds in spring plump up and become silvery and the time the young leaves may be seen clearly sticking out of the ends of the buds "like tiny squirrel ears."

Soil Sterilization. Sterilization or partial sterilization of the soil by the use of chemicals or heat is an effective method of controlling many soil pests. See Soil Sterilization in the main alphabetical sequence in this Encyclopedia.

Spreaders and Wetters. Water, and water solutions, when sprayed on foliage and similar smooth surfaces, particularly if the surfaces are slightly waxy or oily, tend to form globules which run off; as a result, insecticidal and fungicidal sprays may be less effective. To overcome this difficulty, a spreader or wetter which lessens the surface tension of water is added to the spray solution. Soft soap is often used at ½ to 2 oz. per gallon, depending on the hardness of the water. But soft soap is not suitable for certain sprays such as lime-sulphur, Bordeaux mixture or those containing lead arsenate.

There are various other spreaders that are suitable, however, among which are calcium caseinate, glue, wheat-flour paste and resin preparations as well as a number of proprietary wetters and spreaders. Many ready-mixed brand-name sprays have a spreader included in them and therefore need no additives of these particular types.

PRINCIPAL PLANTS—THEIR PESTS AND DISEASES

The following is a list of garden plants most likely to be harmed by pests and diseases, and of the pests and diseases that do the harm. Certain very common pests, such as aphids, mealybugs, red spider mites and scale insects, as well as some prevalent diseases, such as leaf spots, mildews and root rots, may affect plants other than those included in this list.

In most instances, botanical or scientific names are used in this list. If you do not know the botanical name of the plant about which you need information, consult the entry under the plant's popular name in the main alphabetical sequence in this Encyclopedia.

Abies. *Pests:* aphids, bagworms, budworms, mites, sawflies, scales. *Diseases:* blights, cankers, needle blights, needle casts, rots, rusts.

Abutilon. *Pests:* caterpillars, Fuller Rose beetles, root-knot nematodes, red spider mites, whiteflies. *Diseases:* leaf spots, mosaic virus, rots, rust, verticillium wilt.

Acacia. *Pests:* caterpillars, Fuller Rose beetles, mealybugs, root-knot nematodes, scales. *Diseases:* canker, chlorosis, gummosis, leaf spots, rots.

Acalypha. *Pests:* mealybugs, root-knot nematodes. *Diseases:* leaf gall, leaf spots, downy and powdery mildews, rots.

Achillea. *Pests:* aphids, root-knot nematodes. *Diseases:* crown gall, powdery mildew, root and stem rot, rust.

Achimenes. *Pests:* mealybugs, mites, thrips. *Disease:* root rot.

Aconitum. *Pests:* four-lined plant bugs, leaf miners, mites, root-knot nematodes. *Diseases:* downy mildew, leaf spot, rots, rusts, smuts, verticillium wilt, mosaic virus.

Actaea. *Diseases:* leaf spots, rust, smut.

Actinidia. *Pests:* orthezias.

Aesculus. *Pests:* borers, caterpillars, Japanese beetles, mealybugs, scales. *Diseases:* blight, canker, leaf blotch, leaf scorch, leaf spot, powdery mildew, rot.

Agave. *Pests:* mealybugs, scales, thrips. *Diseases:*

Abutilon (Flowering Maple).

Albizzia Julibrissin.

anthracnose, blights, leaf spots.

Ageratum. *Pests:* caterpillars, red spider mites, whiteflies. *Diseases:* crown gall, rots, rust.

Aglaonema. *Pests:* mealybugs, nematodes, red spider mites, scales. *Diseases:* leaf spots, root rot.

Agrimonia. *Diseases:* leaf spots, downy and powdery mildews, root rot, rusts.

Ailanthus. *Pests:* borers, caterpillars, scales. *Diseases:* twig blight, cankers, leaf spots, rots, verticillium wilt.

Ajuga. *Disease:* crown rot.

Akebia. *Pests:* San Jose scale.

Albizzia. *Pests:* caterpillars, scales. *Diseases:* dieback canker, wilt.

Allamanda. *Pests:* mealybugs, red spider mites, scales, whiteflies. *Disease:* chlorosis caused by manganese deficiency.

Almond. *Pests:* aphid, beetles, borers, cater-

Aloe.

Althaea (Hollyhock).

pillars, leaf hoppers, mites, nematodes, scales, thrips. *Diseases:* anthracnose, blights, cankers, crown gall, leaf spot, little leaf, powdery mildew, rots, rust, scab, verticillium wilt, viruses.

Alnus. *Pests:* aphids, borers, caterpillars, flea beetles, scales. *Diseases:* cankers, leaf blisters, leaf spots, powdery mildews, rots.

Alocasia. *Pests:* mealybugs, red spider mites. *Disease:* root rot.

Aloe. *Pests:* mealybugs, scales. *Disease:* root rot.

Alonsoa. *Pests:* aphids, whiteflies. *Disease:* root rot.

Alpinia. *Pests:* mealybugs, red spider mites.

Alternanthera. *Pests:* aphids, mealybugs, nematodes, red spider mites. *Diseases:* root rots, wilt.

Althaea. *Pests:* aphids, borers, caterpillars, hollyhock weevils, Japanese beetles, mealybugs, mites, nematodes, red spider mites, slugs, thrips. *Diseases:* anthracnose, crown rots, hairy root, leaf spots, powdery mildews, root rot, rusts, wilt.

Alyssum. *Pests:* caterpillars, leaf hoppers. *Disease:* club root.

Amaranthus. *Pests:* harlequin bugs, root-knot nematodes, scales. *Diseases:* viruses, white rust.

Amaryllis. See Hippeastrum.

Amelanchier. *Pests:* aphids, borers, caterpillars, curculios, leaf miners, mites, sawflies, scales. *Diseases:* blights (including fire blight), cankers, powdery mildews, rots, rusts.

Amorpha. *Diseases:* leaf spot, powdery mildew, rust, twig canker.

Ampelopsis. *Pests:* aphids, black vine weevils, Japanese beetles, mites, scales. *Diseases:* cankers, downy and powdery mildews, leaf spots, root rot.

Amphicome. *Pests:* aphids, red spider mites. *Disease:* root rot.

Amsonia. *Diseases:* Leaf spot, rusts.

Anchusa. *Pests:* leaf hoppers. *Diseases:* mosaic virus, rust.

Anemone. *Pests:* aphids, blister beetles, cater-

Apple.

pillars, leaf nematodes, root-knot nematodes. *Diseases:* crown rot, collar rot, downy and powdery mildews, leaf spots, rusts, smuts, viruses.

Angelica. *Diseases:* leaf spots, rusts.

Anthurium. *Pests:* mealybugs, red spider mites, scales.

Antirrhinum. *Pests:* aphids, beetles, borers, budworms, bugs, caterpillars, nematodes, red spider mites, slugs. *Diseases:* anthracnose, blights, crown rot, downy and powdery mildews, leaf spot, rots, rust, verticillium wilt, viruses.

Aphelandra. *Pests:* aphids, mealybugs, red spider mites, whiteflies.

Apple. *Pests:* aphids, beetles, borers, bugs, caterpillars, leaf hoppers, maggots, mealybugs, mites, sawflies, scales. *Diseases:* anthracnose, bitter pit, blights (including fire blight), blotches, cankers, chlorosis, crown gall, fruit spots, hairy root, leaf spots, little leaf, powdery mildews, rots, rusts, scab, sooty mold, virus.

Apricot. *Pests:* aphids, beetles, borers, caterpillars, curculios, leaf hoppers, mites, sawflies, scales. *Diseases:* black knot, blights (including fire blight), cankers, crown gall, leaf curl, leaf spots, little leaf, powdery mildews, rots, rust, scab, viruses.

Aquilegia. *Pests:* aphids, beetles, borers, bugs, caterpillars, leaf miners, nematodes, whiteflies. *Diseases:* gray mold blight, leaf spots, rots, rust, smut, virus.

Arabis: *Pests:* aphids. *Diseases:* club root, downy mildew, gray mold blight, leaf spot, root rot, rusts, white rust.

Aralia. *Pests:* aphids, caterpillars, scales, thrips. *Diseases:* leaf spots, powdery mildew, rust, wilt.

Araucaria. *Pests:* mealybugs, scales. *Diseases:* blight, crown gall.

Arbutus. *Pests:* borers, caterpillars, scales, thrips, whiteflies. *Diseases:* anthracnose, canker, leaf gall, leaf spots, rust.

Arctostaphylos. *Pests:* aphids, scales, whiteflies. *Diseases:* anthracnose, canker, crown gall, leaf gall, leaf spots, rust.

Arctotis. *Pests:* aphids, leaf hoppers, root-knot nematodes. *Diseases:* leaf blotch, root rot.

Ardisia. *Pests:* red spider mites, scales. *Disease:* leaf spot.

Arenaria. *Diseases:* leaf spot, powdery mildew, root rot, rusts, smut.

Artemisia.

Argemone. *Diseases:* downy mildew, leaf spots, root rot, rust.

Arisaema. *Diseases:* blight, leaf spots, rust.

Aristolochia. *Pests:* caterpillars. *Diseases:* leaf spots, rot.

Armeria. *Disease:* rust.

Arnica. *Diseases:* leaf spots, powdery mildews, rusts.

Aronia. *Pests:* Borers. *Diseases:* fire blight, leaf spots, rot, rusts.

Artemisia. *Pests:* aphids, mealybugs, gall midges, scales. *Diseases:* downy and powdery mildews, leaf blight, leaf gall, leaf spot, rusts, white rust.

Artichoke, Globe. *Pests:* aphids, caterpillars, root-knot nematodes, slugs. *Diseases:* gray mold blight, crown rot, leaf spots, powdery mildew, rots, virus.

Artichoke, Jerusalem. *Pests:* root-knot nematodes. *Diseases:* crown rot, downy and powdery mildews, leaf spots, rots, rusts.

Asarum. *Diseases:* Leaf spots, rot, rust.

Asclepias. *Pests:* aphids, beetles, caterpillars, leaf miners, scales, thrips. *Diseases:* leaf spots, root rot, rusts, virus.

Asparagus (ornamental kinds). *Pests:* beetles, cutworm, flea hoppers, nematodes, red spider mites, scales, thrips. *Diseases:* cankers, crown gall, leaf mold, leaf spots, rots.

Asparagus (vegetable). *Pests:* aphids, beetles, bulb mites, caterpillars, flea hoppers, garden centipede, harlequin bug, leaf miners, nematodes. *Diseases:* anthracnose, blights, leaf spot, rots, rust.

Aspidistra. *Pests:* mealybugs, red spider mites, scales. *Diseases:* leaf blight, leaf spots.

Aster. *Pests:* aphids. *Diseases:* crown gall, downy mildew, gray mold blight, leaf gall, leaf spots, rots, rusts, viruses. wilt.

Aster, China. See Callistephus.

Astilbe. *Pests:* aphids, Japanese beetles, red spider mites. *Diseases:* powdery mildew, wilt.

Aucuba. *Pests:* aphids, scales. *Diseases:* anthracnose, leaf spots.

Azalea. *Pests:* beetles, black vine weevils, borers, caterpillars, lace bugs, leaf miners, mealybugs, mites, scales, thrips, whiteflies. *Diseases:* blights, leaf galls, leaf scorch, leaf spots, powdery mildews, root rot, rust.

Babiana. *Pests:* aphids, bulb mites, nematodes, red spider mites, thrips. *Diseases:* leaf spots, rots, virus.

Bamboos. *Pests:* aphids, scales. *Diseases:* leaf spot, rust, smut.

Banana. See Musa.

Banksia. *Pests:* scales.

Baptisia. *Diseases:* leaf spots, powdery mildews, rust.

Basil. *Pests:* root-knot nematodes.

Bauhinia. *Pests:* scales.

Lima Beans.

Beans. *Pests:* aphids, beetles, borers, bugs, caterpillars, cutworms, leaf hoppers, maggots, mealybugs, mites, root-knot nematodes, thrips, weevils, whiteflies. *Diseases:* anthracnose, blights, blotch, leaf spots, downy and powdery mildews, rots, rust, viruses, wilts.

Beaumontia. *Pests:* mealybugs, red spider mites, scales.

Beets. *Pests:* aphids, beetles, bugs, caterpillars, cutworms, leaf hoppers, leaf miners, maggots, nematodes, weevils, wireworms. *Diseases:*

Azalea.

Angel Wing Begonia.

blights, crown gall, crown rot, downy and powdery mildews, heart rot, leaf spots, rots, rusts, scab, viruses, white rust, wilt.

Begonia. *Pests:* aphids, black vine weevils, caterpillars, Fuller Rose beetles, leaf nematodes, mealybugs, mites, nematodes, scales, whiteflies. *Diseases:* gray mold blight, crown gall, leaf spots, oedema, powdery mildew, root and stem rots, virus, wilt.

Belamcanda. *Diseases:* leaf spots.

Bellis. *Pests:* root-knot nematodes. *Diseases:* gray mold blight, leaf spot, rots, virus.

Beloperone. *Pests:* mealybugs, red spider mites, whiteflies.

Berberis. *Pests:* aphids, beetles, caterpillars, mites, root-knot nematodes, scales, whiteflies. *Diseases:* anthracnose, leaf spot, powdery mildew, root rot, rusts, wilts.

Betula. *Pests:* aphids, beetles, borers, caterpillars, galls, leaf miners, scales, weevils. *Diseases:* cankers, dieback, leaf blister, leaf spots, powdery mildews, rots, rust, virus dieback.

Bignonia. *Pests:* aphids, mealybugs, red spider mites, root-knot nematodes, scales, whiteflies. *Diseases:* gray mold blight, leaf spot.

Blackberry. *Pests:* beetles, borers, caterpillars, galls, leaf hoppers, leaf miners, maggots, mealybugs, mites, sawflies, scales, weevils, whiteflies. *Diseases:* anthracnose, blights, blotches, cankers, crown galls, downy and powdery mildews, fruit spot, leaf spots, rots, rusts, viruses, wilt.

Blephilia. *Diseases:* leaf spots, rust.

Blueberry. See Vaccinium.

Boltonia. *Diseases:* leaf spot, powdery mildew, rust, smut.

Borago. *Diseases:* leaf spot.

Bougainvillea. *Pests:* aphids, red spider mites, scales. *Diseases:* leaf spot, virus.

Bouvardia. *Pests:* aphids, leaf nematodes, mealybugs, root-knot nematodes. *Disease:* rust.

Breynia. *Pests:* mealybugs, red spider mites, whiteflies.

Broccoli. Pests and diseases as for Cabbage, which see.

Buxus (Boxwood).

Brodiaea. *Diseases:* rusts.

Browallia. *Pests:* aphids (including root aphids), leaf hoppers, root-knot nematodes, whiteflies. *Disease:* wilt.

Brussels Sprouts. Pests and diseases as for Cabbage, which see.

Bryophyllum. *Pests:* aphids, scales, mealybugs. *Diseases:* crown gall, crown rot, powdery mildew.

Buddleia. *Pests:* beetles, caterpillars, root-knot nematodes, thrips. *Diseases:* canker, root rot.

Buxus. *Pests:* leaf miners, mealybugs, mites, root nematodes, psyllids, scales. *Diseases:* blights, cankers, leaf spots, rots, mosaic virus.

Cabbage, including Broccoli, Brussels Sprouts, Cauliflower, Kale, Kohlrabi. *Pests:* aphids, beetles, bugs, caterpillars, cutworms, flea beetles, maggots, root-knot nematodes, slugs, thrips. *Diseases:* anthracnose, blights, club root, downy and powdery mildews, leaf spots, molds, rots, viruses, white rust, wilt.

Cacti. *Pests:* aphids, mealybugs, orthezias, red spider mites, root-knot nematodes, scales. *Diseases:* anthracnose, crown gall, root and stem rots, scorch, stem spots.

Caesalpinia. *Pests:* mealybugs, red spider mites. *Disease:* cane blight.

Caladium. *Pests:* root-knot nematodes. *Diseases:* crown rot, leaf spot, rot.

Calathea. *Pests:* mealybugs, red spider mites. *Diseases:* leaf spots.

Calceolaria. *Pests:* aphids, leaf nematodes, red spider mites, whiteflies. *Diseases:* root and stem rots, virus, wilt.

Calendula. *Pests:* aphids, beetles, borers, bugs, caterpillars, leaf hoppers, mites, root-knot nematodes, thrips, whiteflies. *Diseases:* gray mold blight, crown rot, leaf spots, powdery mildews, rots, rust, smuts, viruses.

Callistemon. *Pests:* mealybugs, scales.

Callistephus. *Pests:* aphids (including root aphids), beetles, borers, bugs, caterpillars, cutworms, leaf hoppers, leaf miners, root-knot nematodes, tarnished plant bugs, thrips. *Diseases:* anthracnose, gray mold blight, stem canker, crown rot, downy and powdery mildews, leaf spots, rots, rust, viruses, wilts.

Calluna. *Pests:* beetles, red spider mites, scales.

Calonyction. *Pests:* beetles, mealybugs, leaf nematodes, orthezias, thrips. *Diseases:* leaf spot, rust, white rust.

Campanula (Bellflower).

Camassia. *Diseases:* blight, leaf spot, smut.

Camellia. *Pests:* aphids, black vine weevils, caterpillars, Fuller Rose beetles, mealybugs, mites, root-knot nematodes, scales, whiteflies. *Diseases:* bud and flower blights, canker, crown gall, leaf gall, leaf spots, oedema, rots, scab, viruses.

Campanula. *Pests:* aphids, root-knot nematodes, slugs, thrips. *Diseases:* crown rot, leaf spots, powdery mildew, rots, rusts, virus.

Campsis. *Pests:* plant hoppers, scales, whiteflies. *Diseases:* leaf blight, leaf spots, powdery mildews.

Canna. *Pests:* beetles, caterpillars, scales. *Diseases:* bud rot, crown rot, leaf spot, root rot, rust, virus.

Capsicum. *Pests:* aphids, beetles, bugs, caterpillars, cutworms, maggots, mealybugs, mites, red spider mites, root-knot nematodes, weevils, whiteflies. *Diseases:* anthracnose, blights, blossom end rot, crown rot, downy mildew, leaf molds, leaf spots, rots, viruses, wilt.

Caragana. *Diseases:* blight, hairy root, leaf spot, root rot.

Carica. *Diseases:* flower blight, leaf spots, powdery mildew, rots.

Carnation. See Dianthus.

Carpinus. *Pests:* scales. *Diseases:* twig blight, cankers, leaf blister, leaf spots, powdery mildews, rots.

Carrot. *Pests:* aphids, beetles, carrot flies, caterpillars, leaf hoppers, millipedes, root-knot nematodes, thrips, weevils, wireworms. *Diseases:* blights, crown rot, heart rot or black heart, leaf spots, rots, rusts, scab, viruses.

Carya. *Pests:* aphids, beetles, borers, caterpillars, curculios, scales, weevils. *Diseases:* anthracnose, blights, cankers, crown gall, leaf blotch, leaf spots, little leaf, powdery mildews, rots, scab, virus.

Cassia. *Pests:* lacebugs, root-knot nematodes, scales. *Diseases:* dieback, root rots.

Castanea. *Pests:* aphids, beetles, borers, caterpillars, scales. *Diseases:* blights, cankers, leaf spots, powdery mildews, rots.

Casuarina. *Pests:* scales. *Disease:* root rot.

Catalpa. *Pests:* aphids, bugs, caterpillars, mealybugs, nematodes, scales. *Diseases:* crown rot, leaf spots, powdery mildews, rots, wilt.

Cauliflower. Pests and Diseases same as for Cabbage, which see.

Ceanothus. *Pests:* aphids, borers, caterpillars, lacebugs, mealybugs, scales, thrips. *Diseases:* crown gall, leaf spots, powdery mildew, rots, rust.

Cedrus. *Pests:* scales, weevils. *Diseases:* canker, root and wood rots.

Celastrus. *Pests:* aphids, scales. *Diseases:* canker, crown gall, leaf spots, powdery mildews.

Celery.

Cherries.

Celery. *Pests:* aphids, beetles, borers, caterpillars, flies, leaf hoppers, stem nematodes, red spider mites, tarnished plant bugs, thrips, weevils. *Diseases:* blights, leaf spots, rots, viruses, wilts.

Celosia. *Pests:* aphids, red spider mites, root-knot nematodes. *Diseases:* leaf spots, rot, curly top virus.

Celsia. *Pests:* aphids, red spider mites, whiteflies.

Celtis. *Pests:* borers, caterpillars, galls, scales, spittle bugs, whiteflies. *Diseases:* blight, canker, downy and powdery mildews, leaf spots, root and wood rots.

Centaurea. *Pests:* aphids (including root aphids), leaf hoppers, root-knot nematodes. *Diseases:* crown rot, downy and powdery mildews, rots, rusts, virus yellows, white rust, wilt.

Centradenia. *Pests:* red spider mites, whiteflies.

Cercis. *Pests:* caterpillars, scales, whiteflies. *Diseases:* canker, leaf spots, rots.

Cestrum. *Pests:* mealybugs, scales.

Chaenomeles. *Pests:* aphids, bugs, Japanese beetles, mealybugs, root-knot nematodes, scales. *Diseases:* blights (including fire blight), canker, crown gall, leaf spot, rots, rusts.

Chamaecyparis. *Pests:* aphids, bagworms, caterpillars, scales, weevils. *Diseases:* blights, rots, rust, sun scorch.

Cheiranthus. *Pests:* aphids, beetles, caterpillars.

Diseases: gray mold blight, club root, crown rot, leaf spot.

Chelone. *Diseases:* leaf spot, powdery mildews, rust.

Cherry. *Pests:* aphids, beetles, borers, caterpillars, curculios, fruit flies, root-knot nematodes, scales, thrips. *Diseases:* black knot, blights, cankers, crown gall, leaf blisters, leaf spots, powdery mildew, rots, rust, viruses.

Chionodoxa. *Pests:* nematodes.

Choisya. *Pests:* mealybugs, whiteflies.

Chorizema. *Pests:* aphids, whiteflies.

Chrysanthemum. *Pests:* aphids, beetles, borers, caterpillars, cutworms, galls, leaf hoppers, leaf miners, leaf nematodes, mealybugs, mites, orthezias, scales, slugs, tarnished plant bugs, thrips, weevils, whiteflies. *Diseases:* blights, crown gall, leaf spots, powdery mildew, rots, rust, viruses, wilts.

Cimicifuga. *Pests:* root-knot nematodes. *Diseases:* leaf spots, rust, smut.

Cineraria (Senecio cruentus). *Pests:* aphids, caterpillars, cutworms, leaf hoppers, mealybugs, red spider mites, root-knot nematodes, slugs, whiteflies. *Diseases:* blight, downy and powdery mildews, root and stem rots, viruses, wilt.

Cinnamomum. *Pests:* mites, scales, thrips. *Diseases:* anthracnose, cankers, leaf spot, root rots.

Citrus (Lemon).

Cissus. *Pests:* aphids, Fuller Rose beetles, mealybugs, scales. *Diseases:* leaf spot, rust.

Citrus. *Pests:* aphids, beetles, borers, bugs, caterpillars, mealybugs, mites, nematodes, scales, thrips, weevils, whiteflies. *Diseases:* anthracnose, blights, cankers, chlorosis, crown gall, leaf spots, powdery mildews; rots of fruit, root, twigs, and wood; scab, sooty mold, virus.

Clarkia. *Pests:* aphids, leaf hoppers. *Diseases:* anthracnose, downy mildew, leaf gall, leaf spot, rusts, stem rots, virus yellows, wilt.

Clematis. *Pests:* blister beetles, borers, caterpillars, red spider mites, root-knot nematodes, scales, whiteflies. *Diseases:* blight, crown gall, leaf spots, powdery mildew, rusts, smut.

Cleome. *Pests:* aphids. *Diseases:* leaf spots, rust.

Clerodendron. *Pests:* mealybugs, red spider mites, root-knot nematodes, scales. *Disease:* leaf spot.

Clethra. *Diseases:* leaf gall, leaf spot.

Coccolobis. *Pests:* scales. *Diseases:* rusts.

Codiaeum. *Pests:* mealybugs, red spider mites, scales, thrips. *Diseases:* leaf and stem spot, root rot.

Coffea. *Pests:* mealybugs, red spider mites, scales, whiteflies.

Colchicum. *Diseases:* leaf spots, rots, smut.

Coleus. *Pests:* caterpillars, leaf nematodes, mealybugs, orthezias, red spider mites, root-knot nematodes, slugs, weevils, whiteflies. *Diseases:* leaf spots, rot, mosaic virus, wilt.

Collards. Pests and diseases as for Cabbage.

Colocasia. *Pests:* root-knot nematodes. *Diseases:* downy mildew, rots.

Columnea. *Pests:* mealybugs, mites. *Diseases:* rots.

Convallaria. *Pests:* root-knot nematodes, weevils. *Diseases:* gray mold blight, blotch, crown rot, leaf spots.

Convolvulus. *Pests:* aphids, beetles, bugs, caterpillars, leaf miners, scales, weevils, whiteflies. *Diseases:* leaf spots, white rust.

Cordyline. *Pests:* mealybugs, red spider mites, root-knot nematodes, scales, thrips. *Diseases:* anthracnose or tip blight, leaf spots, root rot.

Coreopsis. *Pests:* aphids, beetles, leaf hoppers, root-knot nematodes. *Diseases:* blight, crown rot, leaf spots, root and stem rot, rust, viruses, wilt.

Corn.

Corn. *Pests:* aphids, beetles, borers, caterpillars, cutworms, ear worms, maggots, millipedes, wireworms. *Diseases:* bacterial wilt, blight, leaf spots, rots, rust, smut, viruses.

Cornus. *Pests:* aphids, beetles, borers, caterpillars, cicadas, galls, leaf hoppers, scales, whiteflies. *Diseases:* anthracnose, blights, cankers, leaf spots, powdery mildews, rots, leaf scorch.

Cornus Kousa (Japanese Flowering Dogwood).

Corydalis. *Diseases:* downy mildew, leaf spot, rusts.

Corylus. *Pests:* aphids, bugs, caterpillars, mites, scales, weevils, whiteflies. *Diseases:* blight, cankers, crown gall, leaf curl, leaf spots, powdery mildews, root rot.

Cosmos. *Pests:* aphids, root-knot nematodes. *Diseases:* canker, crown rot, leaf spots, powdery mildew, root and stem rots, viruses, wilts.

Cotinus. *Pests:* leaf rollers, scales. *Diseases:* leaf spots, wilt.

Cotoneaster. *Pests:* borers, lacebugs, mites, scales, webworms. *Diseases:* fire blight, canker or twig blight, hairy root, leaf spots, root rots, scab.

Cranberry. See Vaccinium.

Crassula. *Pests:* aphids, mealybugs, mites. *Diseases:* anthracnose, leaf spot, root rots.

Crataegus. *Pests:* aphids, beetles, borers, cater-

Crataegus (Hawthorn).

pillars, mites, scales. *Diseases:* blights (including fire blight), canker, leaf spots, powdery mildews, rots, rusts, scab.

Crinum. *Pests:* bulb mites, caterpillars, mealybugs, scales, thrips. *Diseases:* leaf scorch, leaf spot, mosaic virus.

Crocus. *Pests:* aphids, bulb mites. *Diseases:* rots, rust, scab, virus.

Crinum.

Cryptomeria. *Diseases:* leaf spots, leaf and twig blight, heart rot.

Cucumber. *Pests:* aphids, beetles, bugs, caterpillars, cutworms, leaf hoppers, red spider mites, root-knot nematodes, thrips, whiteflies. *Diseases:* anthracnose, blights; blossom end rot, crown rot, downy and powdery mildews, leaf spots, rots, scab, viruses, wilt.

Cuphea. *Pests:* aphids, mealybugs, red spider mites, whiteflies. *Diseases:* gray mold blight, leaf spot, powdery mildew, root rot.

Cupressus. *Pests:* aphids, caterpillars, mealybugs,

Cycad (Cycas).

mites, scales. *Diseases:* blights, cankers, crown gall, diebacks, needle cast, rots, rust.

Curculigo. *Pests:* mealybugs, scales.

Currants. *Pests:* aphids, beetles, borers, caterpillars, fruitflies, mites, scales. *Diseases:* anthracnose, blights, cankers, leaf spots, powdery and downy mildews, rots, rusts, mosaic virus, wilt.

Cycads. *Pests:* mealybugs, scales, thrips. *Disease:* leaf spot.

Cyclamen. *Pests:* aphids, black vine weevils, mites, root-knot nematodes, thrips. *Diseases:* blights, leaf spots, rots, wilt.

Cynoglossum. *Pests:* root-knot nematodes. *Diseases:* crown rot, downy mildew, leaf spots, stem rot.

Cyperus. *Pests:* mealybugs, thrips, whiteflies.

Cyphomandra. *Pests:* mealybugs, red spider mites, scales, whiteflies.

Cytisus. *Pests:* aphids, mealybugs, red spider mites, scales. *Diseases:* downy mildew, leaf spot.

Dahlia. *Pests:* aphids, beetles, borers, caterpillars, leaf hoppers, mites, nematodes, tarnished plant bugs, thrips, weevils, wireworms. *Diseases:* blights, crown gall, crown rot, leaf spots, powdery mildews, rots, smut, viruses, wilts.

Daphne. *Pests:* aphids, mealybugs, scales. *Diseases:* blight, crown rot, leaf spot, rots, wilt.

Datura. *Pests:* aphids, leaf hoppers, mites, psyllids. *Diseases:* crown rot, root rot.

Delphinium. *Pests:* aphids, beetles, borers, bugs, cutworms, leaf miners, mealybugs, millipedes, mites, nematodes, slugs, sowbugs, thrips. *Diseases:* gray mold blight, cankers, crown gall, crown rot, leaf gall, leaf spots, powdery mildews, rots, rusts, smuts, viruses, wilt.

Deutzia. *Pests:* aphids, Fuller Rose beetles, leaf miners, root-knot nematodes. *Diseases:* leaf spots.

Dianthus. *Pests:* aphids, caterpillars, cutworms, Fuller Rose beetles, mealybugs, nematodes, red spider mites, thrips. *Diseases:* anthracnose, blights, crown gall, crown rot, leaf spots, molds, powdery mildew, rots, rust, viruses, wilts.

Dianthus (Sweet William).

Dichondra. *Pests:* root-knot nematodes. *Diseases:* crown rot, leaf gall, rust.

Dichorisandra. *Pests:* mealybugs, red spider mites.

Dieffenbachia. *Pests:* mealybugs, red spider mites. *Diseases:* anthracnose, leaf spot, root and stem rots.

Diervilla. *Pests:* root-knot nematodes, scales. *Diseases:* leaf spots, powdery mildew, rot.

Digitalis. *Pests:* aphids, beetles, mealybugs, nematodes, thrips. *Diseases:* anthracnose, leaf spots, rots, virus, wilt.

Echeveria.

Dill. *Pests:* caterpillars, nematodes, weevils. *Diseases:* leaf spot, rots, virus.

Dimorphotheca. *Pests:* aphids, whiteflies. *Diseases:* wilt.

Dipladenia. *Pests:* mealybugs, red spider mites, scales.

Dizygotheca. *Pests:* mealybugs, red spider mites, scales.

Dodecatheon. *Diseases:* leaf spot, rusts.

Dolichos. *Pests:* root-knot nematodes. *Diseases:* leaf spot, powdery mildew, root rot, virus.

Doronicum. *Pests:* aphids, nematodes. *Disease:* powdery mildew.

Doxantha. *Pests:* mealybugs, nematodes, scales, whiteflies. *Disease:* root rot.

Draba. *Diseases:* downy and powdery mildews, rusts, white rusts.

Dracaena. *Pests:* mealybugs, root-knot nematodes, scales, thrips, whiteflies. *Diseases:* anthracnose or tip blight, leaf spots, root rot.

Dracocephalum. *Diseases:* crown rot, leaf spots.

Duranta. *Pests:* aphids. *Disease:* crown rot.

Echeveria. *Pests:* aphids, mealybugs, root-knot nematodes, weevils. *Disease:* rust.

Echinacea. *Diseases:* leaf spots, mosaic virus.

Echinops. *Pests:* aphids. *Diseases:* crown rot, virus.

Echium. *Pests:* aphids, whiteflies. *Diseases:* leaf spot, root rot.

Eggplant. *Pests:* aphids, beetles, borers, bugs, caterpillars, leaf hoppers, leaf miners, maggots, red spider mites, root-knot nematodes, whiteflies. *Diseases:* anthracnose, blights, crown rot, downy and powdery mildews, leaf spots, rots, viruses, wilts.

Elaeagnus. *Pests:* aphids, scales. *Diseases:* cankers, crown rot, hairy root, leaf spots, powdery mildew, root rot, rusts.

Endive. *Pests:* aphids, root-knot nematodes. *Diseases:* gray mold blight, downy and powdery mildews, rots (including heart rot or brown heart), crown rot, rust, viruses, leaf spots.

Episcia. *Pests:* mealybugs, mites, red spider mites. *Diseases:* rots.

Flowering spray of Eriobotrya japonica.

Eranthemum. *Pests:* aphids, mealybugs, red spider mites, whiteflies. *Diseases:* leaf spot, oedema.

Erica. *Pests:* scales. *Diseases:* gray mold blight, powdery mildew, rot, rust.

Erigeron. *Pests:* aphids. *Diseases:* gray mold blight, crown rot, leaf gall, leaf spots, downy and powdery mildews, rusts, smut, viruses, wilt.

Eriobotrya. *Pests:* aphids, beetles, borers, bugs, mites, root-knot nematodes, scales. *Diseases:* anthracnose, blights, crown rot, leaf spots, root rots, scab.

Erlangea. *Pests:* mealybugs, red spider mites, whiteflies.

Erythrina. *Pests:* mealybugs, root-knot nematodes, scales. *Diseases:* blight, root rot, wilt.

Erythronium. *Pests:* aphids. *Diseases:* leaf blights, leaf spot, rust, smuts.

Eschscholtzia. *Pests:* root-knot nematodes. *Diseases:* bacterial blight, leaf mold, powdery mildew, rot, smut, viruses, wilt.

Eucalyptus. *Pests:* aphids, borers, caterpillars, mealybugs, mites, scales. *Diseases:* canker, crown gall, leaf spots, oedema, rots.

Eucharis. *Pests:* bulb mites, mealybugs, red spider mites. *Diseases:* gray mold blight, leaf scorch, leaf spots, root rot.

Eugenia. *Pests:* mealybugs, scales.

Euonymus. *Pests:* aphids, root-knot nematodes, scales, thrips. *Diseases:* anthracnose, blight, crown gall, leaf spots, powdery mildews, rots.

Eupatorium. *Pests:* aphids, leaf miners, root-knot nematodes, scales. *Diseases:* gray mold blight, leaf spots, downy and powdery mildews, rots, rusts, smut, virus, wilt.

Euphorbia. *Pests:* aphids (including root aphids), mealybugs, root-knot nematodes, scales. *Diseases:* gray mold blight, canker, crown gall, leaf spots, rots, rusts, scab, wilt.

Eustoma. *Pests:* aphids. *Diseases:* blights, leaf spots, root rot.

Exacum. *Pests:* mealybugs, red spider mites. *Disease:* blight.

Fagus. *Pests:* aphids, borers, caterpillars, leaf hoppers, scales. *Diseases:* cankers, leaf scorch, leaf spots, powdery mildew, rots.

Fatshedera. *Pests:* mealybugs, red spider mites, scales.

Eupatorium (White Snakeroot).

Fatsia. *Pests:* mealybugs, red spider mites, scales.

Feijoa. *Pests:* mealybugs, red spider mites, scales. *Diseases:* rots.

Fennel. *Pests:* root-knot nematodes. *Diseases:* rots.

Ferns. *Pests:* aphids, black vine weevils, caterpillars, cutworms, Japanese beetles, leaf nematodes, mealybugs, scales, slugs, snails, thrips, weevils, whiteflies. *Diseases:* anthracnose, blights, leaf blisters, leaf spots, rusts.

Ficus (Fig).

Ficus. *Pests:* beetles, borers, mealybugs, mites, root-knot nematodes, scales, thrips. *Diseases:* anthracnose, blights, cankers, crown gall, fruit rots, leaf blotch, leaf spots, little leaf, rust, sooty molds, mosaic virus.

Fig. See Ficus.

Forsythia.

Filipendula. *Diseases:* leaf spots, mildew, rust.

Fittonia. *Pests:* mealybugs, red spider mites. *Diseases:* rots.

Forsythia. *Diseases:* blossom blight, canker, crown gall, crown rot, leaf spots, root rot.

Francoa. *Pests:* aphids, red spider mites, whiteflies.

Fraxinus. *Pests:* aphids, borers, bugs, caterpillars, flower galls, nematodes, scales. *Diseases:* anthracnose, cankers, powdery mildew, leaf spots, rots, rust, sooty mold.

Freesia. *Pests:* aphids, bulb mites, root-knot nematodes, thrips. *Diseases:* leaf spot, rots, scab, mosaic virus.

Fritillaria. *Diseases:* leaf spot, rust, mosaic virus.

Fuchsia. *Pests:* aphids, beetles, caterpillars, mealybugs, mites, root-knot nematodes, scales, thrips, whiteflies. *Diseases:* gray mold blight, leaf spot, rots, rust, spotted wilt virus, wilt.

Furcraea. *Pests:* mealybugs, scales, thrips. *Diseases:* leaf spots.

Gaillardia. *Pests:* aphids, beetles, borers, bugs,

leaf hoppers, mites, thrips, wireworms. *Diseases:* leaf spot, powdery mildews, root rot, rust, smut, viruses.

Galanthus. *Pests:* bulb flies, nematodes. *Diseases:* blights.

Galax. *Diseases:* leaf spots.

Galium. *Diseases:* leaf spots, powdery and downy mildews, root rot, rusts.

Galtonia. *Pests:* bulb flies. *Diseases:* leaf spots, mosaic virus.

Gardenia. *Pests:* Fuller Rose beetles, mealybugs, mites, root-knot nematodes, scales, thrips,

Gardenia.

whiteflies. *Diseases:* blight, canker, chlorosis, leaf spots, powdery mildew, root rot, sooty mold, stem gall.

Gasteria. *Pests:* mealybugs. *Disease:* root rot.

Gaultheria. *Diseases:* leaf gall, leaf spots, powdery mildew.

Gaura. *Pests:* aphids. *Diseases:* leaf gall, leaf spots, powdery and downy mildews, root rot, rusts, virus yellows.

Gaylussacia. *Pests:* root-knot nematodes. *Diseases:* leaf blight, leaf galls, leaf spots, powdery mildew, rust.

Gazania. *Pests:* aphids, mealybugs. *Diseases:* rots.

Genista. *Pests:* aphids, mealybugs, scales. *Diseases:* dieback, powdery mildew, rust.

Gentiana. *Diseases:* blight, leaf spots, root rot, rusts.

Geranium (hardy herbaceous kinds). *Diseases:* leaf gall, leaf spots, powdery and downy mildews, rots, rusts, virus. See Pelargonium for pests and diseases of the tender "bedding" or "zonal" Geraniums and of Ivy Leaf Geraniums and Martha Washington Geraniums.

Gerbera. *Pests:* mealybugs, mites, root-knot nematodes. *Diseases:* gray mold blight, crown rot, leaf spot, powdery mildew, rots.

Geum. *Pests:* root-knot nematodes. *Diseases:* downy and powdery mildews, leaf spots, leaf gall, root rot, rust, smut.

Gilia. *Pests:* root nematodes including root-knot nematodes. *Diseases:* powdery mildew, leaf spot, root rot, rusts, virus yellows.

Gladiolus. *Pests:* aphids (including root aphids), beetles, borers, caterpillars, cutworms, leaf hoppers, maggots, mealybugs, mites, root-knot nematodes, scales, tarnished plant bugs, thrips, weevils, wireworms. *Diseases:* bacterial scab, blights, crown rot, leaf spots, rots, viruses, wilt.

Gleditsia. *Pests:* caterpillars, galls, scales. *Diseases:* cankers, hairy root, leaf spots, powdery mildew, rots, rust, virus.

Gloriosa. *Pests:* aphids, mealybugs.

Gloxinia (Sinningia). *Pests:* aphids, black vine weevils, mealybugs, mites, thrips. *Diseases:* bud, crown, leaf and root rots; spotted wilt.

Godetia. *Pests:* aphids, root-knot nematodes, whiteflies. *Diseases:* downy mildew, root rots, rusts, virus.

Gooseberries.

Gomphrena. *Pests:* root-knot nematodes. *Diseases:* leaf spot, virus, white rust.

Gooseberry. *Pests:* aphids, beetles, borers, caterpillars, four-lined plant bugs, maggots, mealybugs, nematodes, scales. *Diseases:* anthracnose, blights, dieback, downy and powdery mildews, leaf spots, rots, rusts, scab, mosaic virus.

Gourds. *Pests:* aphids, beetles, borers, root-knot nematodes, squash bugs, whiteflies. *Diseases:* anthracnose, downy and powdery mildews, fruit spots, leaf spots, root rot, mosaic virus.

Grape. *Pests:* aphids, beetles, borers, bugs, caterpillars, curculios, galls, leaf hoppers, mealybugs, root nematodes (including root-knot nematodes), scales, thrips, whiteflies. *Diseases:* anthracnose, canker, crown gall, fruit rots, fruit spot, leaf blotch, leaf spots, little leaf, powdery and downy mildews, root rots, rust, virus, wood rots.

Grass. See Lawns.

Grevillea. *Pests:* caterpillars, mealybugs, mites, scales. *Diseases:* dieback, leaf spot, root rot.

Gynura. *Pests:* mealybugs, mites, whiteflies.

Gypsophila. *Pests:* leaf hoppers, root-knot nematodes. *Diseases:* gray mold blight, root gall, virus yellows.

Haemanthus. *Pests:* aphids, mealybugs, red spider mites.

Hamamelis. *Pests:* borers, caterpillars, galls. *Diseases:* leaf spots, powdery mildews, rots.

Haworthia. *Pests:* mealybugs. *Diseases:* rots.

Hebe. *Pests:* aphids, mealybugs, red spider mites.

Hedera. *Pests:* aphids, beetles, caterpillars, leaf hoppers, mealybugs, red spider mites, scales, whiteflies. *Diseases:* leaf mold, leaf spots, powdery mildew, root rot, scab, sooty mold.

Helenium. *Pests:* snout beetles. *Diseases:* leaf spots, powdery mildew, root rot, rusts, smuts, virus yellows.

Helianthemum. *Diseases:* leaf spots, rots.

Helianthus. *Pests:* aphids, beetles, bugs, caterpillars, maggots, mealybugs, nematodes, scales. *Diseases:* blights, crown gall, downy mildew, leaf spots, rots, rusts, smut, white rust, wilt, mosaic virus.

Helichrysum. *Pests:* leaf hoppers, root-knot nematodes. *Diseases:* stem rot, viruses, wilt.

Heliopsis. *Pests:* four-lined plant bugs. *Diseases:* leaf spots, mildew, rot, rusts, mosaic virus.

Heliotropium (Heliotrope).

Heliotropium. *Pests:* aphids, caterpillars, mealybugs, orthezias, red spider mites, root-knot nematodes, whiteflies. *Diseases:* blight, leaf spot, rust, wilt.

Helleborus. *Pests:* slugs. *Diseases:* crown rot, downy mildew, flower and leaf spots.

Hemerocallis. *Pests:* root-knot nematodes, thrips, weevils. *Diseases:* blights, leaf spots, root rot.

Hippeastrums (Amaryllis).

Hepatica. *Diseases:* downy mildew, leaf spot, rust, smut.

Hesperis. *Diseases:* club root, downy mildew, mosaic virus, white rust.

Heuchera. *Pests:* black vine weevil, leaf nematodes, mealybugs. *Diseases:* leaf spots, powdery mildews, smut, stem rot.

Hibiscus. *Pests:* aphids, beetles, caterpillars, root-knot nematodes, scales, whiteflies. *Diseases:* anthracnose, blights, crown rot, dieback, leaf spots, root and stem rots, rust.

Hippeastrum. *Pests:* blister beetles, bulb flies, bulb mites, bulb and stem nematodes, caterpillars, cutworms, mealybugs, red spider mites, thrips. *Diseases:* blights, leaf scorch or Amaryllis red blotch disease, leaf spots, rots, viruses.

Hoffmannia. *Pests:* mealybugs, scales.

Horse-radish. *Pests:* beetles, bugs, caterpillars, root-knot nematodes. *Diseases:* club root, crown gall, downy and powdery mildews, leaf spots, rots, viruses, white rust, wilt.

Hosta. *Diseases:* crown rots, leaf spots.

Hoya. *Pests:* mealybugs, scales.

Humulus. *Pests:* aphids, root-knot nematodes. *Diseases:* anthracnose, crown gall, downy and powdery mildews, leaf spots, root rot, rust, virus, wilt.

Hyacinthus.

Jacobinia carnea.

Hyacinthus. *Pests:* bulb flies, bulb mites, bulb and stem nematodes, caterpillars. *Diseases:* bacterial yellows, gray mold blight, mosaic virus, rots.

Hydrangea. *Pests:* aphids, leaf tiers, red spider mites, stem and root-knot nematodes, Rose chafer, tarnished plant bugs, thrips. *Diseases:* blight, chlorosis, crown rot, leaf spots, powdery mildew, rot, rust, wilt.

Hymenocallis. *Pests:* bulb mites, caterpillars, mealybugs, scales, thrips. *Diseases:* leaf scorch, leaf spot, mosaic virus.

Hypericum. *Pests:* root-knot nematodes. *Diseases:* leaf spots, powdery mildew, rust.

Hyssopus. *Pests:* root-knot nematodes, scales.

Iberis. *Pests:* aphids, caterpillars, root-knot nematodes. *Diseases:* club root, downy and powdery mildews, white rust.

Ilex. *Pests:* beetles, caterpillars, leaf miners, mealybugs, mites, scales, whiteflies. *Diseases:* anthracnose, blight, cankers, leaf spots, powdery mildews, rots, rust, scab, sooty molds, wilt.

Impatiens. *Pests:* aphids, beetles, red spider mites, root-knot nematodes, tarnished plant bug. *Diseases:* leaf spots, stem rot, wilts.

Inula. *Diseases:* leaf spot, powdery mildew, rust.

Ipomoea. *Pests:* aphids, beetles, bugs, caterpillars, leaf miners, red spider mites, root-knot nematodes, scales, weevils, whiteflies. *Diseases:* blight, canker, crown rot, leaf spots, root rot, rusts, white rust.

Iris. *Pests:* aphids, beetles, borers, caterpillars, flies, mites, nematodes (including root-knot nematodes), slugs, thrips, weevils. *Diseases:* blights, crown rot, leaf spots, rots, rusts, mosaic virus.

Isoloma. *Pests:* mealybugs, mites. *Diseases:* root rot.

Ixia. *Diseases:* mosaic virus, rots.

Ixora. *Pests:* aphids, mealybugs, root-knot nematodes, scales. *Disease:* root rot.

Jacaranda. *Pests:* mealybugs, scales. *Disease:* root rot.

Jacobinia. *Pests:* mealybugs, red spider mites, scales.

Jasminum. *Pests:* root-knot nematodes, scales, whiteflies. *Diseases:* blight, canker, crown gall, crown rot, leaf spots, root rot, virus.

Juglans. *Pests:* aphids, beetles, borers, caterpillars, curculios, lace bugs, mealybugs, mites, sawflies, scales. *Diseases:* anthracnose, blights, cankers, crown gall, dieback, leaf blotch, leaf spots, powdery mildews, rots, virus, wilt.

Juniperus. *Pests:* aphids, bagworms, beetles, caterpillars, mealybugs, red spider mites, scales, webworms, weevils. *Diseases:* blights, cankers, crown gall, diebacks, needle casts, rots, rusts.

Kalanchoe. *Pests:* aphids, mealybugs. *Diseases:* crown gall, crown or stem rot, powdery mildew.

Kale. Pests and diseases as for Cabbage, which see.

Kalmia. *Pests:* beetles, borers, lace bugs, whiteflies. *Diseases:* blights, canker, chlorosis, leaf spots, rots.

Kerria. *Pests:* Japanese beetles. *Diseases:* blights, canker, leaf spot, root rot.

Kniphofia. *Pests:* root-knot nematodes. *Disease:* leaf spot.

Koelreuteria. *Diseases:* canker, leaf spot, root rot, verticillium wilt.

Kohlrabi. Pests and diseases as for Cabbage, which see.

Laburnum. *Pests:* aphids, mealybugs. *Diseases:* leaf spot, twig blights.

Lachenalia. *Disease:* virus.

Lagerstroemeria. *Pests:* aphids, scales. *Diseases:* blight, blotch, leaf spot, sooty mold, powdery mildews, rots.

Lantana. *Pests:* aphids, caterpillars, leaf nematodes, mealybugs, mites, orthezias, root-knot nematodes, scales, whiteflies. *Diseases:* leaf spot, rot, rust, wilt.

Larix. *Pests:* aphids, bagworms, beetles, borers, casebearers, caterpillars, sawflies, weevils. *Diseases:* blights, cankers, rots, rusts.

Lathyrus. *Pests:* aphids, beetles, bugs, caterpillars, centipedes, cutworms, leaf miners, red spider mites, root-knot nematodes, sowbugs,

Juniperus (Juniper).

Lachenalia (Cape Cowslip).

thrips. *Diseases:* anthracnose, gray mold blight, crown gall, crown rot, leaf spots, mold, powdery mildews, rots, viruses, wilt.

Laurus. *Pests:* caterpillars, psyllids, scales. *Disease:* anthracnose.

Lavandula. *Pests:* bugs, caterpillars, root-knot nematodes. *Diseases:* leaf spot, root rot.

Lavatera. *Pests:* aphids, scales. *Diseases:* anthracnose, rot, rust, virus.

Lawns. *Pests:* ants, aphids, armyworms, beetle grubs, chinch bugs, cutworms, earthworms, grasshoppers, mites, moles, slugs, sod webworms, wasps, wireworms. *Diseases:* anthracnose, blights, blotch, crown rot, downy and powdery mildews, leaf spots, molds, rots, rusts, smuts.

Lettuce. *Pests:* aphids, caterpillars, cutworms, flea beetles, leaf hoppers, millipedes, root-knot nematodes, slugs, whiteflies. *Diseases:* anthracnose, blight, crown rot, downy and powdery mildews, leaf spots, rots, rusts, viruses, white rust.

Leucothoë. *Diseases:* canker, leaf gall, leaf spots.

Liatris. *Pests:* root-knot nematodes. *Diseases:* leaf spots, rots, rusts, verticillium wilt.

Ligularia. *Pests:* aphids, mealybugs, mites. *Diseases:* crown rot.

Ligustrum. *Pests:* aphids, beetles, leaf miners, leaf nematodes, mealybugs, mites, root-knot nematodes, scales, thrips, webworms, weevils,

Lilium (Easter Lily).

Liquidambar (Sweet Gum).

whiteflies. *Diseases:* anthracnose, blights, crown gall, leaf spots, powdery mildew, rots, sooty mold, mosaic virus.

Lilium. *Pests:* aphids, borers, bulb flies, bulb mites, caterpillars, Fuller Rose beetles, root-knot nematodes, thrips. *Diseases:* blights, canker, chlorosis, crown rot, leaf spots, mold, rots, rusts, viruses.

Lily-of-the-Valley. See Convallaria.

Limonium. *Pests:* aphids, red spider mites, root-knot nematodes. *Diseases:* leaf spots, rust, virus.

Linaria. *Pests:* aphids, nematodes (including root-knot nematodes). *Diseases:* anthracnose, crown rot, downy mildew, leaf spots, rots, virus yellows.

Linum. *Pests:* root-knot nematodes. *Disease:* stem rot.

Lippia. *Pests:* root-knot nematodes. *Diseases:* anthracnose, crown rot, leaf spots, root rot.

Liquidamber. *Pests:* caterpillars, scales. *Diseases:* blight, cankers, crown gall, leaf spots, rots.

Liriodendron. *Pests:* aphids, beetles, caterpillars, scales. *Diseases:* blight, cankers, leaf spots, powdery mildews, rots, sooty mold.

Lithospermum. *Diseases:* powdery mildew, rusts.

Lobelia. *Pests:* aphids, bugs, caterpillars, leaf hoppers, root-knot nematodes, wireworms. *Diseases:* gray mold blight, leaf spots, root rots, rust, smut, viruses.

Lobularia. *Pests:* caterpillars, leaf hoppers, root-knot nematodes. *Diseases:* club root, downy mildew, virus yellows, white rust.

Loganberry. Pests and diseases as for Blackberry, which see.

Lonicera. *Pests:* aphids, bugs, caterpillars, flea beetles, four-lined plant bugs, mealybugs, root-knot nematodes, sawflies, scales, whiteflies. *Diseases:* blights, canker, crown gall, hairy root, leaf spots, powdery mildews, root rot, rust.

Lunaria. *Diseases:* club root, leaf spots.

Lupinus. *Pests:* aphids, caterpillars, four-lined plant bugs, root-knot nematodes, weevils, whiteflies. *Diseases:* blights, crown rot, downy and powdery mildews, leaf spots, rots, rusts, smuts, viruses.

Lychnis. *Diseases:* crown rot, gray mold blight, leaf mold, leaf spots, rots, rusts, smut.

Lycium. *Pests:* aphids, borers, caterpillars, galls. *Diseases:* leaf spot, powdery mildew, rot, rusts.

Lycoris. *Pests:* nematodes. *Disease:* leaf scorch.

Lythrum. *Diseases:* leaf gall, leaf spots, root rot.

Maclura. *Pests:* mealybugs, scales, whiteflies. *Diseases:* leaf blight, leaf spots, root rot, rust.

Magnolia. *Pests:* caterpillars, mealybugs, root nematodes and root-knot nematodes, scales, thrips, whiteflies. *Diseases:* blights, cankers, leaf spots, powdery mildews, rots.

Mahonia. *Pests:* aphids, root-knot nematodes, scales, whiteflies. *Diseases:* leaf spots, root rot, rusts.

Maianthemum. *Diseases:* blight, leaf spots, rusts.

Malus. Pests and diseases as for Apple, which see.

Malva. *Pests:* caterpillars. *Diseases:* leaf spots, powdery mildew, root rot, rusts, viruses.

Malvastrum. *Diseases:* root rot, rusts.

Malvaviscus. *Pests:* aphids, mealybugs, red spider mites, whiteflies. *Diseases:* rots, rusts, twig blight.

Manettia. *Pests:* aphids, mealybugs.

Mangifera. *Pests:* flies, mealybugs, mites, scales,

Magnolia stellata.

Malvaviscus.

thrips. *Diseases:* anthracnose, leaf spots, powdery mildew, rots, scab, sooty mold, twig blight.

Maranta. Pests and diseases as for Calathea, which see.

Marrubium. *Pests:* root-knot nematodes. *Diseases:* leaf gall, leaf spot.

Mathiola. *Pests:* aphids, beetles, caterpillars, mealybugs, springtails. *Diseases:* anthracnose, club root, gray mold blight, rots, viruses, white rust, wilt.

Maurandia. *Pests:* aphids, whiteflies. *Disease:* leaf spot.

Meconopsis. *Diseases:* downy mildew, rots.

Medinilla. *Pests:* mealybugs, scales. *Diseases:* leaf spot.

Melastoma. *Pests:* mealybugs, red spider mites.

Melia. *Pests:* mites, root-knot nematodes, scales, whiteflies. *Diseases:* blight, canker, leaf spots, powdery mildew, rots.

Melon. *Pests:* aphids, beetles, borers, caterpillars, leaf hoppers, red spider mites, root-knot nematodes, squash bugs, thrips, whiteflies. *Diseases:* anthracnose, blights, crown rot, downy and powdery mildews, leaf spots, rots, scab, viruses, wilts.

Menispermum. *Diseases:* leaf spots, powdery mildew, smut.

Mentha. See Mint, below.

Mentzelia. *Diseases:* leaf spots, rots, rusts.

Mertensia. *Diseases:* downy and powdery mildews, leaf spot, rusts, smut, stem rot.

Mesembryanthemum. *Pests:* mealybugs, root-knot nematodes, scales. *Diseases:* root rot, mosaic virus.

Mignonette. See Reseda.

Mimulus. *Pests:* caterpillars, mealybugs, red spider mites, thrips. *Diseases:* blight, leaf spots, powdery mildew, virus yellows.

Mint. *Pests:* beetles, grubs, cutworms, flea beetles, four-lined plant bugs, grasshoppers, millipedes. *Diseases:* anthracnose, canker, leaf spots, powdery mildews, rusts, wilt.

Mirabilis. *Pests:* root-knot nematodes. *Diseases:* leaf spot, root rot, rusts, curly-top virus, white rust.

Mitella. *Diseases:* leaf spots, powdery mildew, rust.

Momordica. *Pests:* root-knot nematodes. *Diseases:* anthracnose, downy and powdery mildews, leaf spot.

Monarda. *Pests:* borers, scales. *Diseases:* crown rot, leaf gall, leaf spots, rusts, mosaic virus.

Monstera. *Pests:* mealybugs, red spider mites, scales. *Diseases:* leaf spot.

Montbretia. *Diseases:* blights, crown rot, mosaic virus, rots.

Morus. *Pests:* borers, leaf hoppers, mealybugs, red spider mites, root-knot nematodes, scales, whiteflies. *Diseases:* blights, cankers, hairy root, leaf spots, powdery mildews, rots.

Monstera deliciosa.

Mulberry. See Morus.

Musa. *Pests:* aphids, mealybugs, red spider mites, root-knot nematodes, scales, whiteflies. *Diseases:* anthracnose, leaf blight.

Muscari. *Pests:* nematodes. *Diseases:* rot, smuts.

Mushroom. *Pests:* maggots, mites, slugs, springtails, woodlice.

Mustard. Pests and diseases as for Cabbage, which see.

Myosotis. *Pests:* aphids, caterpillars, flea beetles, slugs. *Diseases:* downy mildew, gray mold blight, rot, rust, virus.

Myrica. *Pests:* caterpillars. *Diseases:* leaf spots, rots, rusts.

Myrtus. *Pests:* aphids, mealybugs, scales. *Diseases:* leaf spot, powdery mildew, stem rot.

Naegelia. *Pests:* mealybugs, mites, thrips. *Diseases:* rots.

Nandina. *Pests:* root-knot nematodes. *Diseases:* anthracnose, leaf spot, root rot.

Narcissus. *Pests:* aphids, bulb flies, bulb mites, caterpillars, mealybugs, millipedes, nematodes, thrips. *Diseases:* blights, leaf scorch, leaf spot, rots, viruses.

Nelumbium. *Pests:* aphids, beetles, borers. *Diseases:* leaf spots.

Nicotiana affinis (Flowering Tobacco).

Nemesia. *Pests:* aphids. *Diseases:* rots.

Nepeta. *Pests:* caterpillars, leaf hoppers. *Diseases:* crown rot, leaf spots, mosaic virus, root rot, wilt.

Nephthytis. *Pests:* mealybugs, red spider mites, scales. *Disease:* leaf spot.

Nerine. *Pests:* mealybugs, thrips. *Diseases:* leaf scorch, virus.

Nerium. *Pests:* aphids, mealybugs, scales. *Diseases:* bacterial gall, canker, leaf spots, root rots, scab, sooty mold.

Narcissi (Daffodils).

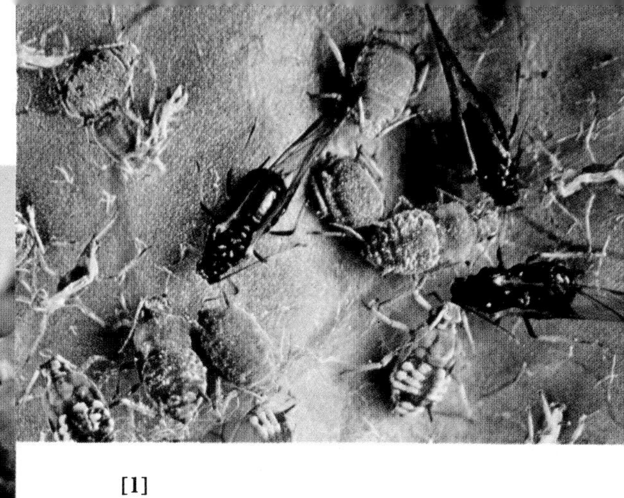

[1]
Bean Aphids

[2]
Aphids on Rose

[3]
Armyworm larva

[4]
Armyworm adult

[5]
Spotted Cucumber Beetle

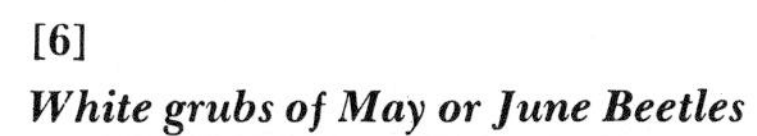

[6]
White grubs of May or June Beetles

[7]
Harlequin Bug

[8]
Cabbage Looper Caterpillar

[9]
Omniverous Looper Caterpillar

[10]
Omniverous Looper adult

[11]
Corn Earworm

[12]
Tomato Hornworm

Nymphaea (Water Lily).

Nicotiana. *Pests:* beetles, caterpillars, cutworms, root-knot nematodes. *Diseases:* downy and powdery mildews, leaf spot, root rot, viruses.

Nierembergia. *Pests:* aphids, mealybugs. *Disease:* crown rot.

Nigella. *Diseases:* stem and root rot.

Nymphaea. *Pests:* aphids, beetles, leaf cutters. *Diseases:* leaf spots, rot, smut.

Nyssa. *Pests:* caterpillars, leaf miners, scales. *Diseases:* blight, cankers, leaf spots, rots, rust.

Ochna. *Pests:* mealybugs, scales.

Odontonema. *Pests:* mealybugs, red spider mites, scales.

Oenothera. *Diseases:* downy and powdery mildews, leaf gall, leaf spots, mosaic virus, rots, rusts.

Okra. *Pests:* aphids, beetles, bugs, caterpillars, cutworms, mites, root-knot nematodes, whiteflies. *Diseases:* blight, crown rot, fruit spots, leaf spots, powdery mildew, rots, virus, wilts.

Olea. *Pests:* beetles, borers, caterpillars, root-knot nematodes, scales, thrips. *Diseases:* anthracnose, bitter pit, chlorosis, leaf spots, root rots.

Onion. *Pests:* armyworms, beetles, bulb flies, bulb mites, cutworms, maggots, nematodes, thrips, weevils, wireworms. *Diseases:* chlorosis, crown rot, downy mildew, leaf spots, rots, rusts, smut, viruses.

Orchids. *Pests:* aphids, beetles, borers, bugs, fly maggots, mealybugs, midges, mites, root nematodes, scales, slugs, snails, thrips, weevils. *Diseases:* anthracnose, blights, leaf spots, mosaic virus, rots, rusts.

Ornithogalum. *Diseases:* crown rot, leaf spots, mosaic viruses.

Osmanthus. *Pests:* aphids, mealybugs, scales. *Diseases:* leaf spots, rots, sooty mold.

Ostrya. *Pests:* aphids, scales. *Diseases:* cankers, leaf blister, leaf spots, powdery mildews, rots, twig blight.

Oxalis. *Pests:* aphids, root-knot nematodes, whiteflies. *Diseases:* leaf spots, root rot, rusts, smut, curly-top virus.

Oxydendrum. *Diseases:* blight, leaf spots, rots.

Pachysandra. *Pests:* mites, root-knot nematodes, scales. *Diseases:* blights, leaf spots.

Paeonia. *Pests:* ants, beetles, bugs, curculios, nematodes, scales, thrips. *Diseases:* Anthracnose, blights, blotch, canker, crown gall, crown rot, leaf spots, oedema, powdery mildew, rots, viruses, wilt.

Palms. *Pests:* aphids, black vine weevil, bugs, caterpillars, leaf miners, mealybugs, nematodes, scales, thrips, weevils. *Diseases:* anthracnose, blights, cankers, leaf scorch, leaf spots, rots, smut, wilts.

Pancratium. Pests and diseases as for Hymenocallis, which see.

Pandanus. *Pests:* mealybugs, scales. *Diseases:* leaf spots.

Onions.

Pansy. Pests and diseases as for Viola, which see.

Papaver. *Pests:* aphids, four-lined plant bugs, leaf hoppers, leaf nematodes, mealybugs, root-knot nematodes, Rose chafers, tarnished plant bugs. *Diseases:* blights, leaf spots, powdery mildew, rot, smut, viruses, wilt.

Parsley. *Pests:* Carrot rust flies, caterpillars, leaf hoppers, root-knot nematodes, stem nematodes, weevil grubs. *Diseases:* blights, leaf spot, rots, viruses.

Parsnip. *Pests:* aphids, beetles, Carrot rust flies, caterpillars, leaf miners, root and stem nematodes, weevils. *Diseases:* crown gall, heart rot, leaf spots, rots, scab, viruses.

Parthenocissus. *Pests:* aphids, beetles, caterpillars, leaf hoppers, mites, scales, weevils. *Diseases:* anthracnose, blight, canker, dieback, downy and powdery mildews, leaf spots, root rot.

Passiflora. *Pests:* caterpillars, mealybugs, root-knot nematodes, scales. *Diseases:* crown rot, leaf spots, rots.

Paulownia. *Diseases:* leaf spots, rots.

Pea. *Pests:* aphids, beetles, borers, bugs, caterpillars, centipedes, millipedes, root-knot nematodes, red spider mites, thrips, weevils, whiteflies. *Diseases:* anthracnose, blights, chlorosis, crown rot, downy and powdery mildews, leaf blotch, leaf spots, rots, rust, scab, viruses, wilts.

Peach. *Pests:* aphids, beetles, borers, bugs, caterpillars, curculios, leaf hoppers, mealybugs, mites, root-knot nematodes, sawflies, scales, thrips. *Diseases:* blights, canker, chlorosis, crown gall, dieback, hairy root, leaf curl, leaf spots, little leaf, powdery mildews, rots, rust, scab, sooty mold, viruses.

Pelargonium (Geranium).

Pear. *Pests:* aphids, beetles, borers, bugs, caterpillars, curculios, fruit flies, leaf miners, mealybugs, midges, mites, psyllids, scales, thrips, weevils. *Diseases:* anthracnose, bitter pit, blights, blotch, cankers, chlorosis, crown gall, fruit spot, leaf spots, powdery mildew, rots, rusts, scabs, virus.

Pecan. See Carya.

Pelargonium. *Pests:* aphids, beetles, caterpillars, mealybugs, mites, scales, slugs, weevils, whiteflies. *Diseases:* blight, crown gall, leaf mold, leaf spots, oedema, rots, viruses, wilt.

Penstemon. *Pests:* aphids, caterpillars, Fuller Rose beetles, root-knot nematodes. *Diseases:* leaf spots, rots, rusts.

Pentas. *Pests:* aphids, caterpillars, mealybugs, red spider mites.

Peperomia. *Diseases:* oedema, ring spot virus.

Pepper. Capsicum, which see.

Peristrophe. *Pests:* mealybugs, red spider mites.

Persea. *Pests:* aphids, beetles, borers, bugs, caterpillars, cutworms, mealybugs, mites, root-knot nematodes, scales, thrips, whiteflies. *Diseases:* anthracnose, blights, blotch, canker, leaf spots, little leaf, powdery mildew, rots, scab, virus.

Persimmon. *Pests:* beetles, borers, caterpillars, mealybugs, thrips, whiteflies. *Diseases:* anthracnose, blotches, canker, fruit spot, leaf spots, powdery mildew, rots, scab, virus.

Petrea. *Pests:* mealybugs, red spider mites, scales.

Petunia. *Pests:* aphids, beetles, caterpillars, grasshoppers, leaf hoppers, mealybugs, mites, orthezias, root-knot nematodes. *Diseases:* blight, leaf blotch, leaf spot, powdery mildew, rots, rust, viruses, wilt.

Phacelia. *Pests:* aphids. *Diseases:* leaf spot, powdery mildew, root rot, rusts, virus.

Philadelphus. *Pests:* aphids, leaf miners, root-knot nematodes. *Diseases:* blight, blotch, leaf spots, powdery mildew, root rot, rust.

Philodendron. *Pests:* mealybugs, red spider mites, scales. *Disease:* leaf spot.

Phlox. *Pests:* beetles, borers, bugs, caterpillars, leaf hoppers, red spider mites, root-knot

Philodendron.

Picea (Spruce).

nematodes, stem nematodes, scales, wireworms. *Diseases:* stem blight, canker, crown gall, crown rot, downy and powdery mildews, leaf spots, rot, rusts, viruses, wilt.

Photinia. *Pests:* caterpillars, lace bugs, scales, thrips, whiteflies. *Diseases:* anthracnose, blights, leaf spots, powdery mildews, root rot, rust, scab.

Physalis. *Pests:* aphids, beetles, caterpillars, nematodes, weevils. *Diseases:* crown rot, leaf spots, rots, rusts, smut, viruses, wilt.

Physocarpus. *Pests:* borers, whiteflies. *Diseases:* leaf spots, powdery mildew.

Physostegia. *Pests:* aphids. *Diseases:* crown rots, downy mildew, leaf spot, stem rot, rust.

Phlox divaricata (Wild Sweet William).

Picea. *Pests:* aphids, beetles, borers, caterpillars, leaf miners, mites, sawflies, scales, weevils. *Diseases:* blights, canker, needle casts, rots, rusts.

Pieris. *Pests:* lace bugs, mites, scales. *Diseases:* dieback, leaf spots.

Pilea. *Pests:* mealybugs, red spider mites.

Pink. See Dianthus.

Pinus. *Pests:* aphids, beetles, borers, caterpillars, leaf miners, mealybugs, midges, mites, sawflies, scales, spittle bugs, weevils. *Diseases:* blights, cankers, needle casts, rots, rusts.

Piper. *Pests:* mealybugs, red spider mites. *Diseases:* rots.

Piqueria. *Pests:* aphids, mealybugs, red spider mites, whiteflies. *Diseases:* root rot, virus yellows.

Pittosporum. *Pests:* aphids, mealybugs, root-knot nematodes, scales. *Diseases:* blight, crown rot, leaf spots, rots, viruses.

Platanus. *Pests:* aphids, bugs, borers, caterpillars, lace bugs, mites, scales, whiteflies. *Diseases:* anthracnose, blights, leaf spots, powdery mildews, rots, wilt or canker stain.

Platycodon. *Diseases:* blight, root rots.

Plum. *Pests:* aphids, beetles, borers, bugs, caterpillars, curculios, flies, leaf hoppers, maggots, mites, root-knot nematodes, sawflies, scales, thrips. *Diseases:* blights, blotch, cankers, chlorosis, leaf curls, leaf spots, little leaf, rots, rust, scab, viruses, wilt.

Populus (Poplar).

Plumbago. *Pests:* Fuller Rose beetles, mealybugs, red spider mites.

Plumeria. *Pests:* mealybugs, red spider mites. *Disease:* rust.

Podocarpus. *Pests:* mealybugs, red spider mites. *Diseases:* leaf spot, root rot.

Podophyllum. *Diseases:* blights, leaf spots, rust.

Poinciana. *Pests:* scales. *Diseases:* anthracnose, crown gall, root rots, rust.

Polemonium. *Diseases:* leaf spots, powdery mildews, rusts, wilts.

Polianthes. *Pests:* root-knot nematodes. *Diseases:* leaf spots, rots.

Polygala. *Diseases:* anthracnose, leaf spots, rusts.

Polygonatum. *Diseases:* leaf spots, mosaic virus, rot, rusts, smut.

Polygonum. *Pests:* beetles, root aphids. *Diseases:* leaf spots, smuts, rust.

Polyscias. *Pests:* mealybugs, red spider mites, scales.

Populus. *Pests:* aphids, beetles, borers, caterpillars, leaf hoppers, mealybugs, sawflies, scales, wasps, weevils. *Diseases:* blight, cankers, chlorosis, leaf blisters, leaf spots, powdery mildew, rots, rusts.

Potato. *Pests:* aphids, armyworms, beetles, borers, bugs, caterpillars, centipedes, cutworms, leaf hoppers, leaf miners, mealybugs, millipedes, mites, nematodes, psyllids, slugs, thrips, weevils, wireworms. *Diseases:* anthracnose, black leg, blights, blotch, canker, chlorosis, leaf spots, powdery mildews, rots, scabs, viruses, wilts.

Potentilla. *Pests:* aphids, weevils. *Diseases:* downy mildews, leaf spots, rust.

Primula. *Pests:* aphids (including root aphids), beetles, black vine weevils, mealybugs, nematodes, red spider mites, slugs, weevils, whiteflies. *Diseases:* chlorosis, gray mold blight, leaf spots, powdery mildew, rots, rusts, virus, wilt.

Prunus. Pests and diseases as for Plum and Cherry, which see.

Pseudotsuga. *Pests:* aphids, beetles, borers, caterpillars, scales, weevils. *Diseases:* blights, cankers, needle casts, rots, rust.

Psidium. *Pests:* fruit flies, mealybugs, root-knot

Quercus palustris (Pin Oak).

nematodes, scales, thrips. *Diseases:* anthracnose, blight, leaf spots, rots.

Pueraria. *Pests:* caterpillars, Japanese beetles. *Diseases:* blights, leaf spots, rots.

Pumpkin. Pests and diseases as for Squash, which see.

Punica. *Pests:* bugs, root-knot nematodes, scales, thrips, whiteflies. *Diseases:* blight, blotches, fruit spot, rots.

Pyracantha. *Pests:* aphids, caterpillars, lace bugs, scales. *Diseases:* blights (including fire blight), cankers, rots, scab.

Pyrostegia. Pests and diseases as for Bignonia, which see.

Quercus. *Pests:* beetles, borers, caterpillars, galls, lace bugs, leaf miners, mites, sawflies, scales, thrips, weevils, whiteflies. *Diseases:* anthracnose, blights, cankers, chlorosis, leaf blisters, leaf spots, powdery mildews, rots, rust, wilts.

Quince. *Pests:* aphids, beetles, caterpillars, curculios, flies, leaf miners, root-knot nematodes, sawflies, scales, weevils. *Diseases:* anthracnose, blights (including fire blight), cankers, crown gall, fruit spots, hairy root, leaf spot, powdery mildews, rots, rusts, scab.

Radish. *Pests:* aphids, beetles, caterpillars, centipedes, leaf miners, maggots, springtails, weevils, wireworms. *Diseases:* blotch, club root, downy and powdery mildews, leaf spots, rots, rust, scab, viruses, white rust.

Ranunculus. *Pests:* aphids, caterpillars, red spider mites. *Diseases:* downy and powdery mildews, gray mold blight, leaf galls, leaf spots, rots, rusts, smuts, viruses.

Raspberry. *Pests:* aphids, beetles, borers, caterpillars, leaf hoppers, maggots, mites, sawflies, scales, spittle bugs, weevils, whiteflies. *Diseases:* anthracnose, blights, cankers, chlorosis, crown gall, downy and powdery mildews, fruit spot, leaf spots, rots, rusts, viruses, wilt.

Reinwardtia. *Pests:* red spider mites, mealybugs.

Reseda. *Pests:* beetles, caterpillars, ear worms, leaf hoppers, red spider mites, root-knot nematodes, thrips. *Diseases:* leaf spot, root rot, wilt.

Rhamnus. *Pests:* aphids, borers, caterpillars, scales, whiteflies. *Diseases:* leaf spots, powdery mildew, root rot, rust.

Rhododendron. *Pests:* aphids, beetles, black vine weevils, borers, lace bugs, mealybugs, midges, mites, scales, thrips, wasps, whiteflies. *Diseases:* blights, cankers, chlorosis, flower spot, leaf galls, leaf spots, powdery mildew, rots, rusts, wilt.

Rhubarb. *Pests:* beetles, borers, caterpillars, curculios, leaf hoppers, mealybugs, root-knot nematodes, scales. *Diseases:* anthracnose, crown gall, crown rots, downy mildew, leaf spots, rots, rust, viruses.

Rhus. *Pests:* aphids, borers, caterpillars, flea beetles, mites, psyllids, scales. *Diseases:* cankers, leaf blister, leaf spots, powdery mildew, rots, rusts, wilt.

Ribes. Pests and diseases as for Currants, which see.

Quinces.

Roses.

Ricinus. *Pests:* aphids, caterpillars, leaf hoppers, leaf miners, red spider mites, scales. *Diseases:* blights, crown gall, crown rot, leaf spots, root rots, wilt.

Rivina. *Pests:* red spider mites. *Diseases:* leaf spot, root rot, rust.

Robinia. *Pests:* aphids, beetles, borers, caterpillars, leaf miners, root-knot nematodes, scales. *Diseases:* blights, cankers, chlorosis, leaf spots, powdery mildews, rots, virus, wilts.

Rochea. *Pests:* aphids, mealybugs, mites. *Diseases:* leaf spot.

Rondeletia. *Pests:* mealybugs, red spider mites, scales.

Rosa. Pests and diseases as for Rose, which see.

Rose. *Pests:* aphids, beetles, borers, bugs, caterpillars, earwigs, galls, leaf hoppers, maggots, mealybugs, midges, mites, root-knot nematodes, sawflies, scales, thrips, weevils, whiteflies. *Diseases:* anthracnose, blights, cankers, chlorosis, crown gall, crown rot, dieback, downy and powdery mildews, hairy root, leaf spots, molds, rots, rusts, viruses, wilts.

Saintpaulia (African Violet).

Rubus. Pests and diseases as for Blackberry and Raspberry, which see.

Rudbeckia. *Pests:* aphids, beetles, borers, bugs, caterpillars. *Diseases:* crown rot, downy and powdery mildews, leaf gall, leaf spots, rots, rusts, smut, viruses, wilt.

Ruellia. *Pests:* mealybugs, red spider mites. *Diseases:* leaf spot, root rot, rusts.

Rutabaga. Pests and diseases as for Turnip, which see.

Saintpaulia. *Pests:* mealybugs, mites, nematodes. *Diseases:* gray mold blight, powdery mildew, ring spot, root and crown rot.

Salix. *Pests:* aphids, beetles, borers, caterpillars, galls, lace bugs, mites, root-knot nematodes, sawflies, scales, thrips, tree hoppers, wasps, weevils. *Diseases:* blight, cankers, crown gall, leaf spots, powdery mildew, rots, rusts, scabs.

Salpiglossis. *Pests:* aphids, nematodes (including root-knot nematodes). *Diseases:* virus yellows, wilts.

Salsify. *Pests:* caterpillars, leaf nematodes, tarnished plant bugs. *Diseases:* blight, leaf spots, powdery mildew, rots, viruses, white rust, verticillium wilt.

Salvia. *Pests:* aphids, beetles, borers, caterpillars, leaf hoppers, leaf nematodes, mites, orthezias, root-knot nematodes, tarnished plant bugs, whiteflies. *Diseases:* downy and powdery mildews, leaf spots, rots, rusts, virus yellows.

Sambucus. *Pests:* aphids, beetles, borers, bugs, caterpillars, mealybugs, scales, thrips. *Diseases:* blights, cankers, leaf spots, powdery mildews, rots, rust, wilt.

Sanchezia. *Pests:* mealybugs, red spider mites, scales. *Disease:* root rot.

Sanguinaria. *Diseases:* gray mold blight, leaf spots, root rot.

Sansevieria. *Pests:* mealybugs, root-knot nematodes. *Diseases:* leaf spots, rots.

Sapindus. *Pests:* aphids. *Diseases:* blights, leaf spots, powdery mildew.

Saponaria. *Diseases:* leaf spots, rust.

A hybrid Saxifraga.

Sassafras. *Pests:* caterpillars, Japanese beetles, scales. *Diseases:* cankers, leaf spots, powdery mildew, rots, virus, wilt.

Saxifraga. *Pests:* aphids, mealybugs, red spider mites. *Diseases:* gray mold blight, leaf spots, powdery mildews, rusts.

Scabiosa. *Pests:* Fuller Rose beetles, leaf hoppers, tarnished plant bugs. *Diseases:* crown rot, powdery mildew, rots, virus yellows.

Schefflera. *Pests:* mealybugs, red spider mites, scales.

Schinus. *Pests:* caterpillars, mealybugs, root-knot nematodes, scales, thrips. *Diseases:* rots, wilt.

Schismatoglottis. *Pests:* mealybugs, red spider mites, scales. *Diseases:* leaf spot, rots.

Schizanthus. *Pests:* aphids, leaf hoppers, nematodes, red spider mites. *Diseases:* anthracnose, stem rot.

Scilla. *Pests:* aphids. *Diseases:* blight, mosaic virus, rot, smut.

Scindapsus. *Pests:* mealybugs, red spider mites, scales. *Diseases:* leaf spot.

Scutellaria. *Diseases:* leaf spots, powdery mildews, rots.

Sedum. *Pests:* aphids, mealybugs, root-knot nematodes, scales. *Diseases:* crown rot, leaf spots, rots, rusts.

Sempervivum. *Pests:* mealybugs. *Diseases:* rots, rust.

Senecio. *Pests:* aphids, root-knot nematodes, whiteflies. *Diseases:* leaf gall, leaf spots, powdery mildews, rots, rusts, smut, virus, white rust, wilts. (For Senecio cruentus, see Cineraria).

Sequoia. *Pests:* borers, caterpillars, mealybugs, scales. *Diseases:* blights, canker, rots.

Sequoiadendron. Pests and diseases as for Sequoia.

Shallot. Pests and diseases as for Onion, which see.

Sidalcea. *Pests:* aphids, red spider mites. *Diseases:* leaf spot, rusts.

Silene. *Diseases:* leaf spots, rusts, smuts.

Silphium. *Diseases:* downy and powdery mildews, leaf spots, rusts.

Smilacina. *Diseases:* leaf spots, rot, rusts, smut.

Smithiantha. *Pests:* mealybugs, mites, thrips. *Diseases:* rots.

Solanum. *Pests:* aphids, caterpillars, red spider mites, root-knot nematodes, thrips, whiteflies. *Diseases:* crown gall, gray mold blight, leaf spots, oedema, viruses, wilt.

Sophora. *Pests:* leaf hoppers, mites, nematodes. *Diseases:* dieback, leaf spot, powdery mildew, root rot, rust, twig blight.

Sorbus. *Pests:* aphids, beetles, borers, caterpillars, leaf hoppers, mites, sawflies, scales. *Diseases:*

Spathiphyllum floribundum.

blights (including fire blight), cankers, crown gall, leaf spots, rots, rusts, scab.

Spathiphylum. *Pests:* mealybugs, red spider mites, scales.

Sphaeralcea. *Diseases:* powdery mildew, rusts.

Spinach. *Pests:* aphids, armyworms, beetles, caterpillars, cutworms, grasshoppers, leaf miners, maggots, springtails. *Diseases:* anthracnose, chlorosis, downy mildew, leaf spots, molds, rots, rust, smut, viruses, white rust, wilt.

Spiraea. *Pests:* aphids, black vine weevil, caterpillars, mites, nematodes, scales. *Diseases:* blights (including fire blight), canker, hairy root, leaf spots, powdery mildews, root rot.

Sprekelia. *Pests:* bulb mites, mealybugs, thrips. *Diseases:* leaf spots.

Squash. *Pests:* aphids, beetles, borers, bugs, caterpillars, leaf hoppers, nematodes, springtails, thrips, whiteflies. *Diseases:* anthracnose, blights, blossom end rot, chlorosis, crown rot, downy and powdery mildews, leaf spots, molds, rots, scab, viruses, wilts.

Stephanotis. *Pests:* mealybugs, red spider mites, scales.

Stevia. See Piqueria.

Stock. See Mathiola.

Stokesia. *Diseases:* blight, leaf spot, mosaic virus.

Strawberry. *Pests:* ants, aphids, beetles, borers, bugs, caterpillars, crickets, curculios, earwigs, leaf miners, mealybugs, millipedes, mites, nematodes, rootworms, sawflies, scales, slugs, spittle bugs, weevils, whiteflies. *Diseases:* anthracnose, blights, crown rots, downy and powdery mildews, leaf scorch, leaf spots, rots, viruses, wilt.

Strelitzia. *Pests:* mealybugs, red spider mites, scales.

Streptocarpus. *Pests:* aphids, black vine weevils, mealybugs, mites. *Disease:* crown rot.

Streptosolon. *Pests:* aphids, mealybugs, red spider mites, whiteflies.

Sweet Pea. See Lathyrus.

Sweet Potato. *Pests:* aphids, armyworms, beetles, bugs, caterpillars, leaf hoppers, maggots, thrips, weevils, whiteflies. *Diseases:* blights, crown rot, leaf spots, rots, rust, scurf, viruses, white rust, wilts.

Symphoricarpus. *Pests:* aphids, caterpillars, scales, whiteflies. *Diseases:* anthracnose, crown gall, leaf spots, powdery mildews, rots, rusts.

Syngonium. *Pests:* mealybugs, thrips. *Disease:* leaf spot.

Syringa. *Pests:* aphids, beetles, borers, caterpillars, giant hornet, leaf miners, scales, whiteflies. *Diseases:* anthracnose, blights, canker, crown gall, dieback, graft incompatibility

Squash.

Syringa (Lilac).

(physiological), leaf spots, powdery mildew, rots, virus.

Tabernaemontana. *Pests:* mealybugs, scales. *Diseases:* leaf spots.

Tagetes. *Pests:* beetles, borers, bugs, caterpillars, cutworms, leaf hoppers, mites, root nematodes, root-knot nematodes, slugs. *Diseases:* blights, crown rot, leaf spots, rots, rusts, viruses, wilts.

Tamarix. *Pests:* borers, scales. *Diseases:* powdery mildew, rots.

Tanacetum. *Pests:* root-knot nematodes. *Diseases:* leaf spot, powdery mildew, rust.

Taxodium. *Diseases:* canker, rots, twig blight.

Taxus. *Pests:* black vine weevils, mealybugs, mites, scales. *Diseases:* blights, rots.

Tecoma. Pests and diseases as for Bignonia, which see.

Teucrium. *Diseases:* downy and powdery mildews, leaf spots, rust.

Thalia. *Pests:* red spider mites. *Diseases:* leaf spot, rust.

Thalictrum. *Pests:* aphids. *Diseases:* downy and powdery mildews, leaf spots, rusts, smuts.

Thunbergia. *Pests:* aphids, mealybugs, red spider mites, root-knot nematodes, scales. *Diseases:* crown gall.

Thuya. *Pests:* aphids, bagworms, beetles, borers, caterpillars, leaf miners, mealybugs, mites, scales. *Diseases:* blights, canker, diebacks, needle cast, rots.

Tilia (Linden).

Tomatoes.

Thymus. *Pests:* mealybugs. *Disease:* root rot.

Tiarella. *Disease:* rust.

Tilia. *Pests:* aphids, beetles, borers, caterpillars, lace bugs, leaf miners, mealybugs, red spider mites, sawflies, scales, whiteflies. *Diseases:* anthracnose, blight, cankers, leaf spots, powdery mildews, rots, sooty mold, wilt.

Tomato. *Pests:* aphids, armyworms, beetles, borers, bugs, caterpillars, centipedes, crickets, cutworms, leaf hoppers, millipedes, mites, psyllids, root-knot nematodes, slugs, springtails, thrips, whiteflies. *Diseases:* anthracnose, blights, blossom end rot, cankers, crown gall, crown rot, downy mildew, fruit spot, hairy root, leaf spots, leaf molds, oedema, rots, scab, viruses, wilts.

Trachelospermum. *Pests:* mealybugs, red spider mites, scales.

Trachymene. *Pests:* aphids, red spider mites, root-knot nematodes. *Diseases:* stem and root rots.

Tradescantia. *Pests:* caterpillars, mealybugs, root-knot nematodes, scales. *Diseases:* blight, leaf spots, rust.

Trillium. *Diseases:* leaf spots, rust, smut, stem rot.

Tritonia. Pests and diseases as for Montbretia, which see.

Trollius. *Diseases:* leaf spots, smut.

Tropaeolum. *Pests:* aphids, bugs, caterpillars, flea beetles, leaf miners, red spider mites,

Tulipa.

root-knot nematodes, thrips. *Diseases:* gray mold blight, leaf spots, rust, viruses, wilt.

Tsuga. *Pests:* borers, caterpillars, leaf miners, mites, scales. *Diseases:* blights, cankers, rots, rusts.

Tulipa. *Pests:* aphids, bulb flies, millipedes, mites, nematodes, wireworms. *Diseases:* anthracnose, blight, crown rot, rots, viruses.

Turnip. *Pests:* aphids, beetles, bugs, caterpillars, curculios, leaf miners, maggots, millipedes, root-knot nematodes, thrips, weevils. *Diseases:* anthracnose, blackleg, club root, crown gall, crown rot, downy and powdery mildews, heart rot, leaf spots, rots, scab, viruses, white rust, wilt.

Ulmus. *Pests:* aphids, beetles, borers, bugs, caterpillars, lace bugs, leaf hoppers, leaf miners, red spider mites, scales, weevils. *Diseases:* cankers, leaf blister, leaf spots, powdery mildews, rots, twig blight, viruses, wilts (including Dutch Elm disease).

Umbellularia. *Pests:* aphids, caterpillars, scales, thrips, whiteflies. *Diseases:* cankers, rots.

Vaccinium. *Pests:* beetles, borers, caterpillars, curculios, galls, leaf hoppers, maggots, scales, spittle bugs, thrips, weevils. *Diseases:* blights, canker, crown gall, galls, leaf spots, powdery mildew, rots, rusts, virus.

Valeriana. *Pests:* Japanese beetles. *Diseases:* leaf spots, powdery mildew, rots, rusts.

Vallota. *Pests:* mealybugs. *Disease:* leaf scorch.

Verbascum. *Pests:* root-knot nematodes. *Diseases:* downy and powdery mildews, leaf spots, root rot.

Verbena. *Pests:* aphids, beetles, bugs, caterpillars, leaf miners, mites, root-knot nematodes, orthezias, scales, thrips, whiteflies. *Diseases:* blight, downy and powdery mildews, leaf spots, rots, rusts.

Veronica. *Pests:* caterpillars, root-knot nematodes. *Diseases:* downy and powdery mildews, leaf galls, leaf spots, rots, smut.

Viburnum. *Pests:* aphids, beetles, borers, bugs, caterpillars, galls, leaf hoppers, mites, plant hoppers, root-knot nematodes, scales, thrips, whiteflies. *Diseases:* anthracnose, blights, canker, crown gall, downy and powdery mildews, leaf spots, root rots, rusts, wilt.

Vinca. *Pests:* aphids, beetles, leaf hoppers, orthezias, root-knot nematodes, scales. *Diseases:* dieback canker, gray mold blight, leaf mold, leaf spots, stem and root rot, virus yellows.

Viola. *Pests:* aphids, beetles, caterpillars, cutworms, mealybugs, midges, mites, root nematodes, root-knot nematodes, sawflies, slugs, sowbugs, wireworms. *Diseases:* anthracnose, crown rots, downy and powdery mildews, leaf gall, leaf spots, oedema, rots, rusts, scab, smut, virus.

Watercress. *Pests:* aphids, beetles, caterpillars, sowbugs. *Diseases:* leaf spot, rust, white rust.

Viburnum Tinus (Laurestinus).

Weigelia.

Watermelon. *Pests:* aphids, beetles, caterpillars, crickets, leaf miners, millipedes, scales, wireworms. *Diseases:* anthracnose, blights, blossom end rot, crown rot, downy and powdery mildews, fruit spot, leaf spots, rots, viruses, wilts.

Watsonia. Pests and diseases as for Gladiolus, which see.

Weigela. *Pests:* four-lined plant bugs, mealybugs, root-knot nematodes, scales. *Diseases:* crown gall, leaf spots, root rot.

Wisteria. *Pests:* beetles, caterpillars, mealybugs, plant hoppers, scales, weevils. *Diseases:* canker, crown gall, leaf spots, powdery mildew, rots, mosaic virus.

Xanthorhiza. *Disease:* leaf spot.

Xanthosma. *Diseases:* rots.

Yucca. *Pests:* aphids, borers, bugs, caterpillars, mealybugs, mites, root-knot nematodes, scale, thrips. *Diseases:* blights, leaf molds, leaf spots, rust, stem rot.

Zantedeschia. *Pests:* aphids, bulb mites, caterpillars, mealybugs, root-knot nematodes, thrips. *Diseases:* blight, crown rot, leaf spots, rots, virus.

Zebrina. Pests and diseases as for Tradescantia, which see.

Zephyranthes. *Diseases:* leaf spots, rot.

Zinnia. *Pests:* aphids, beetles, borers, bugs, caterpillars, leaf hoppers, mealybugs, mites, nematodes (including root-knot nematodes), thrips. *Diseases:* blights, crown rot, leaf spot, powdery mildew, rots, viruses.

INSECTS AND OTHER SMALL PESTS

Many creatures are loosely called insects although they are not insects in the scientific sense. True insects have the body usually divided into three distinct regions in the adult stage: the head, thorax and abdomen. They have three pairs of legs. Some mites have three pairs of legs in the immature stages, and four pairs as adults, so that the mere presence of three pairs of legs is no proof that a creature is an insect.

To laymen, any small crawling or flying creature is usually regarded as an insect, so that mites, sowbugs and symphylids, while not true insects, are looked on as such in the garden and so are included in this section. Included, too, are such creatures as slugs, snails and nematodes.

Many kinds of insects are injurious to plants. Damage is done by sucking the plant juices, by chewing foliage and other parts, by cutting off sap circulation by boring through tissues, and by spreading some diseases. Some insects feed only on one kind of plant or on closely related plants; others range over a wide variety.

Insects cause tremendous crop losses throughout the world and immense sums of money are spent on research, insecticides, equipment and labor to try to keep them under control, yet still they persist. The following list includes insects and other small pests that are most common in gardens.

Ants. There are many kinds of ants, varying greatly in their mode of living and general habits. In gardens some are a nuisance because they nurture aphids and scale insects for the sake of the honeydew these insects secrete. Ant nests in lawns and flower beds are unsightly and likely to be harmful to plants growing nearby.

Chlordane powder dusted where ants run is effective and is reasonably safe to use in houses if

A 10 per cent chlordane dust being sprinkled on and near small hills of soil which ants have thrown up between paving stones.

ants appear. For lawns and borders, dust the powder over the entire nest area. Aldrin and dieldrin dusts and sprays are also effective if used in the same way. Nests may also be destroyed by fumigation. Punch one or more holes, about 8 in. deep and 6 in. apart, in each nest and pour a teaspoon of carbon bisulfide or Cyanogas in each hole and cover with soil. Carbon bisulphide is inflammable; keep flames away from it.

Ant baits are often effective. A poison syrup may be made by dissolving 6 oz. of sugar in 1 pint of hot water, then stirring in 10 grains of sodium arsenite. Saturate pieces of stale bread or sponge with the solution, put them in small tins with holes punched in the lids and sides, then place them near the nests or where the ants run. Prepared ant baits containing chlordane, sodium arsenite or thallium sulfate are sold under trade names. They are easier to handle and perhaps are safer to use where children and pets are about, than the home-prepared syrup.

Argentine Ant (Iridomyrmex humilis) is a small brown ant common in the southeastern United States and in California. Nests are made under pavements, in gardens, lawns and orchards.

Black Carpenter Ant (Camponotus pennsylvanicus) is a large black ant, which is common in the eastern United States. It nests in logs and tree trunks, particularly Pines and Spruces.

Cornfield Ant (Lasius alienus) is a small brown ant which is found over most of North America, and nests mostly in open ground and in rotted wood. It distributes Corn root aphids.

California Harvester Ant (Pogonomyrmex californicus) is common in California and the Southwest. It nests in sandy places, and the light red, vicious workers clear the ground of vegetation.

Imported Fire Ant (Solenopsis saevissima Richteri), a native Argentina which now infests 20 million acres in the South. It stings people and farm animals savagely and feeds on newly-planted seeds and on the bark of Citrus trees.

Red Harvester Ant (Pogonomyrmex barbatus) is red with a black head. It is common in Arizona and other parts of the Southwest. The nests are very deep in the ground. Damage is caused by the ants' clearing away vegetation and leaving bare circles of earth.

Aphids. Aphids or plant lice are widespread pests that feed on a great variety of plants. There are numerous species. Some are green in color, others black, red, brown, purple and yellow. Some are covered with fine waxy particles which give to them a mealy appearance, others are covered with waxen threads and appear woolly.

Aphids are soft-bodied, often winged in the adult stages, always wingless in their immature forms. Their life histories, in some cases simple, in others more complicated, are most interesting. In a simple example, eggs are laid in the fall and hatch in spring into wingless females known as stem mothers. These produce, without fertilization, generation after generation of living young which, in turn, repeat the process with great rapidity. Some of these young may develop wings and migrate to other plants. At the end of the season a generation of true sexual aphids appears and fertilized eggs are laid for overwintering. In warm climates and in greenhouses, living young may be produced for more than a year without an intervening egg stage.

Aphids feed by sucking the sap of plants, thereby causing stunted growth, distorted leaves, and other malformations. Some kinds feed on the roots of certain plants, others cause the formation of galls on leaves, stems and roots and live in these for a period. Aphids, like certain scale insects and mealybugs, secrete a sweet sticky

Aphids suck the juices of the plants they infest. Here they are feeding on the young leaf of a Martha Washington Geranium.

substance called honeydew. This is sought by ants as food and it forms a medium on which sooty mold fungus grows. Plants infested with aphids are often disfigured by a covering of this sootlike fungus growth. In some cases aphids are distributors of mosaic and other virus diseases.

Certain insects play a part in keeping down aphids. Among these are aphis lions (the larvae of lacewing flies), the larvae of hover flies and the larval and beetle forms of lady beetles or ladybugs. These are capable of consuming a great many aphids. Some aphids are killed by a parasitic wasp which lays an egg in the aphid. The young wasp feeds on the host until ready to emerge from the dead body.

Sprays and dusts are usually necessary to obtain complete and satisfactory control. Lindane, 1 level tablespoon of wettable powder in 1 gallon of water, is effective. Nicotine dusts and sprays also give effective control, especially when temperatures are high. Rotenone, pyrethrum and malathion kill aphids. Rotenone and pyrethrum are safe to use on food crops. Thiodan is a new, highly effective aphid killer. Herbaceous plants growing in pots or benches in greenhouses may be protected from aphids by drenching the soil with demeton or OMPA. Every effort should be made to keep down weeds in the vicinity of gardens and in greenhouses. These may harbor aphids and serve as centers of infestation.

Root aphids are not easy to control. Every

Aphids commonly cluster in large numbers towards the tips of young shoots of Roses. Unless they are promptly eradicated they cause serious distortion and damage.

Root aphids are less easy to detect than those that feed aboveground. They are common on China Asters and occur also on many other kinds of plants.

Pineapple-like galls formed at the bases of the young shoots of Spruces are a characteristic symptom of infestation by the eastern Spruce gall aphid.

effort should be made to eliminate ants which transport the aphids from plant to plant. Mixing tobacco powder (ground up tobacco stems and leaves, sold by dealers in horticultural supplies) with the soil at planting time and watering the roots of affected plants with a nicotine insecticide or with lindane are recommended procedures. Bulbs and roots in storage may be dusted with tobacco powder.

Gall-forming aphids that attack Spruces (Picea) and Douglas Firs (Pseudotsuga) are controlled by cutting off and burning the galls on the Spruces before they open and release the aphids in early summer and by applying, if necessary, a dormant oil spray, diluted as recommended by the manufacturer for use on evergreens, before new growth starts in spring. Affected Spruces and Douglas Firs may also be sprayed in the fall or early spring with malathion plus a spreader-sticker.

Bean Aphid (Aphid Fabae) is a dark aphid that winters over on Euonymus and Dock (Rumex) plants, later infesting such plants as Globe Artichokes, Beans, Beets, Dahlias, Nasturtiums, Peas, Rhubarb, Spinach, Thistles and some other weeds.

Grape Phylloxera Aphid (Phylloxera Vitifoliae) makes galls on the leaves and roots. It is not serious on varieties of Grapes that have been developed from native American species, but is destructive to varieties of the European species, Vitis vinifera, which are commonly grown in California. The chief method of control is by grafting vinifera varieties on roots of native American kinds.

Green Peach Aphid (Myzus Persicae) is a green aphid that is known as greenfly in Europe and is widely distributed over the United States and Canada. It is often abundant on fruit trees such as Apricots, Cherries, Oranges, Peaches and Plums and on such vegetables as Beets, Cabbages, Cucumbers, Eggplants, Lettuce, Peppers, Potatoes, Spinach and Tomatoes. It is also common on many ornamentals, including Asters, Calendulas, Carnations, Chrysanthemums, Dahlias, Irises, Lilies, Poppies, Snapdragons, Primroses, Tulips and Verbenas.

Hop Aphid (Phorodon humili) is a pale yellow-green aphid that winters in the egg stage on Apple, Cherry, Peach and Plum trees. Migrants fly to Hops and Sunflowers for the summer.

Lily Aphid (Myzus circumflexus), a yellow and black aphid, is common on Lilies and numerous greenhouse and outdoor plants, including Asparagus, Anemones, Calendulas, Cyclamens, Freesias, Fuchsias, Heliotropes, Hydrangeas, Oxalis, Rudbeckias and Snowberries.

Melon Aphid (Aphis Gossypii), a small aphid, mostly dark green but varying to yellowish, brown or black, is widely distributed over North America. It is very destructive to many kinds of plants in greenhouses and outdoors, and is most serious in the South and Southwest. In the South it is known as the Cotton aphid, in Florida and California as the Orange aphid, because of its prevalence on these plants. Cucumbers, Melons and Squash plants are liable to attack everywhere.

Among other plants that this aphid infests are Asparagus, Asters, Avocados, Begonias, Catalpas, Chrysanthemums, Cinerarias, Dogwoods, Eggplants, Hydrangeas, Lilies, Okra, Pomegranates, Roses, Spinach, Strawberries, Sunflowers, Verbenas and weeds such as Dock, Pigweed and Shepherd's-Purse.

This aphid is a distributor of Cucumber and Melon mosaic disease, a virus infection which also affects Lilies and many other plants.

Norway Maple Aphid (Periphyllus lyropictus) is a large, hairy, green to brown aphid that often causes a heavy summer dropping of green leaves from Norway Maples. Sidewalks and parked cars are made sticky with the copious amount of honeydew dropped on them.

Potato Aphid (Macrosiphum Solanifolii) is a pink and green aphid common through the United States and Canada. It winters in the form of black eggs on Rose bushes. The young feed on the new Rose growth in spring. Later, winged forms develop and fly to Potatoes and other plants. Potato leaves are distorted and the tops often turn brown and die before the tubers mature. Other plants often infected are Apples, Asters, Beans, Corn, Eggplants, Gladioli, Peas, Peppers, Sweet Potatoes, Tomatoes, Turnips and numerous weeds.

Spruce Gall Aphids (Chermes Cooleyi and Chermes Abietis). The first of these, the Blue Spruce gall aphid, infests Colorado Blue Spruce, Sitka Spruce, Engelman's Spruce and Douglas Fir. The second, the eastern Spruce gall aphid, infests Black Spruce, Engelman's Spruce, Norway Spruce and White Spruce.

On Colorado Blue Spruce, Engelman's Spruce and Sitka Spruce, the Blue Spruce gall aphid forms galls at the ends of the shoots. The galls are 1-2 in. long and are composed of thickened stems and enlarged needles (leaves). They are green or purplish at first, but become yellow after the galls open and release the aphids in summer.

Next, the released aphids transfer their attentions to Douglas Fir, upon which they lay eggs in nests made of a white waxy material. From these hatch waxy-fringed green nymphs (immature aphids) which live on the leaves of the Douglas Fir until spring, then lay eggs. Some of these give rise to females, which fly back to the Spruce and there lay eggs which develop into young that cause galls on the new shoots of the Spruce.

Spruce gall aphids must have two alternate hosts, Spruce and Douglas Fir. As a result of the activities of these aphids, Spruces may be stunted or killed, and Douglas Firs may drop their leaves prematurely.

Douglas Firs and susceptible Spruces should not be planted near one another. Other control measures are to cut off and burn the galls before they open in July, and to apply a dormant-strength (for evergreens) miscible oil spray before new growth begins in spring.

The eastern Spruce gall aphid causes cone-shaped galls formed of enlarged leaves at the bases of the young shoots. The galls are ½-1 in. long. They are green marked with purplish division lines; after the aphids are released from them they turn brown. The galls open and the aphids are released in summer. Eggs are then laid, and the young which hatch from them live over winter in crevices around the buds. In spring they complete their growth and lay eggs; these give rise to the young, which cause another batch of galls. Unlike the Blue Spruce gall aphid, the eastern Spruce gall aphid needs no alternate host.

The best control measures are to cut off and burn the galls when this is feasible; to spray in spring, just before new growth begins, with a miscible oil diluted to the dormant strength recommended for evergreens, or with malathion plus a sticker and spreader. The latter may also be used in the fall.

Western Aster Root Aphid (Anuraphis Middletonii) feeds on roots of China Asters, Calendulas, Cosmos, Dahlias, Erigerons, Sweet Peas and other plants.

Armyworms. Armyworms are larvae (caterpillars) of various moths. They are more injurious to field crops than to gardens. Their common name refers to the fact that they move from place to place in large numbers, eating great amounts of vegetation as they go.

Scattering poison mash baits and dusting with a mixture of 1 part calcium arsenate and 3 parts hydrated lime controls these pests. Thuricide is very effective against armyworms.

Armyworms are very destructive caterpillars.

The hanging spindle-shaped bodies shown here attached to a Red Cedar, Juniperus virginiana, are the houses or bags of the evergreen bagworm.

especially recommended for home gardens. A 10 per cent DDT dust gives good results and so does dieldrin.

Armyworm (Pseudaletia unipuncta) is common in the Midwest. This caterpillar is dark green with white stripes down the sides and middle of the back. In epidemic outbreaks this insect travels in vast numbers and devours all vegetation.

Fall Armyworm (Laphygma frugiperda) does not appear until fall in the northern United States. The caterpillars are light tan to green or black with three yellowish hairlines down the back and a V-shaped white mark on the head. Among their food plants are Beans, Cabbages, Corn, Cucumbers, Potatoes and Tomatoes.

Southern Armyworm (Prodenia eridania) is common in Florida, where it is a serious pest of Celery and Sweet Potatoes. The caterpillars are black or are yellow with black markings.

Yellow-striped Armyworm (Prodenia Ornithogalli) often defoliates whole fields of Sweet Potatoes in Florida. In California it infests field and truck crops, flowers, fruits and trees.

Bagworms. Bagworms are caterpillars that carry around with them spindle-shaped houses or bags which are usually covered with bits of leaves and other debris of the plant on which they feed. The commonest kind is sometimes called the evergreen bagworm, although it attacks a wide variety of deciduous (leaf-losing) trees as well as evergreens. This kind, Thyridopteryx ephemeraeformis, is a general feeder on various trees, including Boxelders, Locusts, Maples, Sycamores and Sweet Gum, and is especially damaging to Arborvitaes, Red Cedars and other evergreens. The caterpillars hatch in spring from eggs laid in a sac or bag in the fall. As they feed, each builds a bag for itself and increases the size of this as it grows. The bag is taken along whenever the insect moves to a new location in search of leaves on which to feed.

Collect and burn the bags in winter. Spray with lead arsenate, 3 tablespoons to 1 gallon of water, or with Sevin, 2 tablespoons to 1 gallon of water, when the caterpillars begin to crawl.

Beetles. These comprise the largest group of insects. About 24,000 species are recorded as inhabiting the United States and Canada. A few destroy other insects but many are destructive to plants. Both the larvae and the adults feed by biting and chewing. Beetles that have heads prolonged into conspicuous beaks or snouts with their mouths at the ends are called curculios and weevils and are discussed below under Curculios and under Weevils.

Asiatic Garden Beetle (Autoserica castanea) is a cinnamon-brown beetle that is spreading along the Atlantic seaboard. Its eggs are usually laid in grass. The young grubs do some feeding on roots and then burrow deep into the soil for the winter. In spring they come near to the surface and again feed on roots. Adults emerge in

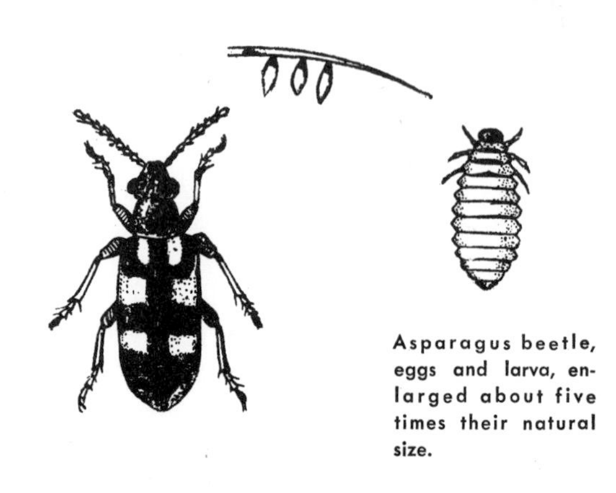

Asparagus beetle, eggs and larva, enlarged about five times their natural size.

[14]
Currants eaten by larvae of the Imported Currantworm, a Sawfly

[16]
Leaf Hoppers

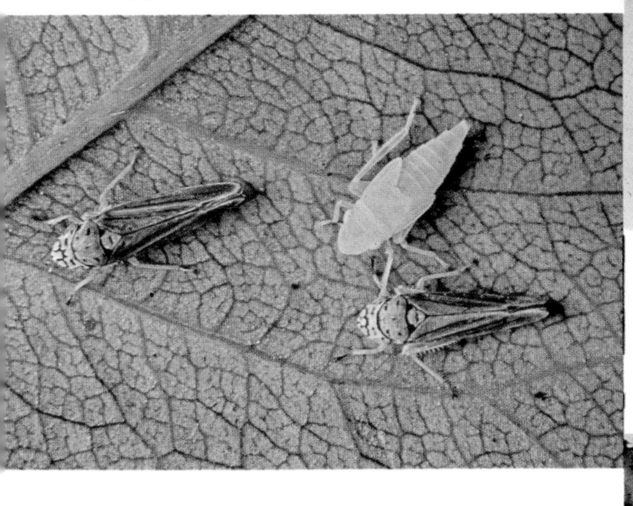

[18]
Seed-Corn Maggot

[13]
Eastern Tent Caterpillar

[15]
Earwig

[17]
Birch foliage damaged by Leaf Miners

[19]
Root-feeding Mealybugs

[20]
Long-tailed Mealybugs

[21]
Millipede

[22]
Bulb Mites

[23]
Two-spotted Spider Mites

[24]
Spruce damaged by Two-spotted Spider Mites

A grub (larva) of the Asiatic garden beetle.

summer and feed at night on the leaves of many kinds of plants. More than one hundred different flowers and vegetables, including Asters, Delphiniums, Roses, Zinnias, Carrots, Corn, Peppers, and Turnips, are liable to their attack, also Cherry and Peach trees and lawn Grasses.

Grub-proof lawns by applying 2.5 per cent aldrin dust at the rate of 52 oz. to 1,000 sq. ft., chlordane 5 per cent dust at the rate of 5 lb. to 1,000 sq. ft., dieldrin 2 per cent dust at the rate of 4 lb. per 1,000 sq. ft., or with 35 oz. of 2.5 per cent heptachlor dust per 1,000 sq. ft. Spray or dust the foliage of ornamentals with these same insecticides, but for vegetables use rotenone, which is nonpoisonous to humans.

Asparagus Beetle (Crioceris Asparagi). A common pest of garden Asparagus, this slender, 1/4-in.-long beetle feeds on the shoots in spring, often almost completely defoliating the plants and staining them with a dark-colored liquid. The beetles are metallic blue-black with a reddish head and three yellow squares on each wing cover. Their eggs are dark brown and are attached by their ends to the Asparagus stems and leaves. From the eggs hatch wrinkled, olive-green or gray larvae, each about 1/3 in. long, and these feed on the stems and leaves of the Asparagus for somewhat less than two weeks, then pupate in the soil. There are two, three or more generations a year. This insect winters as a mature beetle in the places in the garden that are protected and sheltered.

Control is had by cutting the young shoots frequently in spring and by dusting, at that time, with pyrethrum, rotenone or malathion insecticides. It is helpful to apply a 10 per cent DDT dust after the harvesting season has ended.

Another beetle, the spotted Asparagus beetle (Crioceris duodecimpunctata), feeds on the berries only. The adult is reddish-orange or tan colored and has six clearly visible black spots on each wing cover. Control may be had by picking the berries or by following the recommendations given above for controlling the Asparagus beetle.

Bark Beetles include several species of small dark beetles that injure trees by tunneling under the bark. Two species, the small European bark beetle (Scolytus multistriatus) and the native Elm bark beetle (Hylurgopinus rufipes), are considered responsible for the spread of the fungus which causes the Dutch Elm disease.

Control is effected by cleaning up and burning dead wood and badly infested trees. Everything possible, including fertilizing, watering in dry weather, etc., should be done to maintain the trees in good health. Spraying with DDT or with methoxychlor is also effective.

Blister Beetles (species of Epicauta) are long, slender beetles with black, gray or striped wings. The grubs eat the eggs of grasshoppers but the adults chew the leaves and flowers of many plants in summer. Their bodies contain cantharidin, a powerful blistering agent. Gloves should be worn if hand-picking is done.

Control is effected by using 5 per cent DDT dust on ornamentals. A rotenone-pyrethrum dust is safe to use on vegetables. The beetles can be hand-picked or knocked into a container of water with a half-inch layer of kerosene floating on top of it.

Click Beetles are a large family of elongated

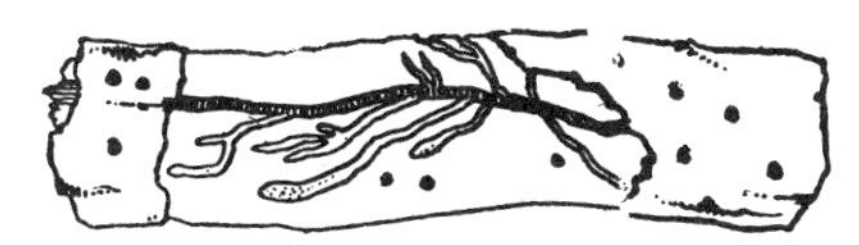

Bark beetles and their grubs attack and injure trees by tunneling just beneath the bark.

The Colorado Potato beetle is a serious pest of Potatoes and botanically related plants. It is yellow with black stripes.

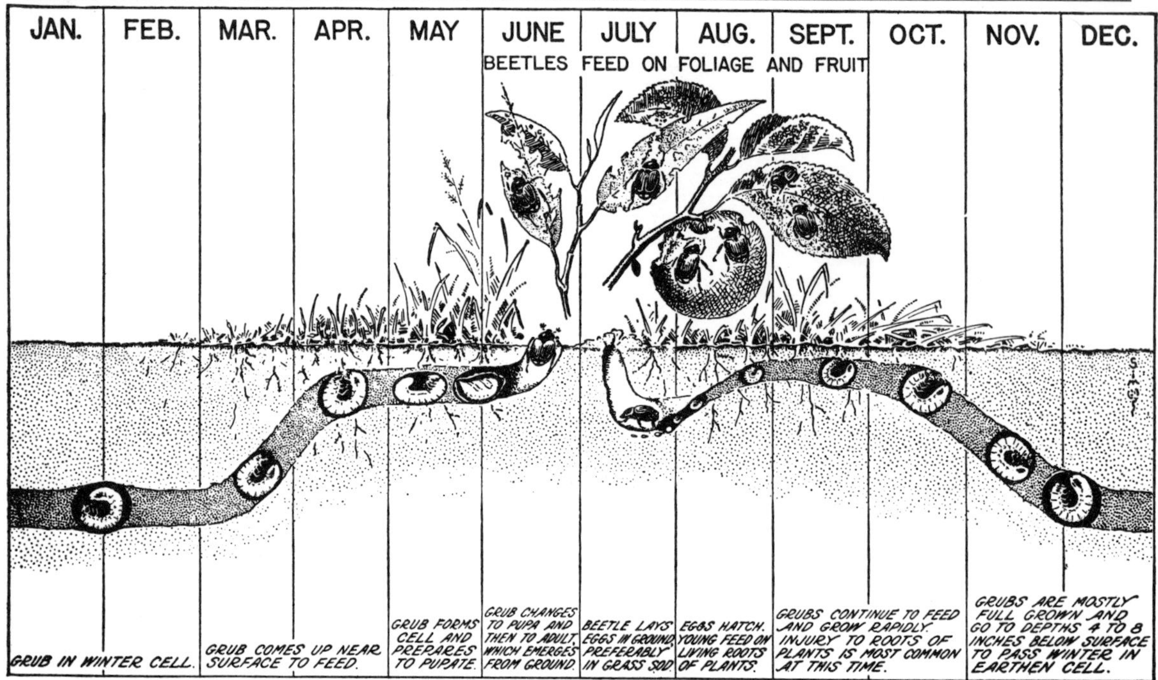

Courtesy U.S. Dept. of Agr.

Seasonal life cycle of the Japanese beetle.

beetles. Most of the damage they do is caused by the larvae, which are called wireworms. See Wireworms, below.

Colorado Potato Beetle (Leptinotarsa decemlineata) is a yellow and black striped beetle which lays clusters of yellowish eggs on the undersides of leaves. These hatch within a week into humpbacked red grubs capable of quickly defoliating Potato plants. They may feed also on botanically related plants such as Eggplants, Peppers and Tomatoes.

Spraying the foliage with 50 per cent Sevin wettable powder at the rate of 2 tablespoons per gallon of water will control this beetle. Spraying or dusting with DDT is also effective.

Flea Beetles comprise a large group of small jumping beetles. Early in the season they eat tiny holes in the leaves of numerous plants, particularly Cabbages, Eggplants, Peppers, Potatoes and Tomatoes.

Spray or dust early with rotenone, methoxychlor or Thiodan. Bordeaux mixture may be sprayed on foliage to serve as a repellent.

Fuller Rose Beetle (Pantomorus Godmani) is a grayish-brown weevil with a short broad snout. It feeds at night on the leaves of various greenhouse plants in the North and on many kinds of outdoor plants in warmer climates. The larvae are white grubs which live chiefly on the roots of Blackberries, Raspberries, Strawberries and Roses.

Apply heptachlor or chlordane to the soil to kill the larvae and as a foliage spray to protect the leaves from the feeding of the adult beetles.

Japanese Beetle (Popillia japonica) is a coppery green beetle most prevalent in the eastern United States within the past forty years. Adults emerge from the ground in early summer and feed on flowers and foliage of many different kinds of plants until September. Eggs are laid in grass during the summer and grubs hatch from them within two weeks. They feed on grass roots before burrowing deeper in preparation for the winter, and again after they move towards the surface in spring. Large areas of lawn and golf course turf have been destroyed by this pest.

Chlordane, applied at the rate of 5 lb. of 5 per cent dust to 1,000 sq. ft.; DDT, 6 lb. of 10 per cent dust to 1,000 sq. ft.; or 4 lb. of 2 per cent dieldrin dust to 1,000 sq. ft., will grub-proof turf for about 3 years. A more even distribution of these materials may be made by mixing the dust with several times its bulk of sand. Apply in spring or early fall and water thoroughly afterwards. A bacterial spore dust which infects the

A leaf severely eaten by the Japanese beetle. A mature beetle can be seen in the center of the leaf.

grubs is slower in action but more lasting in effect. A level teaspoonful of the dust is placed at 10-ft. intervals over the surface of the lawn.

Plants in flower gardens may be protected against Japanese beetle by DDT, malathion or Sevin dusts or sprays. Ornamental trees and shrubs may be sprayed with lead arsenate. For Grapes and other fruits and vegetables a rotenone preparation, because it is nonpoisonous to humans, is preferable. Sevin may be used on vegetable crops. Methoxychlor may also be used, but not within 2 weeks of harvesting.

May Beetles or June Beetles (Phyllaphaga of various species) are large reddish-brown or black beetles. They fly at night and feed on leaves of various trees. The white grubs live in the soil 2-4 years, damaging turf areas by eating grass roots and eating the roots of various plants, especially Corn, Potatoes and Strawberries.

Kill the grubs by treating the soil with chlordane, 5 lb. of 5 per cent dust to each 1,000 sq. ft. or with DDT, 6 lb. of 10 per cent dust to each 1,000 sq. ft., or with dieldrin, 4 lb. of 2 per cent dust to each 1,000 sq. ft. Spray the foliage of trees and shrubs with lead arsenate or malathion.

Mexican Bean Beetle (Epilachna varivestis), as an adult, is 1/3 in. or less long, bronze yellow and marked with 16 black dots, It lays groups of orange-yellow eggs on the undersides of the leaves, and these produce pale yellow, fuzzy larvae which have black-tipped spines. This insect skeletonizes the leaves of all kinds of Beans.

Spraying or dusting with rotenone is effective; so is spraying with Sevin.

Rose Chafer or Rose Bug (Macrodactylus subspinosus) is a slender yellowish beetle with long spiny legs that is common over the eastern part of North America. It feeds on various plants but is most damaging to Rose and Peony flowers. It is most troublesome where sandy soils prevail.

Spray or dust with DDT or malathion. Handpick the beetles.

Spotted Cucumber Beetle (Diabrotica undecimpunctata Howardi) is common east of the Rocky Mountains. The Western spotted cucumber beetle, D. undecimpunctata, takes its place

The underside of a Bean leaf, showing mature Mexican Bean beetles (with black spots), their fuzzy, pale yellow larvae, and a cluster of their orange-yellow eggs.

Beans, those at the left of the stake not sprayed or dusted and severely damaged by Mexican Bean beetles, those at the right protected by a spray and undamaged.

on the western side of the Rockies. They are greenish yellow with twelve black spots on their backs. Besides Cucumbers, Melons, Squash and related plants, they are known to feed on more than 200 other kinds, including fruits, flowers and vegetables. Spray or dust with lindane. DDT may be used on ornamentals but not on parts of fruits or vegetables that are to be used as food. For fruits and vegetables rotenone sprays or dusts are safest to use. Sevin is also effective.

Striped Cucumber Beetles are widely known pests. The kind that is common east of the Rocky Mountains is Acalymma vittata. A. trivittata is common on the Pacific Coast. These are small yellowish beetles marked with three black stripes. The larvae feed on roots of Cucumbers, Melons, Squash and other botanically related plants. The beetles feed on the foliage of these and some other plants, including Beans, Beets, Corn, Apples, Almonds, Peas and Sunflowers.

Control is had by protecting young plants with hotkaps (small paper tents sold by seedsmen) or low frames covered with cheesecloth or fine wire netting. When the plants have outgrown these covers, dust weekly with lindane or with Sevin.

Borers. Borers are larvae of beetles or moths. They work in the insides of plants. There are many different kinds affecting trees, shrubs and herbaceous plants. Trees are most liable to borer attack when checked by transplanting, or if they have been weakened by drought or other causes. A good precaution is to keep the trunks of newly planted trees wrapped in burlap or heavy paper

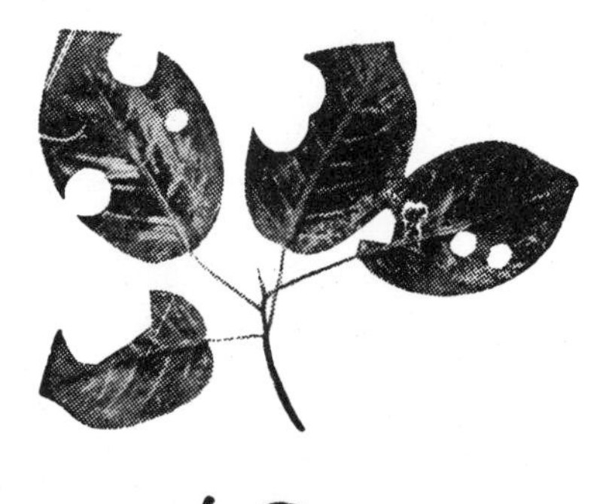

The Rose chafer or Rose bug.

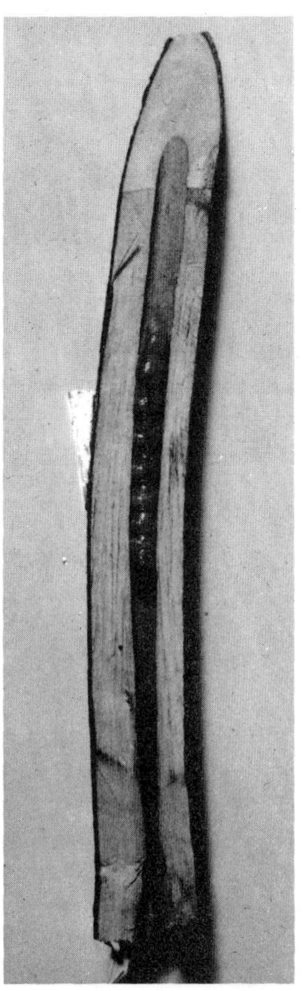

A borer in the stem of an Azalea.

for two years following transplanting. Feeding, watering and other good care are helpful in enabling established trees to resist borer attack.

Carpenterworm (Prionoxystus Robiniae) is a white caterpillar which bores large tunnels in the wood of Oaks, Elms, Maples, Poplars and other trees. The moth is mottled gray and brown and has a 3-in. wingspread. The life cycle takes three or more years. The caterpillar grows to a length of 2 in. or more.

To control this pest, inject carbon bisulphide into the tunnels and close them with clay or putty. Carbon bisulphide is inflammable; keep it away from open flames. Spray the trunks with DDT or with dieldrin after the eggs are laid.

European Corn Borer (Pyrausta nubilalis) is a widespread pest of Corn and is often destructive to Dahlias and other herbaceous plants, including certain vegetables such as Beans, Celery and Potatoes. The yellowish brown moths lay eggs in clusters on the undersides of the leaves. In a week or so, young larvae start feeding—in the case of Corn, first on the tassels and then down into the ears.

Control may be had by dusting with 5 per cent DDT, 1 per cent rotenone or 40 per cent ryania as soon as the tassels show. Repeat 3 or 4 times at 5-day intervals. Ryania and Toxaphene are also effective. Burn all old stems in the fall.

Flatheaded Apple Tree Borer (Chrysobothris femorata) is a yellow-white grub which develops from eggs laid by a flat brownish, blunt-headed beetle. It attacks many different shade trees as well as Apples and other fruit trees and Raspberries and Roses. Damage is mostly on the sunny side of the attacked plant. There large areas of bark may be killed. This borer is particularly destructive to trees that have been recently transplanted and to young trees in nurseries. Excessive pruning and drought are conditions that favor this pest.

To prevent damage, wrap trunks of newly transplanted trees with burlap or paper made especially for the purpose, spray trunks and branches with malathion, DDT or dieldrin about mid-May and repeat twice at two-week intervals.

Iris Borer (Macronoctua onusta). This serious pest of Irises harms the plants by feeding upon them and by spreading the bacteria which cause the destructive soft rot disease. The young borers, larvae of a brown moth which has black markings and a wingspread of about 2 in., hatch in spring from eggs which have wintered over on old Iris leaves and on other debris near Iris plantings. Crawling up the new leaves of the Iris, the young borers enter them through tiny holes they make and then work their way down the leaves between the epidermal layers, feeding on the inner tissues as they go. The paths of the borers are made evident by a ragged, water-soaked appearance of the leaves.

When the borers reach the rhizomes, they feed on the interiors and increase greatly in size, eventually becoming 1½-2 in. long and very much fatter than they are when inside the leaf tissues. The borers are white or pinkish with a dark brown head. In August they leave the rhizomes and pupate in the soil. The mature moths appear in late August and September and at night lay their eggs on Iris foliage and sometimes on other foliage near Iris plantings.

Control measures must include good sanitation. In fall, after frost, all dead leaves as well as any others that are loose enough to be pulled off easily should be removed from the Iris plants and burned at the same time. Good control can be obtained by spraying with 1 part of 47.5 per cent Thimet in 200 to 400 parts of water, at weekly intervals from the time in spring when the leaves are 6 in. high until the flower buds show. Malathion sprays are also effective if applied before the larvae enter the leaves. In spring and early summer, borers in the leaves may be killed by pressing them between the finger and thumb. When Irises are to be divided, this should be done immediately after flowering and well before any borers in the leaves have had opportunity to make their way into the rhizomes. Each rhizome should be carefully inspected at dividing time and borers, if present, cut out.

Lilac Borer (Podosesia Syringae Syringae) is a white caterpillar with a brown head which develops from eggs laid by a wasplike, clear-wing moth in early summer. This creature also damages Ash, Mountain Ash, Privet and other shrubs.

To prevent eggs from being laid on the bushes, spray the trunks with DDT or dieldrin 2 or 3 times at 10-day intervals, beginning in May. Inject carbon bisulphide or nicotine paste into holes from which sawdust exudes and then stop them with clay or putty.

Peach Tree Borer (Sanninoidea exitiosa) is a widely distributed pest of Peach trees and to a lesser extent of Apricots, Cherries, and Plums. Eggs are laid by a blue-black moth with an orange band, from July to September, around the base of the tree. The young worms bore inside the bark, winter in burrows and continue feeding for a time in spring before they pupate. Their presence is indicated by a jelly-like exudation of gum and brown frass (sawdust-like material) about the base of the trunk.

From young trees it may be possible to get the worms by probing or cutting them out with a sharp knife. With older trees the time-tested method is to place a ring of paradichlorobenzine crystals on clean ground about 2 in. from the bark. The dosage varies from ¾ oz. for trees 3 to 6 years old, to 1 oz. for older trees. The time to do this is about mid-September in the North, a month or so later in the South. The crystals are covered with a mound of soil which can be leveled after about a month. Proprietary preparations are obtainable for the control of these borers. Use these according to manufacturers' directions. Good results follow spraying the trunks and lower branches with malathion in early July and repeating this three times at 2-week intervals. Use 1 tablespoon of 50 per cent malathion emulsifiable liquid per gallon of water.

Rhododendron Borer (Ramosia Rhododendri) is a small yellowish grub derived from eggs laid in June by a clear-winged black and yellow moth on stems of Rhododendrons, Azaleas and Mountain Laurel. Its presence is often not suspected until twigs and branches begin to die back.

Cut off and burn dying parts. Inject nicotine paste into holes from which fresh sawdust exudes. Spray the stems with DDT or with dieldrin in May and repeat twice at 3-week intervals.

Squash Borer (Melittia Cucurbitae) is a thick white caterpillar destructive to Squash and Pumpkins and, to a lesser degree, related plants. The wasplike orange and black moths emerge from the soil in late spring and lay many eggs on the stems and leafstalks.

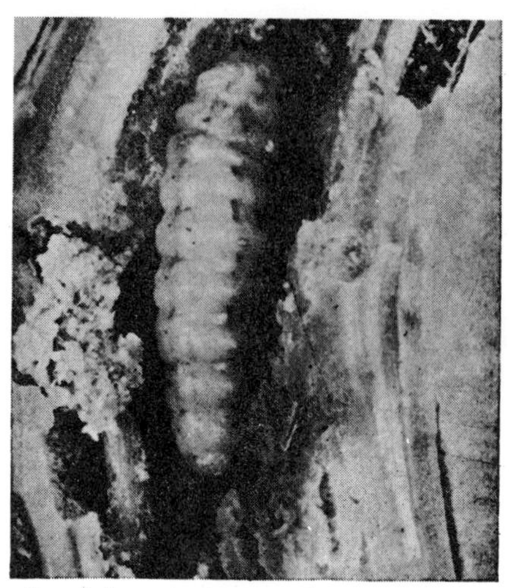

Squash borer in the stem of a Squash plant.

Protect plants by keeping the stems covered with 1 per cent rotenone dust or with lindane from an early stage of their growth. If a vine wilts, slit the stem with a knife and kill the borer within, then mound soil over the stem joints to encourage new roots to develop. Burn old vines after the harvest.

Stalk Borer (Papaipema nebris) is a brownish caterpillar that tunnels in the stems of many plants, including Asters, Cosmos, Dahlias, Delphiniums, Lilies, Peonies, Phlox, Potatoes, Tomatoes and Zinnias. The grayish-brown moths lay eggs on Ragweed and other weeds.

To control, spray or dust the stalks of plants with chlordane or DDT before the borers enter, and keep them covered with a protective coating of these chemicals at all times. Clean up all weeds and plant trash in the fall.

Twig Pruner or Oak Twig Pruner (Elaphidion villosum) is the larva of a narrow, brown beetle which develops from eggs laid in twigs of various trees, particularly Oaks, Hickories, Pecans, Maples and Walnuts. The larvae burrow in the twigs, then sever them and fall to the ground. Clean up and burn fallen twigs.

Budworms. See Caterpillars.

Bugs. Most insects are commonly called bugs, but to the entomologist the only true bugs are members of the family of insects named Hemiptera. The upper wing parts of true bugs are

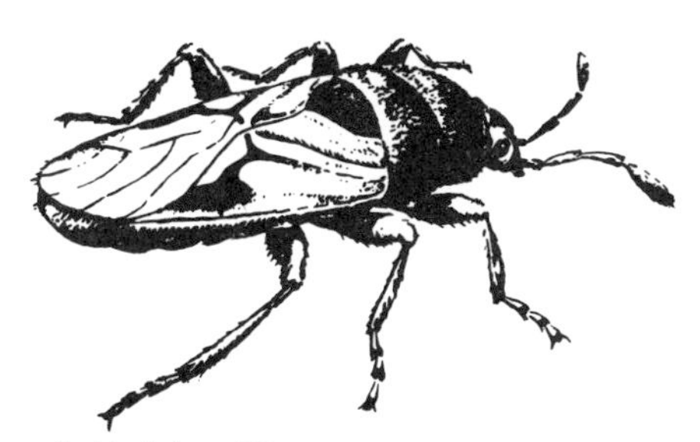

A chinch bug. This tiny insect causes great damage to lawns.

thick and leathery, the lower parts thin and membranous.

Chinch Bug (Blissus leucopterus hirtus) is a small dark-colored bug that causes brown patches in sunny lawns. Chinch bugs winter as adults in tall grass and weedy places, migrating to lawn areas in spring to lay eggs. The nymphs which hatch from the eggs are red at first, and like the adult bugs suck the juices from the bases of grass blades, causing the leaves to discolor from green to yellow to brown. The damage done by chinch bugs is often wrongly ascribed to dry weather. A second brood appears in late summer. Chinch bugs can only be seen by close inspection of the turf at ground level, after roughing up the grass. They are only about 1/6 in. long at maturity.

Control of this pest is effected by applying Diazinon or Sevin as recommended by the manufacturer.

Four-lined Plant Bug (Poecilocapsus lineatus), a hard-shelled, greenish-yellow bug, is about 1/4 in. long. It is marked with four black stripes on its wings. It is widespread east of the Rocky Mountains. Eggs are laid before winter in the stems of Currants and other plants. They hatch in spring into small red nymphs, which cause spotting of the leaves by sucking plant juices. The damage is done in a period of about six weeks in the early part of the season. A great many plants are affected, including Chrysanthemums, Dahlias, Delphiniums, Gaillardias, Mint, Roses, Sunflowers and Zinnias.

Control may be had by spraying or dusting ornamentals with DDT or methoxychlor. On Mint and other food plants, use a 1 per cent rotenone dust.

Harlequin Bug (Murgantia histrionica), also called calico back and fire bug, is a very serious pest of a wide variety of plants in the South and is especially troublesome on Cabbages, Cauliflowers, Collards, Brussels Sprouts, Turnips, Kohlrabi, Radishes, Horse-Radish and other plants that belong in the botanical family Cruciferae (the Mustard family). The bug is flat, about 1/3 in. long, black conspicuously patterned with bright red. There are 2-4 generations each season. Attacked plants wilt, turn brown and finally are killed.

Control is not easy. Keeping down weeds and trash and especially the removal and destruction of old parts of Cabbages and other host plants after harvest are very necessary. Hand-picking is recommended. Heavy applications of rotenone are helpful.

Lace Bugs (species of Stephanitis and Corythuca) are small lacy-winged bugs common on Azaleas, Mountain Laurel, Pieris, Rhododendrons, Cotoneasters, Hawthorns, Japanese Quinces, Oaks, Pyracanthus and Sycamores. Both the nymphs, which are spiny, and the adults suck the plant juices from the undersides of leaves, which they cover with brown, varnish-like excrement. The upper surfaces of affected foliage take on a pale, stippled appearance. In the South the first brood appears early in the season, in the North in May or June. This is followed by a second brood some weeks later.

To control this pest, spray with white oil emulsion, nicotine-soap solution or lindane. Use 1 tablespoon of 25 per cent wettable lindane powder to 1 gallon of water. Apply so that the undersides of the leaves are thoroughly wetted.

Spittle bugs on stems of Lavender.

Two or three applications, ten days apart, are usually needed.

Spittle Bugs, small dull-brown insects, are not true bugs but are closely related to leaf hoppers. They are often called frog hoppers. The small pale nymphs live in frothy masses of their own making. Two common kinds are the Pine spittle bug (Aphrophora parallela), found on Pines, Spruces and other evergreens, and the meadow spittle bug (Philaenus leucophthalmus), which feeds on Strawberries, causing distorted foliage and berries, and on other plants.

To control these, spray forcefully with nicotine, pyrethrum, rotenone or malathion.

Squash Bug (Anasa tristis) is a grayish-brown, hard-shelled bug which attacks Squash and related plants. It gives off a disagreeable odor when crushed. Adults winter under rubbish and around buildings. Patches of golden-brown eggs are laid on the undersides of leaves. The nymphs which emerge from these cause wilting and perhaps death of leaves and runners.

To control, dust freely with pyrethrum or sabadilla dusts. Clean up and burn old vines and trash as soon as the fruits are harvested.

The tarnished plant bug is a serious pest that attacks fruits, flowers and vegetables. These Chrysanthemum blooms have been severely distorted as a result of its activities.

Tarnished Plant Bug (Lygus lineolaris), a small (1/4 in. long), brown, mottled, oval bug, is widely distributed throughout North America. The greenish-yellow nymphs are marked with black dots. This insect is injurious to many fruit, flower and vegetable plants. Fruit-tree buds are liable to attack in early spring and later shoots and buds of other plants are blackened and deformed. There may be three or more generations a year. The bugs winter over as adults under bark, leaves, stones, etc., and on weeds.

To control these bugs, spray or dust with methoxychlor or sabadilla. DDT, a 3-5 per cent dust or 2 level teaspoonfuls of 50 per cent wettable powder to 1 gallon of water, also gives good control but should not be used on food plants. Clean up trash about the garden and all weeds.

Cankerworms. See Caterpillars.

Carpenterworms. See Borers.

Casebearers. See Caterpillars.

Caterpillars. Caterpillars are the larval or grub stages of butterflies and moths. The name is also given to the grubs of some sawflies, since these are of similar shape and appearance. For these latter, see Sawflies, below. Caterpillars of butterflies and moths have up to five pairs of sucker feet in addition to three pairs of ordinary walking legs, whereas those of sawflies have seven pairs of sucker feet, together with three pairs of ordinary legs. There are many kinds, some feeding on a wider variety of plants than others. Some are commonly known under the names of their adult forms (see Moths), others are known as worms.

The caterpillar of the imperial moth.

Budworms are small caterpillars that web leaves together and bore into opening buds. Spruce budworm (Choristoneura fumiferana) is destructive in forest plantings and likely to be troublesome in gardens on Firs, Larches, Hemlocks, Pines and Spruces. The moth is dull gray with brown markings, the caterpillars

Foliage of Broccoli eaten by Cabbage caterpillars.

reddish-brown with yellowish tubercles. Other species of budworms may attack Apples, Roses, Irises, Hydrangeas, Snapdragons and Verbenas.

Spray with lead arsenate when larvae appear or with DDT just after the buds open. DDT increases the mite population. Do not use it on plants subject to mite injury except together with a miticide (pesticide that kills mites).

Cabbage Caterpillars. The larvae of three different insects feed ravenously on Cabbages, Cauliflowers, Broccoli and related vegetables, flowers and weeds, chewing large holes in the foliage. The Cabbage looper (Trichoplusia Ni) is a humped, greenish caterpillar with white lines. The adult is a brownish mottled moth which lays many small round eggs singly on the leaves. The Cabbage worm (Pieris Rapae) is a smooth green caterpillar with light and dark stripes. The adult is the common white Cabbage butterfly.

The caterpillars of the diamondback moth are greenish-yellow with black hairs. The moth is small and dark colored, and has white markings in the shape of a diamond.

These Cabbage caterpillars may be controlled by dusting with rotenone as soon as feeding is noticed. In the home garden, eggs and young caterpillars may be collected by hand. Dusting with DDT is effective but should not be done to edible plant parts within a month of harvesting.

Cankerworms. These are larvae of small moths that are widely distributed in North America. They are known also as inch worms and measuring worms because of their habit of progressing by looping along. There are two common species, the fall cankerworm (Alsophila pometaria) and spring cankerworm (Paleacrita vernata). The common names refer to the time of year the moths emerge. The females are wingless. They crawl up tree trunks to lay their eggs. Caterpillars of both kinds feed on the leaves of many fruit and shade trees in spring. They sometimes lower and raise themselves by a silken thread.

Some protection is afforded by banding trees with a sticky compound called Tanglefoot to prevent the females from crawling up the trunk but this method is less popular than formerly. The best control is to spray with lead arsenate, 3 lb. to 100 gallons of water, or Sevin, 2 lb. of 50 per cent wettable powder to 100 gallons of water, as soon as feeding is noticed. Cankerworms are much more prevalent some springs than others.

Casebearers. These are caterpillars of small moths (mostly species of Coleophora) which feed on various fruit and nut trees. The young larvae spin cases in which they live and move around. They winter over in this stage and some feeding may be done in fall. Control may be had by spraying with lead arsenate when feeding begins.

Centipede, Garden. See Symphylid, below.

Corn Earworm (Heliothis Zea). A widely distributed pest, doing great damage to Corn and numerous other plants, especially in the South. It is known also as Tomato fruitworm, Tobacco budworm and Cotton bollworm when found working on these plants. Other favored food plants are Geraniums, Grapes, Okra, Peaches,

The Tomato fruitworm or Corn earworm feeding on a Tomato fruit.

Peanuts, Pears, Peppers, Roses, Squash and Strawberries. The yellow-green to dark brown caterpillars grow to nearly 2 in. long. Many eggs are laid by the adult insects, which are grayish-brown moths with dark markings. There are 2-3 generations a season. On Corn, eggs are laid on the silks and the larvae feed downwards to the tip of the ear. On Tomatoes they feed on the leaves before eating into the green fruit.

To control this pest on Corn, inject 1/4 teaspoon mineral oil mixed with pyrethrum extract (this may be bought ready prepared) into the tip of each ear as soon as the silks begin to wilt or dust the silks with 5 per cent DDT and repeat 2 or 3 times at 3-day intervals. Dust Tomatoes with 10 per cent methoxychlor as the fruits set. On ornamentals use DDT or chlordane.

Cutworms. Cutworms are the caterpillars of various night-flying moths. They feed mostly at night and hide during the day, usually just below the soil. Some work at ground level, cutting off young plants when they are set out in spring, others climb up stems to eat leaves and buds.

The most troublesome in gardens are the black cutworm (Agrotis ipsilon), a surface feeder, and the variegated cutworm (Peridroma margaritosa), a climbing feeder damaging to garden and greenhouse plants. In greenhouses the variegated cutworm is active in winter, often climbing up the stems of Carnations to eat holes in the buds. This caterpillar is light brown with dark mottlings and yellow dots. During the day they coil up just under the surface of the soil.

The black cutworm varies in color from gray or brown to almost black. It is especially damaging to vegetables, cutting off young plants of Tomatoes and other kinds.

A cardboard collar placed around a young plant to protect it from cutworms.

On a small scale such plants as Cabbages and Tomatoes may be protected by placing a 4-in. cardboard collar around each plant at the time it is planted outdoors, setting the base of the collar about an inch down in the soil. Hand-picking may be effective but dusting with 5 per cent DDT or chlordane is likely to be easier and surer.

Hornworms. These are large green caterpillars, up to 4 in. long. The Tomato hornworm (Protoparce quinquemaculata) and the Tobacco hornworm (P. sexta) are the larvae of large hawk or humming-bird moths. The Tomato hornworm

A cutworm.

A hornworm, the larva of a hawk moth.

has 8 diagonal white stripes along the body and a prominent black horn at the rear end. The Tobacco hornworm has 7 white stripes and a red horn. Both feed on Tomatoes, Peppers, Eggplants, Petunias and related plants. One generation occurs in the North; there are usually two in the South.

Hand picking may be sufficient control. Methoxychlor is effective.

Leaf Cutters. These caterpillars of moths cut pieces out of the leaves of their hosts. The Maple leaf cutter (Paraclemensia acerifoliella) is chiefly a pest of Maples but also infests Beeches and Birches. Its larvae are dirty white with brown heads and are ¼ in. or less long. The Morning Glory leaf cutter (Loxostege obliteralis) has greenish larvae with dark spots. They hide during the day in folded, wilted leaves and at night eat holes in the leaves and cut through the stalks. They are about ¾ in. long and infest Dahlias, Mint, Sunflowers, Zinnias and some other plants, as well as Morning Glories. The Waterlily leaf cutter (Nymphula obliteralis) cuts oval pieces out of the leaves of Waterlilies and other aquatic plants and fastens the cut-out pieces to the remainder of the leaves to form hiding places. The larvae are cream colored with a dark stripe along their backs; when fully grown they may be 1 in. long.

The Maple leaf cutter and Morning Glory leaf cutter may be controlled by spraying or dusting with lead arsenate, by raking up and burning fallen leaves and by hand picking. The Waterlily leaf cutter is more difficult to control. Hand picking should be carefully done. In severe cases, remove all fish from the pool, lower the water and dust the foliage with a mixture of equal parts of pyrethrum powder and tobacco dust. Repeat the dusting in 20 minutes and change the water in the pool before placing any fish in it.

Leaf Rollers. These are caterpillars which feed under the protection of a rolled-up leaf. They are larvae of many species of small moths. Two kinds in particular work on a great variety of plants.

The fruit-tree leaf roller (Archips argyrospilus) is found all across the northern half of North America and is especially damaging to Apples. It also feeds on other fruit trees and many other deciduous (leaf-losing) trees and shrubs. The pale green caterpillars have brown heads. The oblique-banded leaf roller (Archips rosaceana) feeds on many trees, shrubs, vegetables and flowering plants in the garden and greenhouse. The pale green caterpillars are black-headed. The red-banded leaf roller (Argyrotaenia velutinana) feeds on the same plants. The caterpillar is greenish.

To control leaf rollers, pick off rolled leaves containing the caterpillars. Spray or dust with DDT or lead arsenate. The former is not effective against the red-banded leaf roller. Natural parasites are sometimes active and effective.

Leaf Tier (Udea rubigalis). This pest ties leaves together with silken threads. It is especially damaging to Celery, but feeds on many vegetables as well as garden and greenhouse flowers. The young green, black-headed caterpillars turn yellow with a white stripe down the back when full grown. The mature insect is a night-flying brown moth.

Control leaf tiers by using pyrethrum or rotenone on vegetables, DDT or lead arsenate on ornamentals. These should be used while the larvae are young.

Omnivorous Looper (Sabulodes caberata). This is a serious pest on Avocados and many other trees and plants in California. The caterpillars vary from green to pink or yellow with colored stripes and black markings. The adult is a dull brown or yellowish moth. There may be four or more generations a year.

Control is had by spraying or dusting with lead arsenate or with malathion.

Red-humped Caterpillar (Schizura concinna). This is a widespread pest, feeding on many fruit and ornamental trees. The caterpillars, which are also known as red-humped Apple worms, are reddish-yellow with colored stripes and a red head and hump. The adult is a grayish-brown moth.

To control this pest, spray or dust with lead arsenate or with malathion. Collect and destroy young colonies of these caterpillars.

Tent Caterpillars. These are the larvae of several species of Malacosoma moths and are widely distributed over most of North America. Egg masses are laid on twigs in early summer, and

The eastern tent caterpillar constructs large, conspicuous tentlike webs, each of which houses a large number of destructive caterpillars.

hatch into ravenous caterpillars as the young leaves are developing the following spring. In most cases the caterpillars spin webby tents in crotches, and they gather in these tents at night. They feed on many fruit and ornamental trees. The eastern tent caterpillar (Malacosoma americanum) is especially conspicuous on Wild Cherry trees in certain years, but also infests Peaches, Plums, Apples and other kinds.

To control these pests, egg clusters should be collected from twigs in winter wherever possible, and whole nests of young caterpillars may be demolished in early mornings before the caterpillars have left the tents to feed. Spraying the foliage with lead arsenate is effective.

Webworms. Some kinds of caterpillars which feed under webs are commonly known as webworms. They infest many different kinds of plants, including some vegetables as well as many shrubs and trees. The most common webworms are discussed in the following paragraphs.

The fall webworm (Hyphantria Cunea) is a hairy caterpillar which feeds on more than a hundred kinds of deciduous (leaf-losing) trees and shrubs, and is widely distributed in North America. The nests are at the ends of branches rather than in crotches, unlike those of tent caterpillars. The caterpillars are yellow or light green with a yellow stripe along each side and a dark stripe along their backs. The adults are satiny white moths. The first brood of caterpillars appears in June, the second and more destructive in late summer.

The garden webworm (Loxostege similalis) feeds on certain field crops, Clover and Alfalfa especially, and on garden vegetables such as Beans and Beets, and on Strawberries. It is more common in the Southwest, where there are up to five generations in a season. The moth is brownish with light markings. The caterpillars are yellow or light green with numerous pale spots and are hairy.

The Juniper webworm (Dichomeris marginella) is a small brownish moth which lays eggs in June on the new growth of some kinds of Junipers. The partly grown reddish-brown caterpillars web the needles together, spend the winter inside the nests they make and resume feeding in spring.

Sod webworms (various kinds of Crambus) are the larvae of small yellow to light brown moths which may be seen flying slowly over grassy areas at dusk. The caterpillars damage lawns in many parts of North America by cutting off and skeletonizing the leaves of grass, especially Bluegrasses and Bent Grasses. They shelter in slender silk-lined tubes which they construct.

Spray trees and shrubs with lead arsenate or Sevin when larvae are small. Where possible, cut off and burn webbed branches. Use rotenone on vegetables. Apply 5 per cent chlordane on lawns.

The larva and adult insect of the sod webworm.

Yellow-necked Caterpillar (Datana ministra) grows up to 2 in. long, has a black head, yellow neck and the rest of the body yellow and black. It is widely distributed and feeds on a wide variety of fruit trees, ornamental trees and shrubs. The moth is brownish-yellow with narrow lines. Spray or dust with lead arsenate.

Yellow Woolly Bear (Diacrisia virginica) is a very hairy yellow caterpillar marked with black lines. It feeds on many different kinds of vegetables and flowers. The moth is yellowish brown with white wings spotted black.

Spraying or dusting with lead arsenate, malathion or rotenone gives control.

Centipede, Garden. See Symphylid, below.

Curculios. Curculios are beetles which have heads extended into long curved snouts with biting parts at the tips.

Plum Curculio (Conotrachelus Nenuphar) is the most common species. It is very damaging to stone fruits such as Apricots, Cherries, Peaches and Plums and to Apples. It occurs east of the Rocky Mountains. The adult insect, dark brown and gray, about 1/4 in. long, sometimes feeds on leaves, but most injury is done to young fruits by feeding and puncturing them to lay eggs. The white grubs feed in the fruit for two weeks or more, then drop to the ground and pupate. Adults of the new brood continue to feed and scar fruit.

To control curculios, collect and destroy them by jarring them out of the trees on to sheets spread beneath. Lead arsenate sprays, 3 lb. of lead arsenate to 100 gallons of water, are effective, the first being applied to Apples when the petals fall, the second as the shucks (remains of the calices) are falling from the young fruits, and the third two weeks later. For stone fruits, such as Plums and Cherries, use lead arsenate at the rate of 2 lb. to 100 gallons of water with 8 lb. of hydrated lime mixed in. Malathion and methoxychlor may also be used to control curculios.

Cutworms. See Caterpillars.

Earthworms. Considering their activities as a whole, earthworms (Lumbricus terrestris) cannot be said to be pests, certainly not in the sense that they damage living plants. Earthworms feed only on fallen leaves and other dead vegetable matter. The burrows they make greatly assist in the

The loosening of the surface soil and the presence of wormcasts (soil that has passed through the bodies of earthworms) often give the first indication of the presence of earthworms among the roots of potted plants.

Earthworms damage the roots of pot plants by tunneling among them.

drainage and aeration of the soil and an immense amount of plant nutrients are made available in the fresh soil (known as wormcasts) which they bring to the surface.

Useful as the wormcasts may be, they are a definite nuisance on lawns and golf greens. They may be swept up periodically when dry. Many gardeners, however, prefer to kill the worms in the lawns, for which purpose the following methods are all satisfactory.

Bichloride of mercury, dissolved in water at the rate of 1/2 oz. to every 15 gallons of water, may be used to water the lawn. The worms will then come to the surface. Bichloride of mercury is exceedingly poisonous and must be handled with care. Birds must not be allowed to eat the dead worms.

Lime water may also be employed for watering the lawn. This is made by mixing 20 lb. of fresh quicklime with 40 gallons of water and allowing to stand until clear. It is the clear liquid which is used.

Another very simple way of getting rid of worms in lawns and paths is to apply permanganate of potash, 1½ oz. in 2 gallons of water per sq. yd. The forms will soon come to the surface and can then be swept up. Arsenate of lead spread at the rate of 10 lb. to 1,000 sq. ft. or 50 per cent wettable chlordane powder at the rate of 1 lb. to each 1,000 sq. ft. will usually free a lawn of earthworms. If this is not effective the application may be repeated in about two months' time.

Earthworms in the pots in which plants are growing have a bad effect on the drainage of the soil. They may be removed by picking them out when repotting or at other times when this can be done without unduly disturbing the roots or after bringing them to the surface by watering with lime water, mowrah meal or permanganate of potash.

Earwigs. The common earwig (Forficula auricularia) is destructive to a great variety of plants and fruits, eating holes in the tissues of various parts of the plants. It is particularly destructive to Dahlias and Chrysanthemums and may destroy a large percentage of the buds. When the damage is caused early in the year it induces numbers of weak side buds to develop into thin, weak branches.

The mature earwig is ½-¾ in. long, hard, and dark brown, and has a conspicuous pair of pincers protruding from the rear. The small, round white eggs are laid in the soil, or under some shelter, in batches of fifty to ninety. These eggs are laid in the spring and the females remain close to them and to the young that hatch from them until they undergo their first molt. Apart from plants, the food of earwigs consists of decaying vegetable matter, small insects and each other; in fact, earwigs will eat practically anything. During hibernation the earwigs collect in large numbers under the bark of trees, under stones and in similar damp places.

The well-known remedy of catching the earwigs in a trap consisting of a flowerpot loosely filled with hay, straw or paper and inverted over the top of a stake or stout bamboo cane is undoubtedly effective; the traps should, however, be examined at regular intervals during the day and the earwigs shaken out into a vessel containing water and kerosene.

Chlordane, lindane and DDT dusts are also effective against earwigs.

Earworm. See Caterpillars, above.

Eelworm. See Nematodes, below.

Flea Hopper (Halticus bracteatus). This is a small black insect which looks like an aphid and hops like a flea. The greenish nymphs appear in early spring, causing pale areas on the leaves of many vegetables and ornamentals as a result of their sucking the plant juices. Adults winter over in weeds and trash.

To control, spray with nicotine sulphate or dust with 5 per cent DDT. On vegetables and other edible plants use rotenone dust. Clean up weeds in the fall.

Flies. These are 2-winged insects, some of which are destructive to certain plants. The larvae are grublike, soft, white or yellowish. They are known as maggots. Some maggots are pests and are known by the common name of the maggot rather than that of the fly. For these see the discussion of maggots below.

Black Flies are small creatures that frequently hover around potted plants in houses. They emerge from maggots that develop in organic matter in the soil. Apparently they are not harmful. They may be eliminated by watering with nicotine sulphate, 1 teaspoon to 1 gallon water, or by dusting with lindane.

Bulb Flies. Two species of flies attack bulbs, the Narcissus bulb fly (Lampetia equestris) and the lesser bulb fly (Eumerus tuberculatus). The first-named produces only one generation during the year, the flies appearing from early May until the end of June, when each female lays about 40 eggs, singly, on the soil close to a bulb, on the foliage, or even on the bulb itself, which it reaches via the tubelike cavity formed by the dying foliage. On hatching, the grub enters the bulb and eats out the center, becoming fat and ½ in. long and completely ruining the bulb.

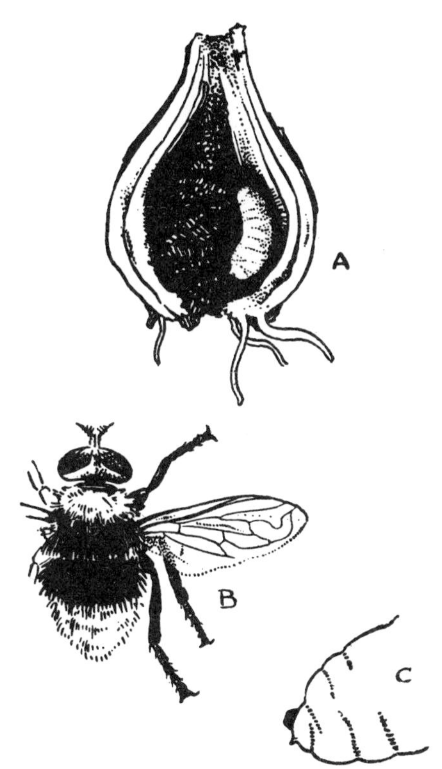

The Narcissus bulb fly. (A) Larva or grub in bulb. (B) The adult fly. (C) The hind end of the larva or grub, by which the grub of the Narcissus bulb fly can be distinguished from the grub of the lesser Narcissus bulb fly.

Usually only one maggot develops in each bulb.

The lesser bulb fly produces two generations in a year, appearing from early May until October. The eggs are deposited in groups around the bulb; they enter through the neck of the bulb and soon reduce it internally to a putrid mass.

These bulb flies attack Narcissi, Amaryllis, Galtonias, Hyacinths, Snowdrops, Leucojums, Scillas and other bulbs.

All bulbs should be examined at lifting time and any that are soft and spongy should be burned. If grubs are discovered in any bulbs, the lot should be dipped for 10 minutes in a heptachlor or an aldrin solution as recommended by the manufacturer. Immersion in water at a constant temperature of 110 degrees F. for 1 hour kills the maggots without harming the bulbs.

Dusting the beds of bulbs at 10-day intervals from early May until the end of July with DDT or benzene hexachloride is effective in preventing egg-laying. After being lifted, bulbs should be kept under cover, not in the open where they will provide a very attractive target for the egg-laying flies.

Carrot Rust Fly (Psila Rosae). The larvae or maggots of this insect bore into the roots of Carrots, Parsnips, Celery, Celeriac, Parsley, Turnips, Radishes and Eschscholtzia, causing a typical "rusty" appearance accompanied by rotting. Often the growth of the roots is severely checked. The tops of badly affected plants turn yellow or reddish.

The flies appear in May and June and lay eggs just below the surface of the soil close to the plants. The young maggots, yellowish white in color and 1/4 in. in length, eat their way into the roots. When fully fed, they pupate in the soil. There are usually two generations of the flies during the year, the second generation of flies appearing in July and August.

Damage may be prevented or considerably reduced by working aldrin into the soil prior to seeding. 1 oz. of the active ingredient per 1,000 sq. ft., is the usual dosage. Since the flies are particularly attracted to the beds of Carrots by the smell when thinning is carried out, this operation is best done in the evening, when the flies are less active. Always firm the soil about the seedlings that are left, and dust at once with chlordane, or failing that, DDT powder. Thin sowing should be the rule, to reduce the need for seedling thinning to a minimum, and all young plants pulled

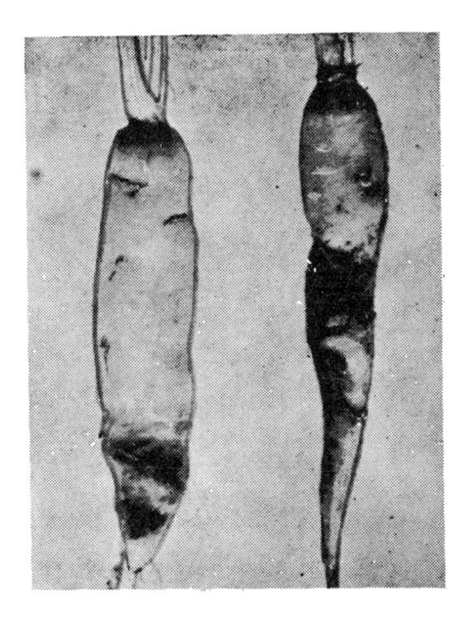

Carrots damaged by maggots of the Carrot rust fly.

out should be removed and destroyed at once.

Cherry Fruitflies. Two species of small flies cause wormy Cherries. The black Cherry fruitfly (Rhagoletis fausta) has a black body, the Cherry fruitfly (R. cingulata) is black and yellow with white bands. These insects emerge from the soil and fly to the trees in late spring, feed for a time on leaves, then lay eggs in the fruit. The maggots that result cause deformed and wormy fruit. These fruitflies also damage Plums and Pears.

Malathion or methoxychlor sprays are effective if applied when adult flies first appear. Rotenone dusts or sprays are safer in the home garden. Apply the spray or dust as soon as flies are active and repeat a week or so later.

Galls. Galls are abnormal growths on leaves, stems, buds and other plant parts caused by irritation of the tissues. They are often caused by mites and insects as well as by bacteria and fungi. Galls caused by bacteria and fungi, such as the destructive crown gall and the Azalea leaf gall, are discussed below under Diseases.

Apart from being disfiguring, many galls caused by mites and insects usually do little harm; in any case, little can be done to control most of them, other than to cut off and destroy the affected parts. Among the commoner insect- and mite-induced galls are the Blueberry stem gall, the Dogwood club gall (this may cause the stems to die back for several inches), various Hickory leaf galls, Maple spindle gall, mossy Rose gall, numerous Oak galls and Willow cone gall. There is no practical control for any of these.

Galls on the trunk of a Maple tree, caused by mites.

Mossy Rose galls on the Sweet Brier Rose.

Cattleya Midge (Parallelodiplosis cattleyae). The yellow maggots of this tiny fly cause galls to form on the roots of Cattleyas and many other Orchids.

Repot infested plants, cutting all galls of the roots and destroying them. When the adult flies are in evidence, spray with lindane or DDT.

Chrysanthemum Gall Midge (Diarthronomyia Chrysanthemi) is a midge or gnat, less than $\frac{1}{10}$ in. long and orange colored, that affects Chrysanthemums in greenhouses and outdoors. The eggs, which are laid on new shoots, hatch to produce minute maggots, which bore into stems and leaves and cause tiny cone-shaped galls. As a result, stems may be twisted and flower buds distorted. Control consists of picking off and burning infested foliage and spraying with lindane.

Maple Bladder Gall is caused by a mite (Vasates quadripes), and shows itself as bladder-like growths, each about $\frac{1}{8}$ in. in diameter, on the leaves. The galls are red in color. This gall can be controlled by applying a dormant-strength spray of lime sulphur about the time the Maples are in bloom, just before the leaves expand.

[25]
Effects of Root-Knot Nematodes

[26]
Bristly Rose Slug, the larvae of a Sawfly

[27]
Black Scale

[28]
Hemisphaerical Scale

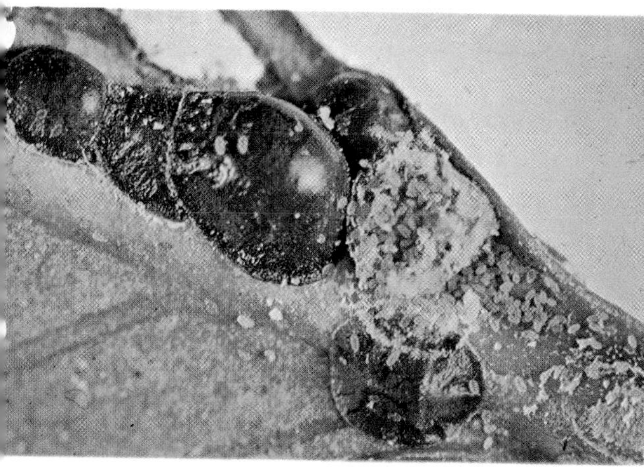

[29]
Brown Garden Snail

[30]
Slug

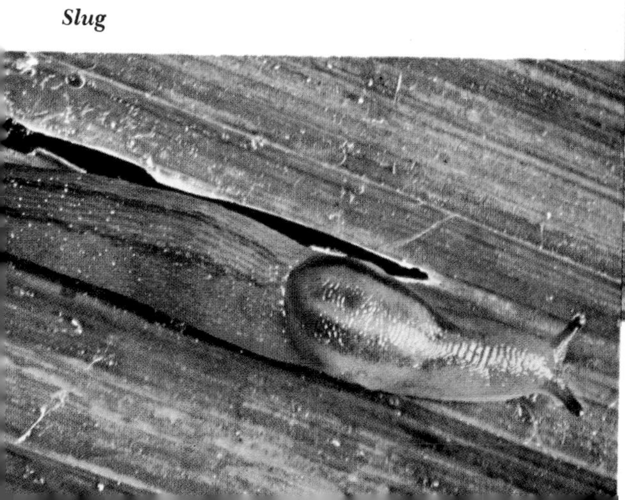

[31]
Sowbugs

[32]
Springtails

[33]
Thrips

[34]
Greenhouse Whitefly.

[35]
Peony damaged by Botrytis disease

[36]
Stem Rot of Geranium (Pelargonium)

For Spruce galls, caused by aphids, see Aphids, above.

Grasshoppers. These ravenous insects are the true locusts. They feed by chewing leaves and other plant parts, and thus differ from cicadas. Cicadas are sometimes misnamed locusts (the so-called seventeen-year locust is a cicada), but feed by sucking the juices from plants. Grasshoppers are more destructive than cicadas. In the West they migrate in large swarms, and special community measures are taken to eliminate them by the use of poison baits as well as chlordane and other insecticides. In other areas grasshoppers are sometimes destructive to garden crops. Dusting with chlordane usually gives satisfactory control.

Several different species of grasshoppers, belonging to a number of distinct genera, prey on plants in different parts of North America. They vary in length at maturity from one to two inches.

Hornet. See Wasps, below.

Hornworm. See Caterpillars, above.

Leaf Hoppers. Leaf hoppers are jumping insects with wedge-shaped bodies. They are close relatives of plant hoppers and tree hoppers. They cause loss of color and of vigor in various garden plants by sucking on the undersides of leaves. Some leaf hoppers are carriers of plant diseases, notably Aster yellows and Peach yellows.

DDT is an effective insecticide against leaf hoppers. A miticide such as Aramite or Ovex should be added to it for plants that are subject to attacks by red spider mites. Rotenone, pyrethrum and nicotine preparations are also used to control leaf hoppers.

Cranberry Blunt-nosed Leaf Hopper (Scleroacus Vaccinii). This short, light brown insect possesses, as its common name suggests, a blunt nose. It produces one brood each year, in May, from eggs wintered over on the Cranberry plants. The chief harm this pest does is to spread the virus infection called Cranberry false blossom. Dusting with pyrethrum and flooding the Cranberry bogs in late June to kill the young leaf hoppers are the standard methods of control.

Elm Leaf Hopper (Scaphoideus luteolus). This insect occurs commonly on Elms and is a menace because it transmits the virus of the Elm phloem necrosis disease. The adult leaf hoppers are brown with faint mottling. The insects hatch in spring from eggs that overwinter on the bark. They feed throughout the summer.

Plum Leaf Hopper (Macropsis trimaculata). This pest transmits the serious virus disease called Peach yellows. The Plum leaf hopper is short, blunt and marked with three dark spots. It hatches in May from eggs laid on the twigs the previous July.

Potato Leaf Hopper (Empoasca Fabae) is sometimes injurious to Potato plants, causing leafburn and curl, and also to Dahlias, causing leafburn and stunt. African Marigolds may be stunted as a result of the activities of leaf hoppers.

Rose Leaf Hopper (Edwardsiana Rosae) is common on Roses and Apples. It also feeds somewhat on botanically related plants. The pale yellow adult insects often disfigure Rose leaves late into the fall.

Six-spotted Leaf Hopper (Macrosteles fascifrons) is greenish yellow with six black spots. It seriously affects Asters and many other garden flowers, transmitting the virus disease known as yellows. In many areas Asters and Dahlias are grown under cheesecloth enclosures to keep out this pest.

Leaf Miners. Leaf miners are maggots, grubs or caterpillars that tunnel between the upper and lower leaf surfaces, feeding on the tissues as they go and forming pale blotches or meandering ribbon-like surface tracings.

It is important to attack leaf miners when they are most susceptible. Because they are protected by the surface skin of the leaf through which they are tunneling, they are easiest to kill when the adults emerge to lay their eggs. At that time spraying with nicotine or DDT insecticides is effective. Because DDT favors an increase in the population of mites, add to it a miticide such as Aramite or Ovex when using it on Spruces or other plants subject to mite injury.

Lindane and malathion are useful against some leaf miners, and for others spraying or dusting with arsenate of lead is recommended. Lindane, dieldrin and aldrin kill young leaf miners working within the leaves. They should be used in early summer.

Numerous garden plants, in addition to the

ones listed below as being the hosts of particular leaf miners, and including Chrysanthemums and related plants, Columbines, Delphiniums, Lilacs and Verbenas, may be attacked by various leaf miners. Protect these with DDT sprays or dust.

Some leaf miners, such as the Birch leaf miner and the Columbine leaf miner, winter in the ground and emerge in spring. Others, such as the Holly and Boxwood leaf miners, live over winter in the leaves. The larvae become adult flying insects which deposit their eggs on suitable foliage. The young larvae which hatch from the eggs bore into the leaves and begin feeding.

Arborvitae Leaf Miner (Argyresthia Thuiella) is a small green, reddish-tinged caterpillar with a black head. It causes the foliage to become whitish or tan colored. The eggs are laid by small gray moths in May and June.

At that time, spray two or three times at ten-day intervals with DDT, adding a miticide to control spider mites.

Birch Leaf Miner (Fenusa pusilla) is a white maggot that develops from eggs laid in the young leaves by a small black sawfly. It produces a blighted appearance, the leaf tissues dying in conspicuous patches. The first brood appears in spring when the new leaves are about half grown; a second brood appears in late June.

Birch leaves damaged by the Birch leaf miner.

Spray with chlordane or lindane when the leaves are about half grown, again in late June, and repeat 10 days later. Summer spraying with aldrin or dieldrin kills the miners inside the leaves.

Pupae of the Boxwood leaf miner in a Boxwood leaf.

Leaves of Columbine (Aquilegia) damaged by the Columbine leaf miner.

Boxwood Leaf Miner (Monarthropalpus Buxi) is a small yellow to orange maggot which causes blistered leaves and gives to Boxwood bushes a most unhealthy appearance. The adults emerge as small orange flies in late April or May (earlier in the South than farther north) and begin egg laying at once.

Spray with DDT, 2 tablespoonfuls of 50 per cent wettable powder to 1 gallon water, just before the flies emerge. If young larvae are found in new leaves, spray with lindane.

Columbine Leaf Miner (Phytomyza minuscula). Conspicuous white meandering lines on the leaves of Columbines, Aquilegia, indicate the presence of this common pest. The tunnels through the leaf tissues that cause the visible white markings are the work of the larvae of a small brownish fly. There are several generations each year.

Picking off and burning affected foliage and spraying with lindane are the recommended controls.

Holly Leaf Miner (Phytomyza ilicis) is a pale yellow maggot. The adult emerges as a small black fly when new leaves are beginning to grow and actively lays eggs for about three weeks.

Spray with DDT as soon as the flies emerge and repeat this spray in 10 days. Dilute the DDT as recommended for the Boxwood leaf miner and add a miticide to control mites.

Locust Leaf Miner (Xenochalepus dorsalis) is a yellowish grub that develops from eggs laid on young leaves by a small beetle which has a black stripe inside its orange wing covers. This pest is widespread on Locust trees in eastern North America and sometimes occurs on Birches, Dogwoods, Wild Cherry and other trees.

Lead arsenate sprays have been used extensively, but chlordane or lindane sprays are likely to be more effective.

Leaf Nematodes. See Nematodes.

Leaf Rollers. See Caterpillars.

Leaf Tier. See Caterpillars.

Maggots. The larvae of flies are called maggots. In some cases these pests are known by the name of the flies. For these, see the discussion of flies, above.

Apple Maggot or Railroad Worm (Rhagoletis Pomonela) is a serious pest in the northeastern United States and neighboring Canada. Unless adequate control measures are taken, 100 per cent of the fruit may be wormy. The maggots are the larvae of white-banded black flies almost as large as house flies. The adults emerge from pupae in the soil in late June or July and lay eggs in punctures they make in the skins of the developing fruits. The maggots tunnel through the fruits and completely or partially destroy them.

Control may be effected by applying two sprays of lead arsenate, the first when the flies come out of the ground and the second two weeks later, at the rate of 3 lb. of lead arsenate to 100 gallons of water. Fruits subjected to these sprays should be washed thoroughly to remove arsenical residues before they are eaten. Moderately effective results can be had by spraying three times at 10-day intervals, beginning when the first flies appear, with methoxychlor at the rate of 2 lb. to 100 gallons of water. Pick up promptly and burn, or otherwise dispose of, all dropped fruits so that the maggots they contain cannot enter the soil and provide future generations of the pest.

Blueberry Maggot (Rhagoletis Pomonella) is a form of the Apple maggot that causes wormy Blueberries. It is controlled by dusting with 5 per cent rotenone when the flies of which the maggots are the larvae first appear in numbers, and again 10 days later.

Cabbage Maggot (Hylemya Brassicae). Plants attacked by this pest develop a bluish-green tint, and are small compared with healthy plants; wilting often accompanies the other symptoms, particularly in hot, dry weather. In severe cases, yellowing of the leaves and death of the plant ensue. The damage is due to the maggots' feeding on the roots and subsurface stems. This pest attacks Cabbages, Cauliflowers, Broccoli, Brussels Sprouts, Kale, Radishes, Turnips, Rutabagas and various weeds belonging to the Mustard family, Cruciferae.

The flies of the first generation appear in late

A tar paper disc applied to control Cabbage maggots.

April or early May and egg laying continues for about a month. The eggs are small, white and elongate and are laid singly or in small batches on the stem just at soil level. Small white maggots hatch from the eggs, make their way to the roots and feed voraciously on them.

The plants thus attacked often make fresh roots at a higher level, and sometimes manage to withstand the attack in this way, if the number of maggots is not great. When fully fed, the maggots turn into dark brown barrel-shaped pupae in the soil. There are several generations in a year.

Chemical deterrents which keep the flies away from the plants, especially the seedlings, and so prevent eggs from being laid, afford a simple and effective means of combatting this pest. This method is particularly suited for use in the seed beds. Crude powdered naphthalene broadcast at the rate of ½-1 oz. per square yd. at ten-day intervals during the period when flies are on the wing and laying eggs will deter them. Disks or squares of tar paper placed flat on the ground around the stems of newly transplanted seedlings are effective.

The best method of control, however, is to dust the planting holes, and the roots of the seedlings as they are planted, with 4 per cent calomel dust, with a sprinkling around each plant after planting and watering; repeat the applications 2 or 3 times at intervals of 10 days. Dustings of lindane, aldrin or chlordane mixed with the soil before planting are effective.

Stimulation of the plants, to bring about new root formation, by means of slight earthing up and the application of quick-acting nitrogenous fertilizers—for example, sulphate of ammonia or nitrate of soda—is very helpful.

Onion Maggot (Hylema antiqua) is chiefly a pest in the North and is most destructive in wet springs. It is little known in southern gardens. The leaves of Onions which are attacked become limp and yellow. The bulbs become a rotting mass. As many as thirty maggots may be found in each Onion. It is in the seedling stage, however, that the most serious damage takes place, since the stems are eaten off just below the level of the soil.

The flies appear in May and June and lay their eggs in groups of from five to twenty on the necks of the Onion plants, on the leaves or on the soil close by. The maggots hatch out and eat off the stems or penetrate the bulbs.

By the end of June most of the maggots are fully fed. They are white and tapering, rather more than ¼ in. in length. The maggots pupate in the soil. There are two or three generations each year, but the generations overlap considerably so that all the stages of the pest may be found at any time during the summer. The last brood overwinters in the pupal stage in the soil.

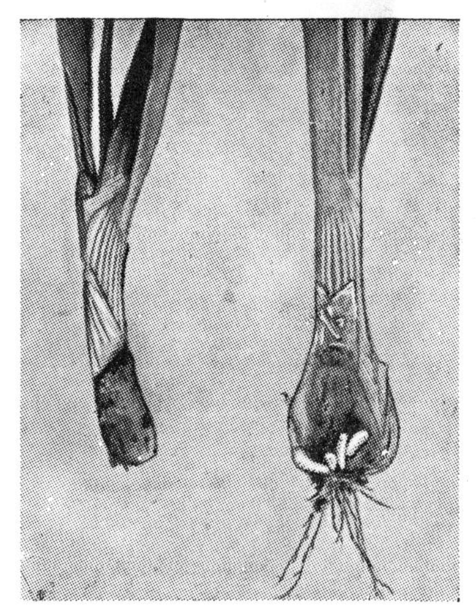

Onion seedlings infested by the Onion maggot.

The pest can be avoided to some extent by suitable cultural measures. Early sowing of seed in a frame or greenhouse, so that young plants can be set out in April, results in freedom from the damage caused by the first generation. Small sets which have been kept over the winter and are planted in spring are also less liable to attack. Applications of nitrate of soda or other quick-acting nitrogenous fertilizer do much good by stimulating growth and enabling the plants to "grow away" from the pest (use nitrate of soda at the rate of ¼-½ oz. per sq. yd.).

It is sound practice to water or dust the seed drills with DDT. When the seedlings are about 1 in. high, they should be dusted with 4 per cent calomel powder followed by a second application two weeks later. In place of the dust a solution of 1 oz. of calomel in 5 gallons of water may be sprayed on at the rate of 1 gallon to 25 ft. of row. Diazinon sprays are also effective.

Raspberry Cane Maggot (Pegomya rubivora). The adult flies of this maggot are about half as large as houseflies. In spring they lay eggs on the young shoots of Raspberries, Blackberries, Dewberries, Loganberries and Roses and the maggots that hatch from them girdle the stems, enter them and tunnel along the canes, causing the upper portions of the shoots to wilt.

The best control is had by cutting off and burning all wilted shoots a few inches below the lowest point where damage is visible.

Seed-corn Maggot (Hylema cilicrura) is a yellowish-white maggot with a sharply pointed head which often causes serious injury to germinating seeds of Corn, Beans, Peas, Cucumbers and Melons. Young plants of Cabbages, Beets, Onions, Radishes, Sweet Potatoes and Turnips may be affected. The gray flies which are the mature insects start laying eggs in May in the soil or on seedlings. The worst injury occurs during cool wet periods. There are three or more generations each year.

Delaying planting until the soil is warm enough to permit quick germination is helpful in controlling this pest. Treating the soil with chlordane or lindane before planting is also advised. Seeds may be bought that are coated with Arasan and chlordane as a protection against this pest.

Mealybugs. Mealybugs are small oval sucking insects covered with a white mealy wax which extends in 36 filaments all around the body. Those with filaments of equal length are known as short-tailed mealybugs, those which have longer filaments at the rear than at other parts are known as long-tailed mealybugs. Both types are very injurious. Many kinds are common in greenhouses all over the world and are serious pests outdoors in warm climates; one or two kinds are hardy enough to live over winter outdoors as far north as Connecticut.

Most mealybugs lay 300 to 600 eggs in a waxy

Mealybugs often congregate on the undersides of leaves.

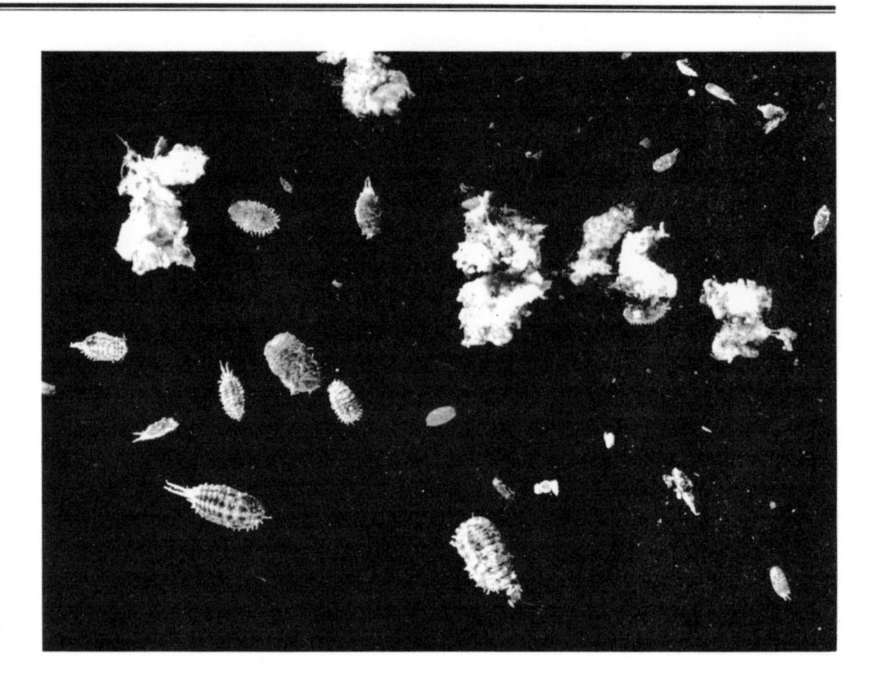

Long-tailed and short-tailed mealybugs.

sac which has the appearance of a mass of cotton. After laying eggs the female dies. The eggs hatch into young crawlers that at first are smooth and pale yellow. The male crawlers change into tiny 2-winged flylike insects, mate and soon die. In greenhouses and in warm climates the life cycle is completed in about a month and generations follow each other without a break. The long-tailed mealybug does not lay eggs but produces its young alive. Mealybugs secrete honeydew, a sweet liquid which is attractive to ants and is a medium upon which sooty mold fungus grows.

Citrus Mealybug (Pseudococcus Citri) is a short-tailed species found on a great many kinds of greenhouse plants and on many plants outdoors in warm climates. It is common on many house plants, especially African Violets, Amaryllis, Cacti, Coleus, Fuchsias, and Poinsettias.

Spray forcibly with a miscible oil spray, a nicotine insecticide or malathion. In greenhouses, spray or fumigate with Cyanogas or aerosol bombs. Most house plants may be kept clean by forceful spraying with water in the kitchen sink or tub, once a week or so. With African Violets and other kinds likely to be injured by spraying, pick off the cottony masses with a soft brush or touch them with a small swab of cotton dipped in alcohol.

Comstock Mealybug (Pseudoccus Comstockii) is a long-tailed species. It is one of the hardiest kinds and infests a number of woody plants, particularly Apples, Umbrella Catalpa and Mulberries. The mealybugs cluster mostly in crotches and crevices. There are two or three generations in a season.

To control these, clean all debris from crotches with a stiff brush. Apply a forceful spray of miscible oil insecticide just before new leaves start. Spray with malathion.

Taxus Mealybug (Pseudococcus Cuspidatae) is a serious pest of Yews in the Northeast. These mealybugs stay on the inner stems and twigs. Plants may become thickly infested before being noticed. The young nymphs winter in bark crevices and give birth to living young in early summer. There may be two or three broods each season. This is a long-tailed mealybug.

Spray the inside of the plant thoroughly with malathion, with a nicotine-soap solution, or with a miscible oil spray.

Midges or Gnats. These are very small flies, some of which cause galls. For the gall-forming kinds, see Galls, above.

Apple Leaf-curling Midge (Dasyneura Mali). The maggots, which are orange colored, infest the curled margins of young leaves.

Foliage of Chrysanthemums damaged by the Chrysanthemum gall midge.

Spraying with DDT at about the time the petals fall is effective.

Catalpa Midge (Itonida Catalpae). The maggots of this midge congregate near the veins on the undersides of the leaves and cause round, dead areas to develop as well as wilting, distortion and premature falling of the foliage. The buds may be killed and the trees stunted as a result.

Chrysanthemum Gall Midge (Diarthronomyia Chrysanthemi). Tiny cone-shaped galls are formed on the upper surfaces of the leaves and on the younger stems of both greenhouse and outdoor Chrysanthemums as the result of irritation instigated by the feeding of the larvae of the Chrysanthemum gall midge, an orange-colored, long-legged gnat about 1/4 in. long. Additional harm done by this creature is distortion of flower buds and of stems. There are two, three or more generations each year.

Control measures consist of picking off and burning infested foliage and of spraying with lindane two or three times at 5-day intervals. The spraying should be done in late afternoon or evening.

Spraying with DDT in May is the best control.

Juniper Midge (Contarinia Juniperina). On Junipers the bases of the leaves may be blistered as a result of the activities of the yellow maggots of this insect and later affected leaves turn brown and may drop off.

Prune out dead twigs and spray with lindane.

Pear Midge (Contarinia Pyrivora). As a result of infestation with the maggots of this midge, Pear fruits become distorted, marked with dark

Millipedes feed chiefly on decaying vegetable matter but sometimes damage seeds and young live roots.

blotches and drop from the trees prematurely.

Spraying with DDT in late April and again in early May is recommended.

Rhododendron Midge (Giardomyia Rhododendri). The whitish maggots of this midge feed on the young leaves of Rhododendrons, causing their edges to be rolled and brown and the growth to be distorted and undeveloped.

Spraying the tips of the shoots with malathion or with lindane gives control.

Rose Midge (Dasyneura rhodophaga). This midge has whitish or orange-colored maggots which feed at the bases of the flowers and on the upper sides of the leaves. As a result the buds blacken and dry up, new shoots die and the leaves turn brown and are distorted. There are several generations each season and this midge infests Roses both outdoors and in greenhouses.

Control may be had by pruning off all infested shoots and buds and by spraying with DDT.

Millepedes. Despite their name, millepedes have many less than a thousand legs. The usual number is from 100 to 400, actually two pairs on each segment of their bodies. They are round in section, brown or pinkish in color and coil themselves like watchsprings. They are primarily feeders on dead and decaying organic matter but they also sometimes damage living roots of such vegetables as Potatoes, Carrots, Parsnips and Turnips.

The recommended control is DDT, lindane or chlordane, sprayed over the ground, under greenhouse benches and in other areas where these creatures congregate.

Mites. Mites are not true insects but very minute creatures related to spiders. From insects they differ in having 8 rather than 6 legs. They are too small to be readily seen and plants are often badly infested before the presence of mites is noticed. There are many kinds of mites and they affect many different plants both in greenhouses and outdoors. They feed by sucking the juices of the plants they infest. The following are the most devastating in gardens:

Broad Mite (Hemitarsonemus latus). This is a pale-colored, almost transparent mite which often occurs together with the Cyclamen mite and is most common in greenhouses but sometimes infests outdoor plants. It is not quite as large as the Cyclamen mite but moves more

An African Violet very seriously damaged by an infestation of the broad mite.

rapidly. It distorts the leaves of numerous plants, including African Violets, Begonias, Chrysanthemums and Verbenas, giving them a glassy appearance and a rather brittle quality. This mite infests susceptible house plants.

Dusting with sulphur is an effective way of eliminating this mite. Aramite or Dimite may also be used with good effect.

Bulb Mites. These pests, Rhizoglyphus echinopus and Steneotarsonemus laticeps (bulb scale mite), attack damaged bulbs, especially in storage, weakening them still further, as a result of which the leaves may be flaked and streaked, and the flowers distorted or of poor quality. The bulb scale mite, barely visible to the naked eye, clusters around the neck of the bulb and is the more harmful of the two.

Care should be taken not to store damaged bulbs. Warm-water immersion for 1 hour as advised above for bulb flies will destroy the mites.

Cyclamen Mite (Steneotarsonemus pallidus). A widely spread pest that attacks a great many greenhouse and outdoor plants. It is particularly damaging to the flowers and leaves of Cyclamen and African Violets. Outdoors it is a very serious enemy of Delphiniums, causing the condition known as "blacks." In some areas it seriously affects Strawberries.

Dusts containing azobenzene or a Dimite spray

A Delphinium flower spike showing Delphinium "blacks," a condition that results from an infestation of the Cyclamen mite.

are especially effective on Cyclamen. Sodium selenate capsules are easy to use on African Violets. Spray into the growing tips of Delphinium shoots with Dimite as soon as they start into growth in spring and repeat every week as growth proceeds. Destroy badly infested plants.

Spruce Spider Mite (Oligonychus ununguis). This mite attacks conifers, especially Spruces, Arborvitaes, Hemlocks and Junipers. The mites spin webs between the needles and cause much discoloration.

Spray with Aramite or Ovex. Frequent forceful sprayings with water may be effective if started early.

Red Spider Mites. The name red spider mite is applied to more than one species of closely related mites that infest a great variety of plants. The commonest kind known by this name seems to be the two-spotted spider mite, which see below. Other kinds are rarely distinguished by gardeners; control measures recommended for the two-spotted spider mite are effective against other kinds.

Two-spotted Spider Mite (Tetranychus telarius). This is the commonest of the red spider mites and is a world-wide pest on a long list of plants in greenhouses and outdoors. It spins webs and thrives at a great rate under hot, dry conditions. Affected foliage loses color, becomes yellowish, light green, grayish-green and usually finely speckled in appearance.

Miticides such as Aramite, Dimite and Kelthane give good control of this two-spotted spider mite. Ovex is more effective against mite eggs than against adult mites and can be used with good effect.

The two-spotted spider mite, a type of red spider mite, causes loss of foliage color and serious slowing of growth of the plants it infests.

Moths. Moths belong, together with butterflies, in a large family of insects known as Lepidoptera. Moths are mostly night fliers. Their eggs are usually rounded or definitely flat, and, in the latter case, are laid in groups overlapping like tiles on a roof. The larvae, commonly called caterpillars, are well known and, though broadly similar in shape, exhibit a great variety in size, color, degree of hairiness and other features. They are provided with two types of legs, true walking legs and sucker feet.

Brown-tail Moth (Nygmia phaeorrhoea). This pest, common in the Northeast, chiefly infests Apples, Cherries, Pears, Plums, Oaks, Hawthorns,

Roses and Willows; occasionally it attacks other trees. The moths are white with a brown mark at the end of the abdomen. They have a 1½-in. wingspread. In July they lay clusters of yellow eggs covered with pale brown hairs, on the undersides of leaves. The larvae which hatch from these are reddish brown to nearly black caterpillars covered with tufts of brown hairs and, at maturity, about 1½-in. long. Their hairs cause a severe rash if they come in contact with the skin and, if breathed into the lungs in quantity, may cause death.

The caterpillars overwinter in large colonies in a nest of silken webbing. In spring they begin feeding voraciously and pupate in June.

Control is had by cutting out and burning the nests in winter, by spraying with arsenate of lead or methoxychlor when the leaves come out in spring, and again in August if the caterpillars are detected feeding then

Codling Moth or Apple Worm (Carpocapsa Pomonella). Apples, Pears and, less frequently, other tree fruits, as well as English Walnuts, are attacked by this most serious pest. The adult insects are grayish-brown moths marked with golden-brown lines on their front wings and measuring ½-¾ in. across. They develop from pupae in spring and lay their eggs on leaves and twigs. Within 1-3 weeks the eggs hatch and the young larvae crawl to the young fruits and bore their way inside through the calyx cups. Once inside the fruit, they tunnel through it, eating its substance as they go and sometimes causing the fruits to drop prematurely. Eventually they leave the fruits through holes they bore through their sides and leave behind a mass of brown excrement.

There are usually two generations a season. The larvae of the second generation enter the fruits at any point, not preferring the calyx cup ends. The codling moth winters as a full-grown, brown-headed, pinkish caterpillar contained in a silken cocoon hidden under loose bark and in similar protected places.

Control is had by following a careful spray schedule based on the use of lead arsenate, methoxychlor or DDT. Because timing of the sprays is important, it is advisable to consult the local County Agricultural Agent or the State Agricultural Experiment Station regarding this and to follow their recommendations exactly.

The larvae of the codling moth, often known as Apple worms, are extremely destructive unless controlled by careful spraying.

European Pine Shoot Moth (Rhyacionia buoliana). This is a small reddish-brown moth with silver cross lines on its front wings which lays its eggs in the tips of Pine shoots in early summer. The small brown, black-headed caterpillars which hatch from the eggs winter in or on the buds. In spring they bore into young growing shoots, which become crooked and die. Usually quantities of coagulated sap are to be seen where the caterpillars bore into the shoots. In the North there is one generation only each year but in the South there are 2 or more.

Cut out and burn all infested tips that are

Masses of coagulated sap or pitch on the buds and young shoots reveal the presence of the larvae of the European Pine shoot moth.

within reach in April or May, before the caterpillars change to moths. Spray with lead arsenate or dust with DDT when the young caterpillars appear, normally in late June or early July. Three applications at 2-week intervals are recommended.

Gypsy Moth (Porthetria dispar). This serious pest occurs chiefly in New England, where it does great damage to a wide variety of trees. The female moth, which is whitish with dark markings and is barely able to fly, lays oval egg masses coated with light brown hairs on tree trunks, poles, buildings and other hard surfaces. The brown hairy caterpillars hatch from the eggs in early May.

To control this pest, kill the egg masses by daubing creosote on them during winter. Spraying with lead arsenate or with Sevin, or dusting with DDT kills the caterpillars.

Oriental Fruit Moth (Grapholitha molesta). This small gray moth is a particular enemy of Peaches and also attacks Quinces, Apples, Plums, Cherries and some other fruits. The pinkish caterpillars, which at maturity are about 1/2 in. long, first bore into the young twigs, causing their tips to die. Later they attack the fruits, tunneling through them and rendering them worthless. The fully grown caterpillars overwinter in cocoons on dried fruits that fall to the ground, and on bark, weeds and trash. In spring they pupate and become moths and lay their eggs on the twigs and leaves of their host plants. The number of generations each season is 2-4 in the North, more in the South.

Spraying with DDT or with Sevin gives good control, starting after the flower petals fall and repeating at intervals until 3 weeks before harvesting. The exact timing of the sprays varies in different localities. Check with local County Agricultural Agents about this.

White-marked Tussock Moth (Hemerocampa leucostigma). This is a common pest in the East, feeding on a variety of deciduous (leaf-losing) trees, including orchard and city street trees. Large, conspicuous masses of eggs are laid on trunks, branches and dead leaves by the gray wingless female moths. The red-headed, hairy caterpillars are about 1 1/2 in. long at maturity and have conspicuous tufts of hairs along their bodies in addition to two projecting slender tufts of long black hairs at the head and one tuft at the rear. The caterpillars have a prominent black stripe bordered by broad bands of yellow along their backs. They feed in spring and early summer, and then pupate and emerge as moths. These lay eggs that produce a second brood of caterpillars, which feed in late summer. In the South there are usually 3 broods each season.

To control this pest, daub the egg masses with creosote in winter. Spray with malathion or lead arsenate as soon as caterpillars are feeding.

Nematodes. Nematodes are microscopic wormlike creatures which are often known as eelworms. They are quite distinct from true worms. They live in soil, water, decaying organic matter and as parasites in plants and animals. Their presence is usually detected at first by the symptoms they produce; the diagnosis can be confirmed by microscopic examination of the plant tissues. Some nematodes that affect plants confine their attentions to roots (root nematodes) others invade foliage (foliar or leaf nematodes) and others bulbs and stems (bulb and stem nematodes).

Few pests are able to increase so rapidly or cause so much serious damage in a short space of time. There are a great number of kinds of nematodes and several are able to attack a great variety of plants. They have, however, the peculiarity that they may exist in what are known as biologic races.

A biologic race is a collection of individuals of a particular species which can only attack a certain range of plants. Where different biologic races exist in one species they are indistinguishable from each other in appearance and structure and must, therefore, be classified as belonging to one and the same species, the only distinction lying in the particular range of plants which each biologic race is alone able to attack.

Bulb and Stem Nematodes (Ditylenchus Dipsaci and related species). These attack a wide variety of plants, including Anemones, Campanulas, Galtonias, Garlic, Foxgloves, Hyacinths, Narcissi, Onions, Primroses, Phlox and Sweet Williams. The symptoms they produce vary somewhat according to the kind of plant infested. Bulbs of Narcissi, Hyacinths, Onions, etc., fail

Characteristic symptoms exhibited by a Phlox plant infested with bulb and stem nematodes.

to grow satisfactorily, may show brown rings when cut through and often have their foliage twisted, stunted and marked with yellow spots. Phlox and some other plants are commonly crippled and exhibit much distortion and stunting; they often fail to bloom and die prematurely.

The only effective control with nonbulbous plants is to dig up affected specimens, burn them and take care not to replant susceptible kinds in the same ground for 3 or 4 years unless the soil is first sterilized with chloropicrin, D-D or some other killing agent. Valuable bulbs may be freed of infestation by soaking them for 3 hours in water held at 110 degrees F.

Chrysanthemum Leaf Nematode (Aphelenchoides ritzema-bosi). This is perhaps the most serious pest of Chrysanthemums in greenhouses and outdoors, and many other kinds of plants are affected by it. Both the eggs and the nematodes live in the soil and in old parts of infested plants. The nematodes travel up the stems when the stems are covered with a film of moisture and enter the leaves through the stomata or pores. As a result of infestation the leaves develop dark spots on their undersides and soon become yellow, then brown or black, in distinct triangular-shaped patches between the main veins. The lower leaves are normally first affected and the condition gradually travels upwards. Finally the foliage withers and dies and remains hanging on the stems.

To control this pest, burn all old Chrysanthemum tops (stems and foliage) in the fall. Avoid overhead watering. Keep the surface of the soil mulched with peat moss, buckwheat hulls, pulverized corn cobs or some similar material that offers a barrier to the nematodes swimming through films of moisture along the stems from the soil to the leaves. Propagate new Chrysanthemums by means of cuttings taken from parts of the plant not in contact with the soil and so not likely to have been infected by water splashed on them from the soil. Do not propagate by root division. Spray frequently with a nicotine insecticide from the time spring growth begins until late summer.

Sodium selenate gives good control but must not be applied to soil that is to be used for growing vegetables for 4-5 years. Dissolve 1 oz. of crystals of sodium selenate in 1 gallon of water and dilute this stock solution at the rate of 1 teacupful to a gallon of water. Apply this to the soil at the rate of 1 pint to 1 sq. ft. Then sprinkle with plain water. Repeat this treatment in 3-4 weeks. Be sure to label the crystals and stock solution "poison," and wash the hands thoroughly after using.

Meadow Nematodes (species of Pratylenchus). These are pests of a considerable variety of plants, including Apples, Cherries, Peaches, Boxwood and Peonies, and are widely distributed. They are confined to the roots but do not cause galls to form, as do root-knot nematodes. A sloughing away of a part of the root tissue results, and attacked plants show general debilitation, stunting and the dying of branches and sometimes the entire plant. The earliest effects of meadow nematodes are lesions that are yellow, brown or black, and appear on the fine feeder roots. These are followed by the death of much of the root system.

Control is best assured by sterilizing the soil with D-D mixture before planting. Affected

Boxwood infested with meadow nematodes, showing the witches'-broom effect that often results.

plants can be encouraged to resist the ill effects of these nematodes by fertilizing them adequately and making sure they do not suffer from lack of water during dry weather. Mulching with organic materials such as rotted manure and compost appears to be helpful.

Root-Knot Nematodes (various kinds of Meloidogyne). These cause irregular swellings or galls on the roots of hundreds of kinds of plants. The swellings must not be confused with the beneficial bacteria-filled nodules that are found on the roots of plants in the Pea family, Leguminosae, such as Peas, Beans, Clover and Lupines. The nodules on the roots of legumes are readily detached, those caused by nematodes are not. Root-knot nematodes are more prevalent and longer-lived under warm conditions in light sandy soil than in heavy soils or where winters are severe. In the South they are a very major problem; they sometimes are, too, in greenhouses in colder regions.

For plants in greenhouses, steam sterilization of soil is effective but is usually not practicable except in large commercial operations. The soil fumigant called D-D is effective and easy to apply to vacant greenhouse beds and to soil outdoors. Planting can follow about 2 weeks after treatment. Other materials that are effective in controlling nematodes are Vapam and V-C 13. Small infested plants may be cleaned by immersing the roots in water held for 30 minutes at 113 degrees F.

Orthezia (Orthezia insignis). The insect called greenhouse orthezia and orthezia scale is closely related to mealybugs and scale insects. It infests a wide variety of plants, including Cacti, Coleus, Chrysanthemums, Heliotropes, Lantanas, Salvias, Petunias and Verbenas, and seriously harms them by sucking their juices. In the North this is a pest chiefly in greenhouses; in the South it infests garden plants. The mature females, which are most conspicuous, are about 1/3 in. long and are surrounded by a white waxy fringe; they may also carry a long, white, fluted egg sac. The immature insects (nymphs) are smaller and covered with tiny waxy scales.

Control is by spraying with malathion, nicotine or oil sprays.

Plant Hoppers. These energetic jumping insects, which are also called lantern flies, generally resemble leaf hoppers but are larger. They are close relatives of leaf hoppers and tree hoppers. The commonest kinds, which are also known as mealy flata, frequent shrubs and vines, especially Boxwoods, Catalpas, Hawthorns, Grapes, Honeysuckles, Japanese Cherries, Mulberries, Privets and Viburnums. They also infest some nonwoody plants including Dahlias, Lilies and Salvias.

Mealy Flata (Ormenis Pruinosa and Ormenis septentrionalis). At maturity, these exceed 1/4 in. in length. The first kind has brownish or purplish wings conspicuously covered with a white powdery or mealy material; the other species is pale bluish-green. The nymphs (immature insects) of both species are greenish and are concealed beneath great masses of white, woolly strands which are conspicuous on the branches of infested trees and shrubs and may be mistaken by people unfamiliar with garden pests for mealybugs or woolly aphids.

Mealy flata do no serious harm and it is not

worth while taking measures to eliminate them.

Corn Plant Hopper (Peregrinus Maidis) is also known as the Corn leaf hopper. It causes damage by killing young Corn plants before they have formed their tassels. The mature insects are 1/6 in. long and are yellowish green with transparent wings that have dark markings near their tips.

Control is obtained by dusting with sulphur or pyrethrum dust.

Psyllids. These very active jumping insects are usually less than 1/4 in. long. They obtain their food by sucking the juices of plants, and in doing so seriously weaken their hosts; in addition, many of them excrete honeydew (a sweetish liquid), which gathers on the leaves and forms a fertile material for the sooty mold fungus to grow upon. The most important of the psyllids that affect garden plants are here listed.

Blackberry Psyllid (Trioza tripunctata). This yellowish-brown insect with banded wings infests Blackberries and related fruits. Shortly after new growth begins in spring, both adults and immature insects, which have wintered over in trash and other protected places, puncture the stems and cause the leaves to curl. A severe attack causes stunting and distortion.

Mealy flata at rest on the stem of a shrub.

Control is obtained with two or three sprays of a nicotine insecticide, applied 5-7 days apart, the first being given at the very first sign of attack.

Boxwood Psyllid (Psylla Buxi). A characteristic symptom of infestation is that the terminal leaves on Boxwood shoots are cupped and the young growth stunted. The adult psyllids are green with transparent wings; as nymphs (immature insects) they are grayish green with a conspicuous covering of a white, cottony, waxy substance.

An effective control measure consists of three sprays of a nicotine insecticide or of malathion, applied 10-14 days apart, the first being given when new growth begins in spring.

Laurel Psyllid (Trioza alacris). This pest of Laurus nobilis and Prunus laurocerasus is about 1/12 in. long and greenish yellow to light brown, marked with darker and lighter spots. The nymphs (immature insects) are pale yellow and orange and are covered with powdery white wax. They cause the leaves of infested plants to become thickened, distorted and reddish at their edges and often to form galls. Premature dropping of foliage occurs.

Repeated spraying with a nicotine insecticide or malathion gives control.

Pear Psyllid (Psylla Pyricola). This serious pest of Pears also sometimes attacks Quinces. It results in loss of vigor, premature dropping of foliage and disfiguring of the fruits. Large amounts of honeydew are excreted. Because of this, the leaves and fruits of infested trees are usually more or less blackened with the sooty mold fungus that grows on the honeydew.

The mature psyllid is less than 1/8 in. long and reddish brown. After living over winter in crevices in bark or in trash on the ground, it lays its eggs in spring on the buds. The eggs hatch into minute nymphs (immature insects) which feed on the host and in a short time become adult. Several generations of Pear psyllids occur in a season, the later generations laying their eggs on the foliage.

Control is had by applying a miscible oil spray (dormant strength) before growth begins in spring and by spraying with a nicotine or with a rotenone spray during summer months.

Potato or Tomato Psyllid (Paratrioza Cockerelli). The adults of this insect are less than 1/8 in. long and are at first green but later become black with white edges. Chiefly in warm weather eggs (bright yellow and each attached by a tiny, distinct stem) are laid on the undersides of the leaves. These hatch into nymphs (immature insects), which at first are yellow or orange but later become green, surrounded with a fringe of hairs.

A serious effect of infestation is caused by the feeding of the nymphs. These inject into the host plant a toxic substance, the action of which is not localized but affects the whole plant. The terminal leaves of the shoots become reddish or purplish, the lower parts of the edges of the leaflets become yellow and turn upwards, the older leaves become brown and die. Growth of stems is checked or stopped and the nodes of the stem become swollen. Potatoes produce dwarfed shoots that are swollen at their bases and bear undersized, distorted leaves.

Dusting or spraying with DDT or dusting with sulphur gives the best control.

Sawflies. Sawflies are closely related to bees and wasps. Their larvae, however, resemble the caterpillars of butterflies and moths or slugs. Some of these larvae are called caterpillars, others slugs. The name sawfly refers to the saw-like ovipositor (egg depositor) which the female uses to slit stems and to lay eggs in them. Various kinds of sawflies attack evergreens such as Larches, Pines and Spruces. Among deciduous (leaf-losing) trees, Elms, Mountain Ashes, Pears, Pin Oaks and Willows are attacked.

Control of the larvae of sawflies is obtained by prompt spraying or dusting with lead arsenate, DDT or rotenone as soon as they begin to feed; this treatment is repeated as often as necessary.

Of sawflies the larvae of which attack garden plants the following are most important:

Ash Sawflies (Tethida cordigera and Tomostethus multicinctus). The larvae of the first of these, the black-headed ash sawfly, are whitish or yellowish with black heads; those of the other, the brown-headed ash sawfly, are yellowish white or greenish with brown heads. Both defoliate Ash trees in spring, change to adult insects in late May or June and live in the ground during the remainder of the year.

A Rose leaf eaten by the bristly Rose slug.

Birch Sawfly or Dusky Birch Sawfly (Croesus latitarsus). Chiefly a pest of Gray Birch (Betula populifolia), this insect sometimes attacks other kinds. The larvae are about 1 in. long, green with black markings, and have black heads. They are fond of congregating and feeding on the leaf edges, which they do from late spring to early fall. There are two generations each year.

Blackberry Sawfly (Pamphilius dentatus). The larvae are bluish green, about 3-4 in. long. They roll themselves inside the leaves, upon which they feed, and are active as larvae from May to June. They spend the remainder of the year as adults in the soil.

Bristly Rose Slug (Cladius isomerus). This pest defoliates Roses north of central Virginia, east of the Mississippi and also in California. The greenish-white sluglike larvae are furnished with long bristles. There are 5 or 6 broods each season.

Curled Rose Sawfly (Allantus cinctus). This kind takes its name from the fact that the larvae curl up like cutworms. They are green above, marked with white dots, and beneath are grayish. Their heads are brown. There is 1 generation in the North, and there are 2 in the southern regions of the area in which the pest occurs, which is from Virginia to Maine and westwards to Minnesota.

Elm Sawfly (Cimbex americana). Fully mature

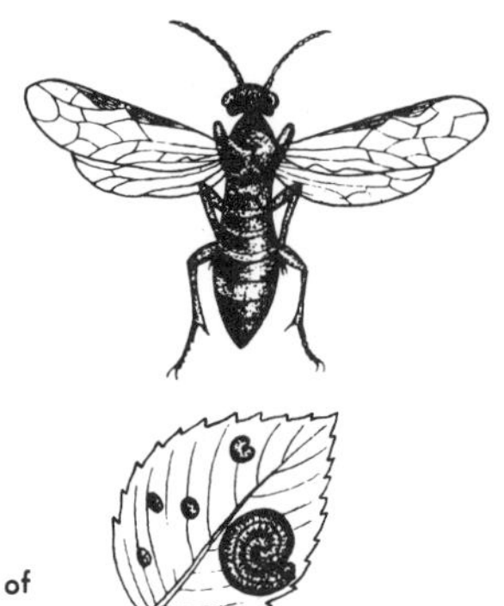

Adult and larvae of Rose Sawfly.

Imported Currantworm (Nematus Ribesii). This pest of Currants and Gooseberries feeds on the leaves. The larvae are green with black heads and have black spots on their bodies. When disturbed, they raise their front and rear ends. A first brood appears when the Currants or Gooseberries are first in full leaf, a second in July or August.

Larch Sawfly (Pristiphora Erichsonii). The larvae measure 1¾ in. long. They are light yellowish green with a black stripe down the back. When feeding, they coil the rear ends of their bodies around twigs. They are active from late spring until frost.

European Apple Sawfly (Hoplocampa testudinea). The white larvae of this pest bore into the young fruits and leave a dark brown frass or sawdust at the entrance to their borings.

DDT does not seem to be effective against this pest, but rotenone, applied when the petals fall and again a week later, gives good results. The European Apple sawfly is troublesome in southeastern New York and southern Connecticut.

Branches of Currants stripped of their foliage by the imported currantworm.

The imported currantworm is the larva of a sawfly.

larvae of this insect are grayish green with black heads and legs. They feed in gangs and seriously defoliate Larches. As a result of severe attacks trees may be killed.

Mountain Ash Sawfly (Pristiphora geniculata). This species seriously defoliates Mountain Ash. The larvae are green marked with black dots. There are 1 or 2 generations a year.

Peach Sawfly (Pamphilius Persicus). The light bluish-green larvae of this sawfly roll themselves in the leaves they feed upon.

Pear Slug or Cherry Slug (Caliroa Cerasi). The dark green to orange-colored larvae are slimy, about ½ in. long and resemble slugs. They attack Cherries, Pears, Plums, Quinces, Hawthorns and Mountain Ash, skeletonizing the leaves by feeding on their upper surfaces. There are two broods each season. For the second brood on fruit trees it is best to use a nicotine insecticide rather than lead arsenate, DDT or any other type that is likely to leave a poisonous deposit on the fruits.

Pine Sawflies. Several kinds of sawflies attack various species of Pines. The most common are the European Pine sawfly (Neodiprion sertifer), which has green larvae with black heads; the introduced Pine sawfly (Diprion simile), larvae yellowish green with black and yellow stripes; the Loblolly Pine sawfly (Neodiprion americanum), larvae greenish white with a green stripe, black spots and brown heads; the red-headed Pine sawfly (N. Lecontei), larvae white at first but yellow with black spots and red heads later; and the White Pine sawfly (N. Pinetum), the larvae of which are yellowish with black spots and black heads.

These larvae vary in color and size but all seriously harm their host plants by devouring their foliage. As a result young Pines may be killed, older ones seriously weakened. The larvae usually feed together in large gangs. Some of the sawflies that infest Pines have only one generation a year, others more.

Plum Web-spinning Sawfly (Neurotoma inconspicua). The larvae, which are grayish yellow and about 3/4 in. long, feed beneath the protection of webs they spin at the ends of the branches. They attack Plums and Sand Cherries.

Poplar Sawfly (Trichiocampus viminalis). The bright yellow larvae, marked with rows of black spots and having black heads and tufts of white hairs on their bodies, attain a length of about 3/4 in. They seriously defoliate Lombardy and Carolina Poplars by feeding in gangs. The Willow sawfly, which see below, also attacks Poplars.

Raspberry Sawfly (Monophadnoides geniculatus). Raspberries, Blackberries, Dewberries and Loganberries are seriously defoliated by the light green larvae of this sawfly, which feed on the undersides and the margins of the leaves.

Rose Slug or Rose Sawfly (Endelomyia aethiops). This dark green or yellow-green sluglike larvae is of velvety appearance and 1/2 in. or less long. It skeletonizes foliage and causes it to become brown. This pest occurs east of the Rocky Mountains and has but one brood each season.

Spruce Sawflies. Spruces are attacked by the European Spruce sawfly (Diprion Hercyniae), the yellow-headed Spruce sawfly (Pikonema alaskensis) and the Balsam Fir sawfly (Neodiprion Abietis). The larvae of the first named are pale green at first, later becoming darker and marked with five white stripes. The larvae of the yellow-headed Spruce sawfly are yellowish green, striped with gray, and have brown heads. The larvae of the Balsam Fir sawfly are green, striped with brown and deeper green, and with black heads. All devour the foliage of their hosts.

Violet Sawfly (Ametastegia pallipes). Pansies and Violas are often damaged by this pest. The larvae feed at night. They are about 1/2 in. long, bluish black or greenish.

Willow Sawfly or Yellow-spotted Willow Slug (Nematus ventralis). The larvae of this species are sluglike and greenish black and have heart-shaped spots of yellow along their sides. They feed in gangs and produce more than one generation a year. This sawfly attacks Poplars as well as Willows.

Scales or Scale Insects. Scale insects are of many kinds and occur on a wide variety of fruit and ornamental trees, shrubs, vines and many other plants, both outdoors and in greenhouses. Scale insects which have hard coverings are called armored scales, those without this

Scale insects on English Ivy.

protection are unarmored or soft scales. The female scales do most harm to plants. They are without wings and are able to move from place to place only when very young. Later, they insert their mouth parts into a stem or leaf and remain there, looking like small lumps or bumps and sucking sap, until they die. The males, at maturity, are tiny winged insects. In some cases the females bear living young.

Scale insects, like aphids and mealybugs, excrete a sweet, sticky substance called honeydew. This is a favorite food of ants, and these insects are likely to frequent plants infested with scales. A black fungus called sooty mold commonly grows on the honeydew and this may seriously disfigure plants that are more or less covered with it.

Control of scales is effected by applying dormant oil sprays or dinitro compounds at dilutions recommended by the manufacturers just before new growth begins in spring, by spraying with malathion and by using a nicotine spray at times when the young scale insects are in the crawling stage. This latter can be determined by examining the plants very carefully. A keen-eyed observer can just see the young scales moving about, but a good hand lens makes it very much easier to do this, and such a lens should be part of the equipment of every gardener.

Spraying is the obvious way to eliminate scale insects on outdoor plants and in greenhouses where considerable numbers of plants are infested. But if only a few must be dealt with, as is often the case with house plants or in a small greenhouse, a simpler method and one less wasteful of spray is to mix a small amount of the insecticide at the correct dilution, dip a sponge in it, squeeze it nearly dry and then rub each leaf and stem with it vigorously enough to remove the scales but without harming the plant tissues. After the plant has been cleaned in this way, rinse it off with a forceful spray of plain water. Among the principal scale insects that infest garden plants are the following kinds:

Black Scale (Saissetia Oleae). This is a widespread pest, especially destructive to Citrus trees. It also attacks other fruit and ornamental trees outdoors and a wide variety of plants in greenhouses. Added injury is caused by the sooty mold fungus, which develops in the honeydew secretion these scale insects exude. The mature females are hemispherical, less than 1/4 in. in diameter and dark brown to black.

Black Thread Scale (Ischnaspis longirostris). This dark brown or black scale attains a length of about 1/16 in. and is very slender. It is a particular pest of Palms.

Cottony-Cushion Scale (Icerya Purchasi). This reddish-brown scale insect is conspicuous at egg-laying time because of its white fluted sac containing 600 to 800 bright red eggs, which is in evidence then. It occurs generally in the South and in California on a great variety of plants. Sooty mold fungus often grows on the honeydew secretion that is exuded by this insect.

Cottony Maple Scale (Pulvinaria innumerabilis). This scale insect occurs especially on Silver Maples and on many other trees and shrubs. It covers the undersides of the branches and twigs with conspicuous cottony masses which contain

A black, threadlike scale insect on Ficus.

the numerous eggs. The scales in winter are brown, flattened and about 1/8 in. long. They grow rapidly in spring. There is one generation each season.

Cottony Taxus Scale (Pulvinaria floccifera). This pest occurs both outdoors and in greenhouses and is especially partial to Yews (Taxus), Camellias, Acalyphas and Abutilons. The scale itself is light brown and about 1/8 in. long. It becomes conspicuous in spring when it lays its eggs in long, narrow cottony masses. It infests both leaves and branches and often causes serious injury.

Euonymus Scale (Unaspis Euonymi). This pest is extremely destructive to many kinds of Euonymus and is also common on Celastrus and Pachysandra. The stems of infested plants are often completely whitened by the countless numbers present. When that condition occurs the best course is to cut out and burn the worst affected branches and then to spray several times to clean the remainder. The female scales resemble miniature oyster shells, and are dark brown and about 1/16 in. long. The males are clear white and very slender. A first brood of young (crawlers) hatches in late May or June, a second generation in late August and September.

The Euonymus is commonly infested with scale insects. The white ones shown here are the female insects.

European Elm Scale (Gossyparia spuria). This pest occurs on Elms of various kinds and causes yellowing and unseasonally early dropping of the leaves as well as dying back of twigs and branches. In severe cases infested trees may be killed. At their maturity the females are up to 3/8 in. long, reddish brown fringed with white. The males, in early spring form conspicuous white cocoons. This pest produces much honeydew.

European Fruit Scales (Leucanium Corni and L. Persicae). These closely similar insects infest fruit and ornamental trees and shrubs. L. Corni (Brown Apricot Scale or Brown Elm Scale) is up to 1/8th inch long, more or less hemispherical, convex, and glossy brown. Individuals of Leucanium persicae (European Peach Scale) are somewhat larger, longer and less convex.

Fern Scale (Pinnaspis Aspidistrae). Males and females of this species are conspicuous although quite different in appearance. The former are pure white and slender, the latter brown, pear-shaped or oyster-shaped and larger than the males. They infest Ferns, Aspidistras, Citrus fruits, Orchids, Palms and some other plants. It is important not to confuse these insects with the natural spore-bearing bodies which occur on the undersides of the leaves of many Ferns. These bodies always form regular patterns on the leaves and occur there only and not on the stems; the scales often are found on leafstalks as well as the flat surfaces of the leaves and are distributed haphazardly rather than in definite patterns.

Florida Red Scale (Chrysomphalus aonidum). This is a small reddish-brown circular scale that is common on Citrus and many ornamentals in Florida and the Gulf States. In the North it is familiar on the leaves of English Ivy, Rubber plants, Begonias and many other plants that are grown in greenhouses and homes.

Hemispherical Scale (Saissetia hemisphaerica). This glossy brown tortoise-like scale measures at maturity 1/8 in. across. It is common on many plants outdoors in warm climates and on a considerable variety of plants grown in greenhouses

Oystershell scale insects on Lilac.

and houses everywhere. A characteristic of this scale is its great height; it is raised very prominently above the surface on which it grows. The hemispherical scale exudes much honeydew (a sweet secretion) and upon this the sooty mold fungus develops abundantly.

Juniper Scale (Diaspis Carueli). This pest occurs chiefly on Arborvitaes, Cypress and Junipers which are in ornamental plantings and soon causes them to be in ill health and assume a shabby appearance. The scales are about 1/20 in. in diameter, round, of an off-white color with a yellowish center to each scale. They often occur in great numbers on the foliage. The young (crawlers) hatch in late May or early June.

Magnolia Scale (Neolecanium cornuparvum). At maturity this scale measures as much as 1/2 in. in diameter. It is brown, but this color is more or less obscured by a covering of white wax. Magnolias affected by this insect are likely to make poor growth and appear sickly. A great deal of the sticky secretion called honeydew is produced and on this the sooty mold fungus is likely to grow.

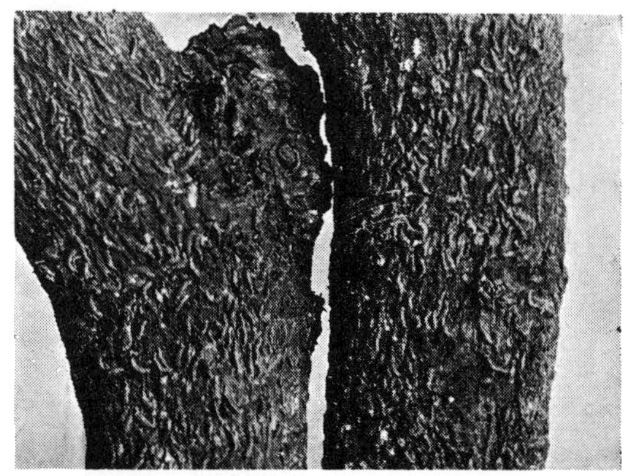

Branches of an Apple tree heavily infested by the oystershell scale.

Oleander Scale (Aspidiotus Hederae). This is a circular, flat, pale-yellow scale, about 1/10 in. in diameter, that is found on many different kinds of plants outdoors in the South and in greenhouses everywhere; it is especially prevalent on Oleanders and English Ivy.

Oystershell Scale (Lepidosaphes Ulmi). This scale insect is widely distributed and occurs on many deciduous (leaf-losing) trees, shrubs and other plants, including Lilacs, Maples, Willows, Apples, Figs, Grapes, Birches, Poplars, Peonies, Camellias, Tulip Trees and Yuccas. It is easily recognized by its oyster shape and oystershell-like markings. These insects may be gray or brown, or brown with a yellow fringe. Mature scales are 1/8 in. long.

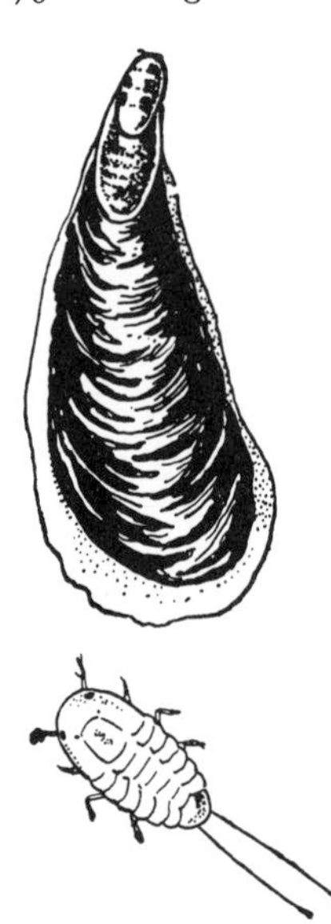

A female oystershell scale insect and a larva.

Pine Needle Scale (Phenacaspis Pinifoliae). This common kind is found on Pines, Spruces, Firs, Hemlocks and Incense Cedars and is most prevalent in the eastern half of North America. Both the males and females are white. The females are about 1/10 in. long, the males not much more than a third as long. The scales are considerably longer than broad. The foliage of severely infested plants turns yellow and eventually dies. Two generations of young appear each season, the first in May, the second in late July.

Rose Scale (Aulacaspis Rosae). This pest is by no means confined to Roses, although they are one of its favorite hosts. It infests, too, Blackberries, Dewberries, Loganberries, Raspberries and closely related plants. The scales are white, round, and about 1/5 in. in diameter, and they occur on the stems in such numbers that entire canes may be covered. The young hatch in May or June; there is a second brood in August.

San Jose Scale (Aspidiotus perniciosus). A widely spread circular gray waxy scale about 1/16 in. in diameter, with a yellow ring around its center. It is especially injurious to Apples and other fruit trees and is also found on a great many other trees and shrubs. There are 2 to 6 generations a year, the greater number where long warm summers prevail.

Soft Scale (Coccus hesperidum). This soft, flattish, yellowish, greenish or brownish scale insect is very common in greenhouses and, in mild climates, outdoors. It infests a wide variety of plants, including Abutilons, Apples, Auracarias, Bougainvilleas, Clerodendrons, Gardenias, Pittosporums and Willows. The young of this kind are born alive. This scale produces a great amount of sweet, sticky honeydew and on this the sooty mold fungus is likely to grow and disfigure the foliage.

Terrapin Scale (Lecanium nigrofasciatum). This is a glossy, dark-brown soft scale, 1/8 in. in diameter, that occurs on various fruit trees, shade trees and shrubs, chiefly on the twigs and branches. Its back is marked by black bands which radiate from the center to the circumference. Sooty mold grows freely on the honeydew secretion which is produced in abundance by this insect. Among trees commonly infested are Boxelder, Hawthorns, Maples and Sycamores.

Tulip Tree Scale (Toumeyella Liriodendri). This large, soft scale infests Tulip Trees, Liriodendron, as well as Magnolias and Lindens, Tilia. The female is hemispherical, dark brown and measures at maturity about 1/3 in. in diameter. These insects tend to crowd together along the branches and branchlets.

The large rounded scale insects which attack the Tulip Tree, Liriodendron Tulipifera.

Spraying with a dormant-strength oil emulsion in spring is the recommended control. Spraying with Malathion in August is also helpful.

Slugs. Slugs are not insects but are classed along with snails, clams and oysters as molluscs. They differ from snails in not being protected by a large, hard shell, although some kinds have a much reduced shell located internally or near the rear of their bodies. Some slugs cause serious damage to a great variety of plants. Not all slugs are pests; some are harmless and others are actually beneficial. The beneficial kinds live below the surface of the soil and are carnivorous, feeding on earthworms, slugs, wireworms and soil grubs. These carnivorous slugs should not be destroyed. They can be distinguished by the presence of a small shell near the tail end of their bodies. In addition to true slugs, the larvae of some sawflies are called slugs. For these, see under Sawflies, above.

Slugs feed largely at night when conditions are damp; on dull, damp days they may feed to some extent during daylight. They lay white, semitransparent eggs in the soil and in other damp locations. The young slugs are like their parents. They grow until they are fully mature, and, in turn, lay eggs. Slugs are hermaphrodite—that is, each individual possesses both male and female organs. However, mating between distinct individuals is necessary for reproduction. Slugs travel by means of crawling and they leave conspicuous silvery trails of mucus wherever they go.

To reduce the danger of damage by slugs the hiding places frequented by them should be removed or made unsuitable for them. Walls should be well pointed (any cavities between bricks or stones should be filled with cement). Rubbish heaps should be kept sprinkled with lime and turned at intervals.

Acid soils are particularly favorable to slugs. Liming is therefore indirectly beneficial.

Various substances may be used around plants to keep slugs away from them. Such substances need to be renewed frequently in wet weather. Lime or lime and coal soot may be sprinkled around seedlings or other plants. Powdered coke and fine coal cinders have also been found effective.

Several methods have been devised whereby slugs may be killed by applications made to the soil. Lime is effective if applied at a fairly heavy rate. Dry Bordeaux mixture is also used. Powdered copper sulphate or a copper sulphate in solution is extremely effective, but can only be used when the ground is free of plants. A mixture of 1 lb. of copper sulphate and 20 lb. of muriate of potash may be applied at the rate of about ½ oz. per square yard. Slugs put out large quantities of slime when any irritating substance touches them, and this slime, to a large extent, enables them to avoid injury. If, however, a second dressing is applied after a short interval, success is usually attained.

The dressings mentioned above must be applied when the slugs are on the surface of the soil, so that the various materials come into direct contact with their bodies. The period just before dusk is the most satisfactory time for applications to be made.

Hollowed orange skins are effective traps for slugs. Half an orange skin is used, after the fashion of a tent, with a small stone beneath one edge if the soil is level, to allow the slugs to find their way under it. These traps, which attract slugs because they provide shade, moisture and shelter, should be examined regularly and the slugs collected and destroyed. Lettuce leaves, bran and similar substances may be used to attract slugs if the materials are placed under boards.

Spotted garden slugs on the flower of a Dahlia.

A preparation known as metaldehyde is a most effective bait for destroying slugs. This is the basis, often combined with calcium arsenate or sodium fluosilicate, of commercial slug baits sold by dealers in garden supplies. Such baits are poisonous to humans, animals and birds. Dusting with a 15 per cent metaldehyde dust is also an effective method of controlling slugs.

Among the commonest slugs that are destructive in gardens are those listed below. The larvae of certain sawflies—Pear slug and Rose slug—are also sometimes known as slugs. For these, see Sawflies, above.

Gray Garden Slug (Deroceras reticulatum). This is a particularly harmful kind; the general color is gray of various shades, the slime is milky white.

Foliage of Primrose eaten by slugs.

Greenhouse Slug (Milax Gagates). This slug feeds on the roots of plants below the surface of the soil during the day and is very destructive. It is dark gray or black in color.

Spotted Garden Slug (Limax maximus). This kind may grow 6-7 in. in length when fully extended. When young, it is dark gray or black; at maturity it is yellowish or brown, mottled with black.

Snails. These creatures are not insects but, like the slugs, are molluscs. Snails differ from slugs in that they have a conspicuous hard shell into which they can draw their entire body when danger threatens or when at rest or dormant. They move slowly by crawling and usually leave a silvery trail or mucus marking their tracks.

There are many different kinds of snails, varying in color from whitish yellow through brown and gray to black, and in size from 1/4 in. to 9 or 10 in. long. Only a few are of importance in gardens.

Injuries to plants by snails are serious and widespread. Almost any kind of plant is liable to damage, but plants in the seedling stage are particularly favored by these pests; decaying vegetable matter is also eaten. Snails have a long rasplike tongue with which they feed. Feeding takes place largely at night.

Snails spend the winter in colonies among rocks, under loose boards and fence bases, among evergreen ground covers such as English Ivy and Pachysandra, in hedge bottoms, rubbish heaps and similar places. Breeding takes place in the spring and summer. Snails are hermaphrodite—that is, each snail possesses male and female organs, though mating between different individuals is still necessary.

The snails make a nest for their eggs in damp soil; the nest takes the form of a hole 1/4 in. or more in diameter and as much as 1 1/2 in. deep. The eggs are laid in a loose mass, some sixty being present in each nest. The nest is then closed with soil. Each egg is 1/8 in. in diameter. The eggs hatch in about two weeks.

The young snails have very small shells when hatched and they make their way out of the nest and feed upon young and tender plants. As they grow their shells increase in size. It takes nearly two years for a snail to become fully grown.

One of the snails most likely to cause trouble in the garden is the brown garden snail (Helix aspera), which is a serious pest on the West Coast and is especially harmful to citrus fruits, Avocados, and other trees, shrubs, flowers and vegetables. Four or five kinds that most commonly abound in greenhouses are also serious nuisances.

The methods used for the control of slugs are frequently also effective against snails (see Slugs). Snails may, however, be reduced very considerably by systematic hand collection, which is made more feasible than it is with slugs because of the habit snails have of congregating. It is most satisfactory to look for snails when weather conditions are dry. In the average garden, snails are often plentiful in rocky places and along the bases of walls and hedges. The snails should be picked up and dropped into a pail containing a strong solution of salt in water.

Sowbugs or Pillbugs. These form a section of the animal group known as Crustacea (which includes crabs and lobsters); they are not insects. They have seven pairs of legs and are 1/3-1/2 in. long. Their bodies are oval and flattish and consist of several distinct segments. They are gray or brownish. The commonist kinds are the dooryard sowbug (Porcellio laevis) and the common pillbug (Armadillidium vulgaris). Both kinds are sometimes called woodlice.

These pests feed on a variety of different foods, including animal and vegetable refuse. Living plants are also attacked, and sowbugs or pillbugs may do much harm to the roots, leaves and other

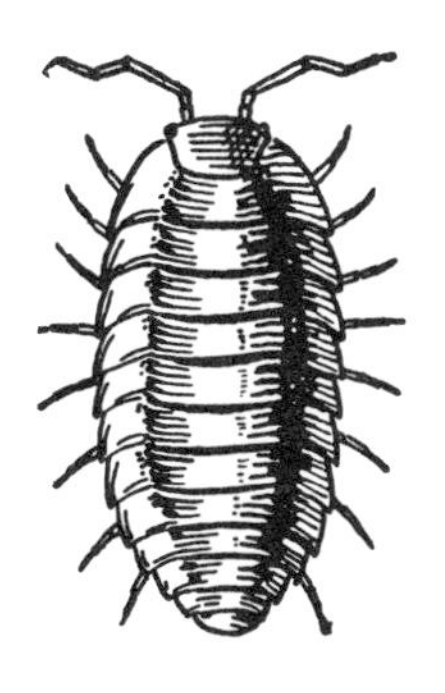

Pillbug or woodlouse. The specimen at the right is rolled up in a characteristic manner.

parts of many greenhouse plants and, to a lesser extent, such plants as Strawberries growing in the open.

Sowbugs or pillbugs are fond of damp, dark places. They are especially likely to be found behind and under rotten wood. The eggs are carried in a kind of pouch by the female. From these the young hatch. They are very much like their parents. The young remain close to their parents for a considerable time. They attain full size in about a year.

To prevent damage, rotten wood, stones, old flats and boxes and similar objects, which provide the damp, dark conditions favored by these creatures, should be removed from the greenhouse. A well-kept greenhouse always suffers less from attacks of sowbugs or pillbugs than one which is in a neglected condition.

Sowbugs or pillbugs may be trapped in pieces of Potato or Apple which have been hollowed out. The pests may be collected by hand and destroyed. A 5 per cent DDT dust or a 2 per cent lindane or chlordane dust sprinkled about the greenhouse or frame will destroy large numbers.

Spittle Bugs. See under Bugs, above.

Springtails. Several species of these very minute insects (Collembola) are of importance as pests. Various plants are attacked. The damage usually takes the form of the bleeding of sap more or less at ground level. The insects congregate in large numbers and, by their continual feeding, keep the damaged tissues from healing.

The most important species is the garden springtail (Bourletiella hortensis). This kind attacks young Marigolds, Beet, Spinach, Beans and Cucumbers as well as other plants, causing a constriction of the stems near ground level. The injuries by springtails principally take place in the early stages of growth. Damp soil is favored by these insects.

Springtails often live in the organic matter in the soil of potted plants and may be seen on the surface or in the saucers in which potted plants stand, especially after watering. As such plants are usually not young, the springtails do them no appreciable harm. Springtails are small, long and narrow or globular in shape. Their name alludes to a springlike process beneath the body, which is used in leaping.

Eggs are laid in groups of 30-40 on damp, decaying leaves or on damp soil near the bases of plants. The young springtails are similar to their parents and become mature and fully grown in about two months. June and July are the months when attacks by springtails are usually most noticeable outdoors.

Dusting the soil surface in early morning or evening with lindane or with malathion powder will provide control. Powdered naphthalene is worthy of trial as a deterrent.

Symphylid or Garden Centipede. The creature commonly known as the garden centipede (Scutigerella immaculata) is not a true centipede but a symphylid. True centipedes have a large number of legs (1 pair to each body segment) and a pair of poison claws. They are not garden pests but are to some extent useful because they destroy snails and some harmful insects. Symphylids are active white creatures which have 12 pairs of legs when mature, are without poison claws and have no eyes. They are about ¼ in. long. They are often troublesome in greenhouses and in warm climates outdoors. They feed on young roots and damage plants so that they become stunted or die. The young symphylids hatch from groups of eggs which are laid several inches deep in the soil. At first they have six pairs of legs, but more develop as the creatures grow. Symphylids favor dark places and are rarely seen above ground.

Steam sterilization of the soil or treating it with D-D mixture two weeks before planting eliminates symphylids. Where plants are growing,

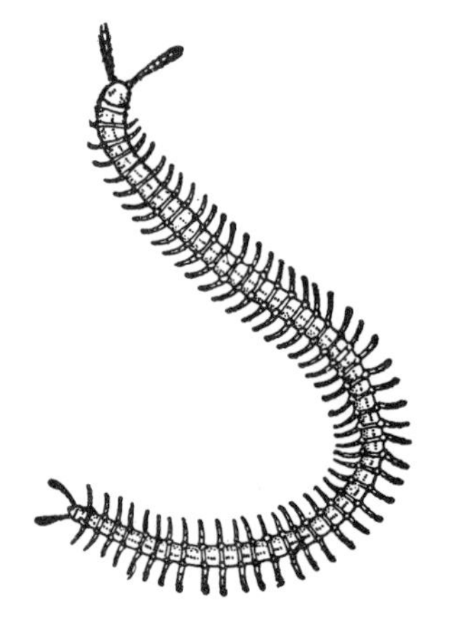

A symphylid or garden centipede is a quick-moving creature that avoids light places.

lindane, 6 oz. of 25 per cent wettable powder in 10 gallons of water applied to 1000 sq. ft., or 10 lb. of 1 percent lindane dust per 1000 sq. ft., is recommended.

Termites. These destructive insects are quite distinct from ants, to which they bear a superficial resemblance. Like ants, they live in large, highly organized colonies. Termites are only slightly constricted at their middles whereas ants have deep constrictions that give them characteristic slender waists.

Termites feed on wood or other forms of cellulose and can destroy buildings and other wooden structures. Often the damage they do is not observed until well advanced because these creatures tunnel within the wood and leave an outer shell intact; but here we are concerned with the damage termites do to plants rather than structures.

The kinds most harmful in gardens are the eastern subterranean termite (Reticulitermes flaviceps) and the western subterranean termite (R. hesperus). They are chiefly feeders on dead wood but they sometimes injure living fruit trees and other kinds as well as many perennial plants that have more or less woody stems. They are not uncommon pests of Chrysanthemums. In the South they may injure vegetable and other crops.

Termites may be deterred by cleaning up all dead and rotted woody material, by mixing chlordane or DDT in the soil about living plants and by taking care to treat fence posts, plant stakes and other wood that is to be placed in contact with the ground with creosote, copper sulphate, copper naphthenate, mercuric chloride or zinc chloride. Creosote should not be used on plant stakes as it is harmful to roots. Redwood is resistant to termite attack.

Thrips. These minute insects (Thysanoptera) are important as pests both out of doors and in greenhouses. They are small, black, reddish or dark brown and are about 1/15 in. in length. They are spindle-shaped. Two pairs of narrow membranous wings, heavily fringed with hairs, are present.

Thrips damage plants by sucking sap and rasping the tissues. The symptoms take the form of silvery mottling of leaves and other portions of the plants attacked. The damage is rather like that produced by red spider mites but lacks the characteristic rusty appearance of injuries caused by the latter pests. Distortion of leaves and other parts of the host plant also occur. Thrips are much attracted by flowers and often cause serious injury to them. Thrips increase most rapidly under hot, dry conditions.

Most kinds of thrips are readily controlled by spraying or dusting with DDT. Because application of this material is often followed by a great increase in red spider mites and some other mites it is wise to mix a miticide such as Aramite or Ovotran with the DDT when spraying or dusting plants such as Roses, Avocados, Carnations and Privets, which are known to be susceptible to attacks by mites. For crops that are to be harvested for food within a month of the application of the insecticide, it is best to use nicotine, pyrethrum or rotenone sprays rather than one that may leave residues on the plants that are poisonous to humans. Lindane and dieldrin are also effective against thrips but should not be used on food crops approaching the harvesting stage.

Bulbs (corms) of Gladioli and other bulbs that are infested with thrips should be sprinkled with a little 5 per cent DDT dust before storing them for the winter.

Among the commonly troublesome kinds of thrips are the following:

Banded Greenhouse Thrips (Hercinothrips femoralis). This kind is a pest of various plants in greenhouses, and in the Southwest affects plants outdoors. Among the plants especially likely to be attacked are Agapanthus, Aralias, Chrysanthemums, Gardenias, Gerberas, Hydrangeas, Hymenocallis, Nerines, Sweet Peas and Snapdragons. The insect is dark brown or almost black with reddish-yellow areas at front and rear. Its front wings are marked with white.

Chrysanthemum Thrips (Thrips nigropilosus). A common pest on Chrysanthemums in greenhouses and sometimes on those in the open garden, this species causes the leaves to be flecked with white. In cases of heavy infestation the shoots die.

Flower Thrips (Frankliniella Tritici). This common species feeds upon and damages many different kinds of plants, harming only the flowers.

The petals are distorted and browned as a result of the feeding and often buds do not expand or only partly open. Light-colored blooms are more likely to be affected than those of darker hues. The thrips can usually be found congregated most densely near the bases of the petals, on their insides.

This thrips is light yellow when young, brownish when older and about 1/20 in. long when mature. Among the many kinds of flowers this species favors are Daylilies, Peonies, Roses and Japanese Irises. Because the thrips work inside the buds, they are difficult to reach with sprays, and it is necessary to supplement spraying by promptly cutting off and burning all infested buds and all flowers as soon as they begin to fade.

Gladiolus Thrips (Taeniothrips simplex). A common pest of Gladioli, Irises, Delphiniums, Hollyhocks and some other plants, this species is very destructive unless kept well under control. Typical injury consists of a silvered appearance of the foliage caused by the rasping of the surface tissues in the process of feeding, followed by browning and deformed and browned flowers and flower buds. The mature insects are about 1/16 in. long and are brown or black with a whitish band near the bottom of the wings. The young are yellowish or orange-colored and have red eyes. This thrips breeds all summer. During winter, if the temperature is over 50 degrees, the insect breeds on bulbs in storage, damaging them severely and very definitely reducing their possibilities of growth after planting.

Greenhouse Thrips (Heliothrips haemorrhoidalis). This common pest of greenhouses also affects outdoor plants in the southernmost parts of the United States. A characteristic symptom of infestation is silvering of the foliage, a condition caused by the rasping of the surface tissues in the process of feeding. A wide range of plants are affected, including Avocados, Azaleas, Begonias, Citrus, Cyclamen, Ferns, Ficus, Fuchsias, Gloxinias, Hippeastrums, Mesembryanthemums, Orchids, Palms, Roses, Statice and Viburnums.

The greenhouse thrips is about 1/24 in. long and is dark with a network of lines over its head and central body portions.

Onion Thrips (Thrips Tabaci). Not only Onions, but a wide variety of other plants, including many vegetables, weeds and such ornamentals as Campanulas, Chrysanthemums, Dahlias, Gloxinias, Mignonette and Sweet Peas, are affected by this very widely distributed pest. It causes whitish or silvery streaking of foliage, followed by browning and dying and distortion of bulbs and flowers. The insects transmit the spotted wilt virus disease from plant to plant of Tomatoes and many flowers.

This thrips at maturity is about 1/25 in. long and varies in color from pale yellow to dark brown. The wings are gray without lighter bands. Many generations are produced each year, and in warm climates the thrips continues breeding throughout the year.

Pear Thrips (Taeniothrips inconsequens). This pest attacks a great variety of hosts, including Apples, Apricots, Cherries, Grapes, Maples, Willows and grasses and weeds. It is a slender creature about 1/25 in. long and of a dark brown color. Its wings are gray. In early spring it infests the opening of buds, causing them to exude sap or blacken and decay, and bringing about deformation of the leaves and flowers. This thrips overwinters in the soil.

Privet Thrips (Dendrothrips ornatus). The grayish or silvery appearance that Privets often assume in eastern American gardens is usually caused by this pest. The slender, yellow young and the dark brown adults, each marked with a red band, occur in great numbers chiefly on the undersides of the leaves. Because Privet is susceptible to attack by mites a miticide should be mixed with DDT if the latter is employed to destroy the thrips.

Tree Hoppers. These jumping insects, close relatives of leaf hoppers and plant hoppers, injure trees and shrubs as well as Beans, Tomatoes, Watermelons and some other garden crops. Control measures are not entirely satisfactory. Spraying with DDT or a combination of DDT and lindane is sometimes effective and so are nicotine sprays. Good sanitation, the destruction of all weeds and, when practicable, such plants as Alfalfa and Sweet Clover (Mellilotis), which harbor the nymphs (immature insects), is important.

Buffalo Tree Hopper (Stictocephala bubalus). This kind damages a wide variety of trees and shrubs, including many fruit trees and Elms,

Locusts and Poplars, by laying its eggs in curved slits in the bark. The young hatch in spring, drop to the ground and feed on weeds and grasses. The adults are 1/4 in. long, light green, blunt-headed with a brief horn at each upper front corner and, when viewed from above, are triangular. They taper to a point at the rear.

Three-cornered Alfalfa Hopper (Spissistilus festinus). This infests Black Locust, Hickories, Oaks and Viburnums and in parts of the South is destructive to Beans, Tomatoes, Watermelons and some other crops. The insect is yellow green in color and triangular when viewed from above.

Two-marked Tree Hopper (Enchenopa binotata). This species is brown with two yellow spots. A high, curving horn sticks out in a forward direction from the body. The nymphs (immature insects) are covered with a white powdery substance. The two-marked tree hopper injures trees by puncturing the stems and buds to deposit its eggs. Butternuts, Celastrus, Grapes, Hickories, Locusts and Redbuds are most likely to be infested.

Wasps. Most wasps are helpful rather than harmful in gardens, for they are of great value in keeping down the populations of many harmful insects. Two large wasps, however, are troublesome at times.

Cicada Killer or Digger Wasp (Sphecius speciosus). This is a black, yellow-banded wasp that may measure up to 1 1/2 in. in length. It is sometimes a nuisance because of its habit of tunneling in lawns, banks, terraces, paths, etc., in late summer. Its burrows are extensive and the insect itself is of decidedly fearsome appearance.

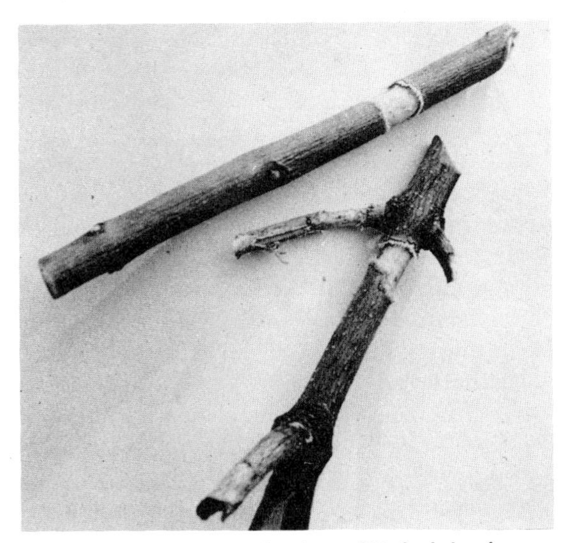

Twigs of Lilac, showing patches from which bark has been removed by the giant hornet.

Control is best had by injecting carbon disulfide or Cyanogas into the burrows and then stopping the holes with soil. Dusting the openings with 5 per cent chlordane dust is also effective.

Giant Hornet or European Hornet (Vespa Crabo). This creature appears in late summer. It is about 1 in. long and dark reddish brown with orange markings. It damages Lilacs and other shrubs by tearing off strips of bark with which it constructs its nests.

Control is by spraying the trunks and branches of affected shrubs with DDT, 2 tablespoons of 50 per cent wettable powder to a gallon of water.

Webworms. See Caterpillars, above.

Weevils. Weevils are beetles which have heads that are extended into snouts with mouth parts at their ends. Some kinds, such as the Fuller Rose beetle, are named beetles and are discussed under Beetles, above. Others, known as curculios, are discussed under Curculio, above. Spraying with DDT or lindane controls most weevils; in some cases chlordane gives most effective control.

Of weevils that infest garden plants the following are important:

Apple Flea Weevil (Rhynchaenus pallicornis). This pest is most destructive in the Midwest but occurs in the East too. The adults are black and about 1/10 in. long. They lay their eggs in spring on the young leaves of Apples, Hawthorns, Quinces, Blackberries and some other hosts. The eggs hatch into tiny grubs which tunnel through the leaf tissues and become weevils in May or June. As a result of their activities the foliage is punctured with numerous small holes. After feeding for a brief period the adult weevils hibernate. They spend the winter among grass or trash beneath the trees they feed upon.

Black Vine Weevil (Brachyrhinus sulcatus). This pest is also known as Cyclamen grub and Taxus weevil. It causes serious damage to Cyclamens, Primulas, Rhododendrons, Yews and many other plants in greenhouses and outdoors. The small white grubs, which are the larvae of this pest, feed on roots, and the dark-colored adult

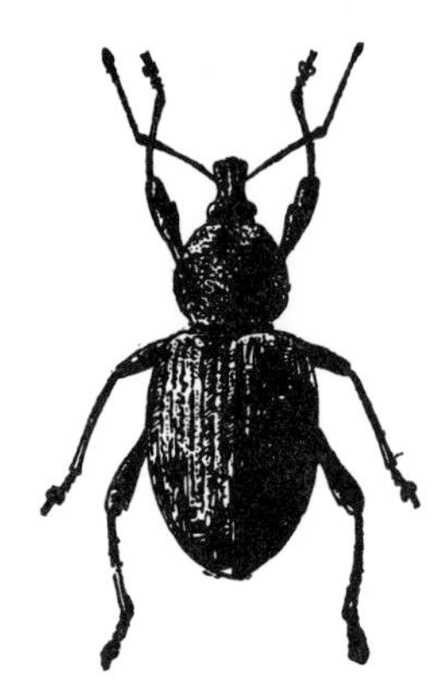

Black vine weevil.

weevils feed at night on foliage. They are particularly fond of the leaves of Rhododendrons and Yews (Taxus). The adults, which are about 3/8 in. long, hide in the soil during the day. The chief damage done to foliage out of doors occurs in June and July; in greenhouses the adults may start feeding earlier than June.

To kill the grubs in the soil, apply 5 per cent chlordane dust to the soil, 1 lb. to 200 sq. ft. To control adults, spray with malathion or with dieldrin. Spray both the plants and the surface soil around them.

Carrot Weevil (Listronotus oregonensis). This dark brown insect at maturity is about 1/4 in. long. It lays eggs in late spring in the leafstalks of Carrots, Celery, Parsnips and other plants belonging to the botanical family Umbelliferae. The white grubs that hatch from the eggs are without legs and attain a length of about 1 1/3 in. They burrow into the roots or hearts of the plants they attack and feed on them for about two weeks, then move to the soil and pupate. A second generation of weevils emerges in August and the cycle is repeated. Sometimes a third generation occurs. For the best control, crops likely to be infested should be grown on land that has not carried susceptible crops for a year or two.

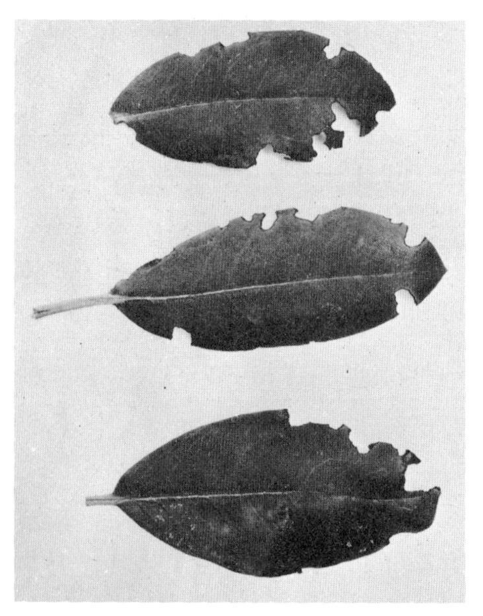

Rhododendron leaves eaten by the black vine weevil.

Cattleya Weevil (Cholus Cattleyae). This pest of Cattleyas and related Orchids is dark colored, with white marks on its back. It damages, by feeding on them, both the leaves and pseudobulbs (bulblike structures at the bases of the leaves). Spraying with DDT and hand picking are effective.

Hollyhock Weevil (Apion longirostre). This black weevil, which is covered with gray hairs, is widely distributed. The adults eat small circular holes in the leaves, and the white larvae (grubs) feed on the developing seeds. Cutting all flowers before they form seeds and removing and burning infested seed pods are effective controls. Dusting or spraying with lindane is also effective.

Orchid Weevil (Diorymerellus laevimargo). This injures Cattleyas, Dendrobiums and some other Orchids by feeding on the leaves, flowers and roots. The adults are about 1/8 in. long and glossy black. Spraying with DDT is effective.

Pea Weevil (Bruchus Pisorum). The eggs of this species are laid on the young pods, and the larvae which hatch from them bore through the pods and eat the developing seeds. The larvae are white with brown heads. The adults are about 1/5 in. long and are brown with markings of white, gray and black. Pull up and burn all vines immediately after the crops are harvested. Dust with rotenone at weekly intervals from the time the flowers begin to fade.

Strawberry Root Weevil (Brachyrhinus ovatus). This pest injures a wide variety of plants including many kinds of evergreens as well as Blackberries, Raspberries, Strawberries and other

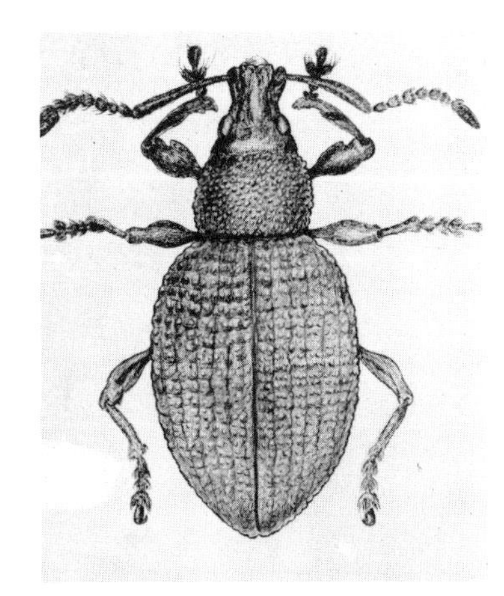
Strawberry root weevil, greatly enlarged.

fruits and a number of vegetables and deciduous (leaf-losing) trees and shrubs. Damage is caused by the grubs' feeding on roots and the adults' feeding upon foliage. The adults are about 1/4 in. long and are dark brown or black; the larvae (grubs) are white and curled. They may be controlled in the manner recommended above for black vine weevil. A commercially prepared bait made of Apple pomace and sodium fluosilicate is also effective.

Strawberry Weevil (Anthonomus signatus). This dark red-brown weevil lays its eggs in the flower buds of Blackberries, Raspberries, Strawberries and a few other plants, causing the buds to wilt. From the eggs, grubs develop; they feed in the buds for about a month, then pupate. The adults appear in June or July and winter among trash on the ground surface. Dusting with lindane about a week before the flowers open is recommended. Spraying or dusting with lead arsenate is also effective, but this should not be done within a month of harvesting a crop that is to be used for food.

White Pine Weevil (Pissodes Strobi). This insect harms Pines and Spruces, especially the White Pine (Pinus Strobus). The larvae, which are yellow and attain a length of about 1/3 in., bore into terminal shoots and cause them to turn brown and die. These grubs hatch from eggs laid in May and June. When fully developed, the larvae pupate and change into adult weevils during the summer. The adults are brown with a white spot on each wing cover and are about 1/4 in. long. They overwinter among trash that is allowed to accumulate on the ground surface.

Control may be had by promptly cutting off all infested shoots below the point where the grub is and burning them, and by spraying in spring with lead arsenate or DDT.

Whiteflies. These insects have somewhat the appearance of tiny moths. They infest a wide variety of greenhouse and house plants and are common outdoors in warm regions. In the North they are often troublesome outdoors in summer on such plants as Fuchsias, Geraniums, Coleus, Heliotropes and other frost-tender kinds. These insects congregate on the undersides of the leaves. The adults fly in clouds if the foliage is brushed against or otherwise disturbed, but soon return. They are more lively in sunny, warm weather than on cool, dull, moist days.

There are several distinct species. Most notable are the Azalea whitefly (Pealius Azaleae), a pest of evergreen Azaleas; the Citrus whitefly (Dialeurodes Citri), which infests a number of

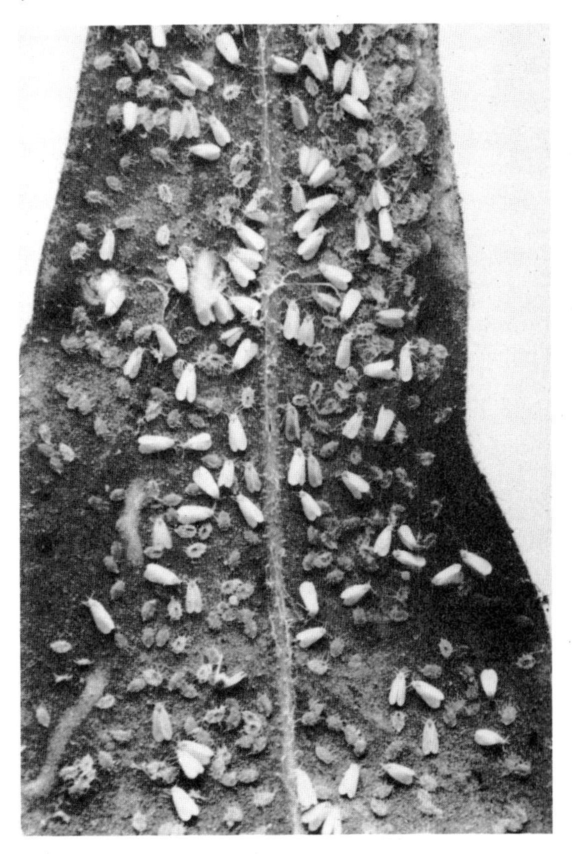
Whiteflies, nymphs and adults, on the underside of a leaf.

different kinds of plants, including Gardenias, Privets, Lilacs and Osage Orange as well as various kinds of Citrus; the Fern whitefly (Aleyrodes Nephrolepidis), a pest of Ferns; the Grape whitefly (Trialeurodes vittatus), which attacks Grapes on the West Coast; and the greenhouse whitefly (Trialeurodes vaporariorum), the most common of all, a kind that infests a great variety of different plants, both in the open garden and in greenhouses and houses. All are similar in appearance, have essentially the same life histories and are controlled in the same ways.

Whiteflies suck the sap of plants through fine needle-like stylets with which they pierce the tissues of the leaves.

Leaves of plants attacked by these pests develop a speckled or mottled yellowish or silvery appearance. The scalelike larvae secrete honeydew, which covers the leaves, blocks the pores (stomata) and prevents the leaves from functioning properly. In addition, a sooty mold fungus grows on the honeydew and further hinders the growth of the plants by cutting out light and by blocking the pores. In very severe attacks, plants may be completely killed.

Whiteflies are usually about 1/25 in. in length. There are four pairs of rounded wings, and the insects are entirely covered with a pure white waxy secretion.

Female whiteflies lay 100-500 eggs each, in circular groups. Each egg has a short, stalklike process at its base, which is inserted in a slit made in the leaf by the ovipositor of the female. The eggs are laid on the undersurfaces of the leaves and hatch in 5-15 days. Hatching is most rapid when the temperature is high.

From the eggs hatch very small flat larvae, rather like scale insects in appearance and of a pale green or yellow color. These larvae soon settle down on the leaves and feed by sucking sap from the leaf. The larvae grow and cast their skins four times, finally emerging as mature insects. The length of the larval period varies considerably, according to the temperature.

Whiteflies are not always easy to control. Spraying repeatedly with malathion, taking care to reach the undersides of the leaves, is often the most satisfactory method for amateur gardeners to use. A DDT spray combined with a summer oil spray also gives good results. For crops that are to be used as food within a month, repeated spraying with a nicotine or rotenone insecticide is recommended. Whenever practicable it is advisable to choose a cool, dull day for spraying because then there is more likelihood of hitting the adults with the spray before they take wing.

Fumigation with Cyanogas is effective in greenhouses. Because of the deadly nature of the gas generated by this material, fumigation with Cyanogas should not be done in greenhouses attached to buildings occupied by people or animals.

Wireworms. These creatures are the grubs or larvae of various kinds of click beetles. They live in the soil and feed on the roots of a great variety of plants. Seedlings are bitten through just below soil level. Fleshy plants like Potatoes, Sweet Potatoes and Turnips are tunneled into by wireworms and may be completely riddled with holes. Wireworms sometimes enter the stems of plants and tunnel within them and may in this way reach a point well above soil level.

Adult click beetles are tapering and have long, narrow wing cases. If they are laid on their backs, they have the power of jumping in the air and turning themselves over with a sharp click. The length of the various kinds varies from rather less than 1/2 in. up to nearly 3/4 in.

The life histories of different kinds of click beetles differ only in small details. The following

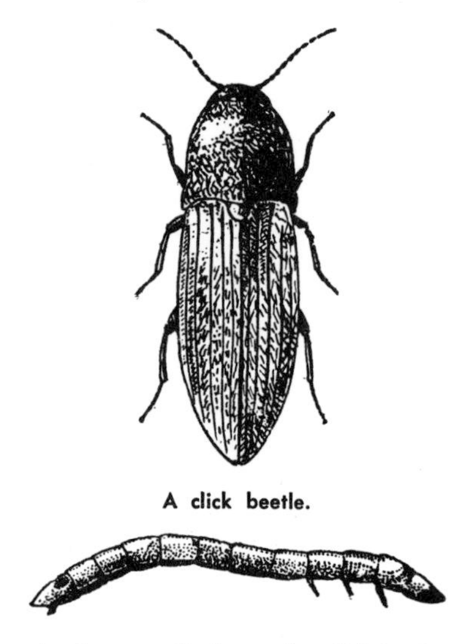

A click beetle.

A wireworm, the larva of a click beetle.

sequence applies to all. The beetles are active in late summer and pass the winter in the soil. The beetles again become active in spring and egg laying takes place in June and July.

The round, white eggs are laid in the soil at a depth of 1-6 in., especially at the roots of grasses. This explains why wireworm attacks are so much worse on crops growing on newly broken grassland or on land which has been allowed to become foul with weeds, grasses in particular.

The young wireworms at first do not greatly resemble those usually found by gardeners, since they are very small, almost white and nearly transparent. For the first year they feed on decayed organic matter. Later they become typically brownish-yellow and begin to do serious harm.

Wireworms usually take 3-4 years to mature to adult beetles, sometimes longer, occasionally not so long. They are wormlike in shape and conspicuously jointed or segmented. They have very tough skins, which are characteristically shiny in appearance, and there are two small, dark pits on the tail end of the body. The mature wireworms turn into white pupae in the soil at a depth of about 6 in. The pupae are found in earthen cells made by the wireworms. About a month after pupation the adult click beetles emerge.

Control of wireworms may be effected by sterilization of the soil with steam or by the use of chemicals. Of the latter, D-D mixture is easy for the amateur to use. Holes 6 in. deep and spaced 1 ft. apart are made in the soil; 2 teaspoonfuls of the material are placed in each and the holes are then filled with soil. Care should be taken not to inhale vapor from the D-D mixture. This treatment cannot be used where plants are growing, and no plants should be set in treated ground for at least 2 weeks following the application of the D-D mixture.

Although they are less rapidly effective than soil sterilization with steam or D-D mixture, good control may be had by treating infested ground with DDT, chlordane or lindane. Mix these with the soil to a depth of 8-9 in. Use DDT at the rate of 1 lb. of 5 per cent dust to each hundred sq. ft., chlordane at the rate of half a pound of 5 per cent dust to each hundred sq. ft., lindane at the rate of 3-4 oz. of 1 per cent dust to each 100 sq. ft. These may be used any time before planting or may be applied to the surface of turf or to the soil in which other permanent crops are growing. One treatment is effective for 3 years or more.

Woodlice. See Sowbugs or Pillbugs.

Worms. This is a general term applied loosely to many different pests. See Armyworms, Bagworms, Borers, Caterpillars, Earthworms, Maggots, Moths and Wireworms.

LARGER PESTS—MAMMALS

In addition to insects and other small pests, certain larger creatures are sometimes troublesome in gardens. The most common of these and ways of controlling them are discussed below.

Cats. Cats are useful for keeping down mice, rats and rabbits, but a nuisance when they scratch in seedbeds or among seedlings. A nicotine spray used in areas they are likely to disturb may deter them, but it is prudent to protect seedbeds with chicken wire or by laying brushwood across them.

Chipmunks. These attractive little ground squirrels have a liking for bulbs. They may be caught in snapback traps baited with peanuts, or, if their burrows can be found, eliminated by inserting some Cyanogas and plugging the entrances to the holes. The traps should be placed in a location where birds cannot be caught in them.

Deer. In some rural and suburban areas deer do considerable damage to garden plants. They are especially fond of Yews and Tulips. Plants may be protected by spraying them with a repellent called Good-rite z.i.p. The recommended dilution is 1 pint to 2½ gallons of water during the dormant season, half that strength when growth is active.

Dogs. A gardener can train his dog not to harm plants, but neighbors' dogs may be nuisances. Choice evergreens and other shrubbery may be protected from damage by well-placed wire guards. Spray repellents may be used from time to time in places where dogs are nuisances. Such repellents are sold by dealers in garden supplies.

Pocket gopher.

Gophers. Where these animals abound, injury to plants is caused by their tunneling and feeding. Special gopher traps may be set in the main runways, or a poison bait may be employed. Cut some pieces of Sweet Potato or Carrot about 1 in. long and ½ in. square, sprinkle them with powdered strychnine, make holes in the runways, drop a couple of pieces of the poisoned bait in each, then close the openings. Strychnine is a deadly poison—handle and store it with great care.

Ground Squirrels. These burrowing rodents are particularly destructive in Iowa, California and Oregon, especially in digging up seeds of Corn, Melons and Soybeans. In California they even climb trees to get fruit and nuts, making it necessary to protect the trees with cylinders of metal around the trunks. Trapping, shooting and poisoning ground squirrels with a powdered strychnine bait, such as described above for gophers, are methods that are also commonly used to control these pests.

California ground squirrel.

Mice. Field mice and other kinds are often very destructive to shrubs and trees and can work havoc among potted bulbs during their rooting period. Most mice work on the surface of the ground; under cover of litter or mulch they gnaw the bark off stems, sometimes killing young trees by completely girdling them.

The Pine mouse works underground, and by burrowing and cutting roots injures fruit trees and ornamentals.

In small areas mice may be caught in snap-back traps, but for extensive protection it is better to use a poison bait. This mixture is recommended: ⅛ oz. each of powdered strychnine and baking soda mixed together dry and sifted over 1 quart of oats and well stirred. Warm the mixture in an oven, then pour over it 6 tablespoons of a mixture of 3 parts melted beef fat and 1 part melted paraffin and stir until the oats are well coated. Place small portions of the bait in the runways of the mice or in containers so that pets and birds cannot reach it.

[37]
Anthracnose on Plane Tree

[38]
Cedar-Apple Rust on Apple

[39]
Fungus Leaf Spot
Disease on Orchid

[40]
Powdery Mildew

[41]
Pachysandra injured by Stem Rot

[42]
Lawn Grass Blight

[43]
Bacterial Wilt of Squash

[44]
Virus Disease, Aster Yellows

Oregon ground squirrel.

Moles. These burrowing animals feed on various soil creatures (many of which are harmful to plants) and other small creatures, such as earthworms, but do damage to plants by heaving up the soil in lawns and flower beds and thus disturbing bulbs and roots. The Oregon mole and Eastern star-nosed mole throw up large mounds, but the common Eastern mole does not. Its presence is shown by loose ridges made as it tunnels just beneath the surface. Moles produce one litter of 3 or 4 young each year in spring.

Moles may be trapped with choker, harpoon and scissors-jaw traps set in the runways. It is advisable to handle the traps with gloves so that no human scent is left on them.

Various methods of poisoning are also used. A

Field mouse.

The mole.

teaspoonful of carbon disulfide, Cyanogas or paradichlorobenzine, placed in the runs at 5-6 ft. intervals, is often effective. In some cases it is possible to attach a hose to the exhaust pipe of a car, put the free end in a main mole run, allow the engine to run for 20 minutes, and so exterminate the moles with carbon monoxide. Mole-Nots are a useful commercial poison and excellent results are had by using the poisoned peanut bait sold as Tat-Mo-Go.

Muskrats. These large aquatic rodents are native over much of North America. They make their homes in the banks of lakes, ponds, streams and irrigation ditches and construct extensive burrows which have underwater entrances. These creatures feed on Water Lilies, Cattails and other aquatic and waterside vegetation. They cause damage to banks, dams and levees by their burrowing activities.

Muskrats may be sighted swimming by day. Other evidences of their presence are the tracks of their broadly spread rear feet and streaks made by their tails in muddy places, large droppings found in the water or on the shore, floating pieces of leaves of Cattails or other vegetation where the muskrats have been feeding, burrow entrances just below water level and usually beneath a clump of sod or near clumps of Cattails, and cave-ins along the banks where the burrows have been stepped on by people or livestock.

Muskrats are controlled by trapping and by poisoning with rolled barley or rolled wheat treated with Warfarin. Take care to set the poisoned bait in special bait boxes or in locations

Muskrat.

Rabbits. *(Left)* Black-tailed jack rabbit. (Center) Cottontail. *(Right)* Brush rabbit.

not available to any desirable animals and birds.

Rabbits. Rabbits cause severe damage to a great variety of plants. They are particularly likely to destroy the foliage of Crocuses and in winter they gnaw the bark off young fruit trees and other kinds of trees, often completely girdling and killing them. They do much damage to vegetables.

Wherever possible, keep rabbits away from trees and crops they are likely to damage. The best method is to use chicken wire guards and fences. These should be of 1 in. mesh and about 3 ft. high. For winter protection the guards should be this height above the top level of any snow that may accumulate, because the rabbits, standing on top of the snow, can reach much higher than when there is no snow. In all instances the chicken wire should extend downwards an inch or two below ground level.

Where chicken wire or other rabbit-proof fences cannot be used, some protection can be obtained by using repellents, although these are by no means always effective.

Repellents useful in the home garden include the following: moth balls or naphthalene flakes scattered around plants; aluminum sulphate sprayed on Lettuce and other vegetables in a dilution of 2 tablespoonfuls to 1 gallon of water; powdered alum, 4 oz. mixed with 2 lb. of tobacco dust and applied as a dust; epsom salts, 3 oz. dissolved in 1 gallon of water and applied as a spray.

Commercial rabbit repellents obtainable from dealers in garden supplies are worth trying.

Rats. These loathsome creatures cause damage by gnawing such crops as Carrots, Beets, Melons and Tomatoes in the garden as well as stored fruit and root vegetables.

Where rats are troublesome, concerted action by entire communities gives best hope of success. Of first importance is the removal of rubbish heaps and other shelters where rats breed undisturbed. Storehouses and other buildings, and stacks and corn cribs should be rendered rat-proof, and holes likely to be used by these animals stopped with a mixture of cement and broken glass. Much good may be done by systematic trapping.

Poisoning is effective and is best carried out in winter and spring when food is short. Barium carbonate is an excellent poison to use, as it is tasteless and odorless. To make the bait, mix 1 part by bulk of barium carbonate with 8 parts of oatmeal. A little water is added to the mixture and the whole kneaded into a stiff dough. The poison bait should be placed well within the burrows, as it is then out of reach of other animals. Commercial rat poisons are available and should be used according to the manufacturers' directions.

Rats become thirsty after taking certain types of poison. It is essential, therefore, to cover all wells, etc., before starting a poisoning campaign.

Baits containing Warfarin are effective in eliminating rats. They kill by preventing clotting of the blood and thus promoting hemorrhages.

Squirrels. Squirrels are amusing to watch but often annoying in the mischief they do to plants. The red squirrel sometimes damages trees by gnawing the bark off young shoots and biting off young growths from evergreens. Gray squirrels are likely to help themselves to Sweet Corn before it is quite ready for the table. Shooting and trapping seem to be the only sure methods of control.

Woodchucks. These large burrowing rodents can work havoc in a garden, especially among vegetables. They may be shot or poisoned in their burrows, which usually have two openings. Place 2 tablespoonfuls of Cyanogas well down in the burrow with a long-handled spoon, and close the entrances with soil. Special woodchuck bombs are obtainable commercially and are effective when used according to the manufacturer's directions.

BACTERIAL AND FUNGUS DISEASES

A great many plant diseases are caused by bacteria and fungi. The former are minute plants, invisible to the naked eye, each consisting of a single cell and devoid of chlorophyll (green coloring matter). They increase rapidly by means of fission (division).

Fungi are also plants without chlorophyll. Individuals usually consist of more than one and often of a large number of cells. Fungi vary in size, according to kind, from very minute to quite large and are very easily visible. Mushrooms and Toadstools are well-known examples of fungi.

Because bacteria and fungi contain no chlorophyll they are generally unable to manufacture foodstuffs from simple elements as do green plants. Like animals, they obtain their nourishment from the bodies of other organisms, dead or alive. Fungi that feed on living organisms are called parasites; those that obtain their nourishment from dead organic matter, saprophytes. The kinds that cause plant diseases are parasites.

A number of fungus diseases of plants are spread by the use of infected seed, the fungus causing the disease being present on the surface of the seed or inside the tissues. It is possible in many cases to kill the fungus and so make the seed healthy by treating it with chemicals. Seed disinfection for this purpose has been practiced by farmers for many years, particularly with cereals, but it is only recently that it has been extended to vegetables and flowers. A much wider range of disinfectants has also become available in recent years, including such commercial preparations as Arasan, Cuprocide, Semesan and Spergon.

Seed disinfection is valuable apart from its control of any specific disease. Young seedlings are delicate and in the early stages of their lives may not survive competition with soil organisms that they can successfully compete with later. Seed treated with fungicidal dust is likely to grow better in soil in which many of the organisms have been killed by the dust. The extra start thus given to the young plants may be very important to their subsequent healthy growth. For the general practice of seed disinfection, dusts are preferable to liquids.

Anthracnose. Diseases called anthracnose are caused by various fungi and are characterized by well-defined dead areas on leaves and lesions on stems and fruits. These symptoms are often accompanied by dying back of twigs and branches. In some instances spots caused by the infection are depressed and are surrounded by slightly raised borders. Anthracnose diseases are most troublesome in wet seasons.

Bean Anthracnose (Colletotrichum lindemuthianum). This is a common fungus disease of Beans. Its effects show chiefly on the pods and seeds in the form of small, round, dark sunken spots from which a pinkish slime oozes in moist weather. On the foliage dark lesions appear along the veins on the undersides of the leaves and on the leafstalks.

To control this disease, sow only seed produced in the West. Spade under or add to the compost pile old Bean tops as soon as the crop is harvested. Avoid working among the plants when they are wet. Do not use the same plot for Beans two years in succession. Sow disease-resistant varieties.

Bramble Spot Anthracnose (Elsinoe veneta). Blackberries, Raspberries and Dewberries may be infected with this disease, which causes circular spots with gray centers and purple margins to appear on the leaves and stems. The spots on the stems often join to produce cankers of considerable size. Other results of infection are premature dropping of the foliage and drying of the fruits.

The best control is had by pruning out and burning all old canes as soon as they can be spared, by spraying with lime sulphur (a delayed dormant application) in spring, and by applying a spray of ferbam a week before the flowers open and again immediately after the fruit is harvested.

Dogwood Spot Anthracnose (Elsinoe Corni). This fungus spot disease attacks the eastern American Flowering Dogwood, Cornus florida. The spots on the leaves are very small, reddish and yellowish gray and their centers break away, forming small holes. On the bracts (petals) the spots are light brown bordered with purple or purple-brown.

Spraying early in the season with maneb gives the best control.

Maple Anthracnose (Gloeosporium apocryptum). This fungus disease is common on Sugar Maples and other kinds. It first shows as light brown spots on the leaves which gradually merge until the entire surface is affected and the leaf is killed.

Spray with Bordeaux mixture or Puratized Agricultural Spray as buds are breaking. If Bordeaux mixture is used, repeat the spray 2 or 3 times at 10-day intervals; one application of Puratized Agricultural Spray is usually sufficient.

Melon Anthracnose (Colletotrichum lagenarium). This fungus disease is most serious on Cucumbers, Muskmelons and Watermelons but appears on Pumpkins and Squash and on some other plants. Small spots, yellow or water-soaked, appear on the foliage and spread until the leaves shrivel and die. Lesions appear on the stems and the young fruits may shrivel and die while more mature ones develop round sunken areas.

To control this disease, treat the seed with Arasan or Spergon. Spray or dust the plants with zineb or ziram when the vines begin to run. Repeat this treatment 3 or 4 times at 10-14 day intervals.

Oak and Sycamore Anthracnose (Gnomonia veneta). The White Oak is the most susceptible of the Oaks to this disease; affected trees often

Anthracnose has caused young leaves of this Sycamore (Platanus) to wither and blacken.

appear as though their foliage has been badly scorched. It is also a common disease on the American Sycamore or Buttonwood (Platanus occidentalis); affected trees often look as though they have been affected by late frost. On the Buttonwood, twigs as well as leaves are infected.

This disease may be controlled in the same manner as the Maple Anthracnose disease mentioned above.

Privet Anthracnose. See Sweet Pea Anthracnose, below.

Rose Spot Anthracnose (Elsinoe Rosarum). This fungus disease is common on Roses. Climbing kinds are more likely to be infected than bush varieties. The disease first shows on the leaves as round brown or blackish spots which later turn grayish with a dark red border. Individual spots measure up to 1/4 in. across; sometimes they merge together to form larger discolored areas. On the canes the spots may be round or spindle shaped, brownish or purplish with gray, sunken centers.

Spraying or dusting with ferbam is the recommended control.

Sweet Pea Anthracnose (Glomerella cingulata). This fungus disease occurs on many different kinds of plants, including such varied kinds as Agaves, Apples, Citrus, Dieffenbachias, Privets and Snowberry as well as Sweet Peas. On Sweet Peas it appears about flowering time, and may be very destructive. It causes areas of the leaves to become whitish and the leaves to shrivel and drop off. The flower stems and buds wither and the seed pods shrivel and lack their normal green color. The fruits of the Snowberry, Symphoricarpos albus, when affected by this fungus, are marked with reddish brown spots and drop early. Twigs and stems of affected Privets die back with the foliage clinging to the younger parts even after it has dried and died. Cankers may be formed at the bottoms of the main stems.

Control of this disease is encouraged by sowing only healthy seeds of Sweet Peas (those that are plump and of good color) and by treating the seed with a fungicide such as Arasan before they are planted. The tops of Sweet Pea plants should be cleared off the ground and burned at the end of the season. Spraying with Bordeaux mixture is likely to be helpful when other plants are affected by this disease, which is also known as canker, dieback, wintertip, stem rot, bitter rot and fruit rot when it attacks various other plants.

Tomato Anthracnose (Colleotrichum phomoides). This fungus causes sunken, water-soaked spots, which later turn brown and in their centers exhibit masses of pinkish, cream-colored or brown spores, to appear on the fruits late in the season. Control is effected by spraying with ferbam or ziram and clearing up all Tomato debris at the end of the season.

Black Knot. This fungus disease (Dibotryon morbosum) produces conspicuous long, black, rough, knotted or cankerlike enlargements on the twigs of Apricots, Cherries and Plums.

Cut out infected twigs and branches at least 4 in. below the swollen portion. Apply a dormant-strength lime-sulphur spray. Remove Wild Cherries and Plums that are near cultivated trees or treat them in the same manner as cultivated specimens.

Blackleg. Certain diseases which cause a distinct blackening of the basal parts of the stems of plants are known as blackleg. They are caused by fungi and bacteria. The following are the most important:

Blackleg or Foot Rot of Crucifers (Phoma Lingam). Many plants of the Mustard family (Cruciferae), such as Cabbage, Cauliflower, Brussels Sprouts, Kale, Radishes, Stocks and Sweet Alyssum, are likely to be afflicted with this disease. The stems turn black and shrivel at ground level and the foliage wilts and turns purplish. The disease is chiefly transmitted by means of infected seeds.

Control measures consist of practicing crop rotation, using seeds that have been grown in uninfected areas (reliable seedsmen supply them), and sterilizing any soil in which infected plants have been grown within a period of three years and in which seeds of susceptible kinds are to be sown.

Potato Blackleg (Erwinia atroseptica). This bacterial disease is readily recognized by its most typical symptom, the blackening of the bases of the stems. Other symptoms are the pale-green or yellow foliage and the somewhat stunted growth of the plants. The margins of the leaflets on the upper leaves are rolled inwards. An affected plant is pulled out of the ground with very little effort.

The blackening of the stem is confined to the base, but, if the upper portions are cut across, three brown spots will be seen marking the position of the conducting tissues. The brown color is due to the bacteria, and it may extend all the way along the stem and occasionally be partly visible externally as black streaks.

Premature decay may prevent tuber formation altogether, and if new tubers are formed some are certain to be diseased. They are soft and discolored, the flesh turns brown and the tuber decays in the soil unless it is only moderately attacked. Affected tubers may also decay in storage and the decay may spread to healthy tubers in contact with them. If even slightly infected tubers are used for planting, the disease will reappear. It is certain that this is how the disease spreads.

Control of this disease consists of planting only seed Potatoes that are certified disease-free and promptly digging up and destroying any affected plants.

Black Mildew. See Mildew.

Black Spot. See Leaf Spots.

Blights. The term blight is used loosely by gardeners and others to include a wide variety of plant diseases and sometimes even infestations of insects and other creatures. It is most properly restricted to diseased conditions the chief symptoms of which are sudden and very noticeable damage to leaves, shoots or flowers; the damage is not confined to definitely limited spots or blotches, and is not a characteristic wilting resulting from an interference with the plant's water-conducting tissues, as is the case with wilt diseases. Blighted foliage usually does not fall prematurely. Blights are caused by bacteria and fungi. Among the more common that affect gardens are the following:

Azalea Petal Blight (Ovulinia Azaleae). This is a serious disease of Azalea flowers in humid areas in the South. Except for the harm done to the flowers, the plants are not injured, but practically overnight whole crops of bloom may be lost, the flowers becoming spotted and decaying rapidly.

The recommended control is to spray with zineb, 1 oz. to 5 gallons of water, starting treatment when the first flowers open and repeating the spray 3 times a week until all flowers are open, then about every 4 or 5 days until blooming is finished.

Bean Bacterial Blight (Xanthomonas Phaseoli). This common bacterial Bean blight is seed-borne. It first shows on the leaves as small water-soaked spots which later spread to form large brown areas with yellow margins. The spots are marked with irregular blotches and much spoilage of the crop may occur.

Seed grown in the Far West is unlikely to produce blighted plants. Refrain from cultivating or picking among the crop when plants are wet. Burn affected plants after harvest. Some varieties are somewhat resistant to this disease. These are listed in seedsmen's catalogues.

Celery Blights. Early blight (Cercospora Apii) is likely to appear on Celery and Celeriac when the plants are only a few weeks old. At first tiny yellow spots appear on the leaves and enlarge to conspicuous gray areas. Late blight (caused by Septoria apii and S. apii-graveolentis) is likely to be more destructive than early blight. Yellow leaf spots develop which spread and fuse in severe infections and cause the leaves and stalks to turn brown and rot.

To control these diseases, tie the seed in

Cherry leaves affected by shot-hole disease.

cheesecloth and dip it in a calomel solution (1 oz. to 1 gallon of water) for 2-3 minutes while keeping the solution stirred. Spray or dust the plants with zineb and repeat this treatment every 2-3 weeks if necessary. Clean up all tops and other refuse at the end of the season and burn it. Practice crop rotation.

Cherry Leaf Blight or Shot-Hole Disease (Higginsia hiemalis). This is a common and destructive fungus disease of Cherries. It affects both sweet and sour kinds. The purplish, circular spots that it causes turn brown and die and the dead tissue falls out to leave a shot-hole effect. Often, the leaves turn yellow and fall prematurely.

It is most important to clean up and burn all fallen leaves. In addition, the application of four sprays is recommended, one at petal fall, one at shuck fall, one 2 weeks later and one after the fruit is harvested. Lime-sulphur at 1-50 dilution may be used for the first 2 sprays, ferbam for the later ones. Cyprex sprays are also effective.

Fire Blight (Erwinia amylovora). This a serious bacterial disease of Pears, Quinces and Apples and occurs also on Cotoneasters, Pyracanthas and many botanically related plants. It affects the blossoms and the leaves on young twigs, which wilt, turn black and die but remain hanging on the stems. The bark shrivels and becomes dark in color. Sometimes sap or gum oozes from it.

The best control measure is to cut off infected branches 6 in. or more below the dead part. Between successive cuts, disinfect the pruning tool with formaldehyde, a corrosive sublimate solution, or denatured alcohol. Spraying fruit trees with weak Bordeaux mixture as they come into full bloom aids in preventing the flowers from being infected. Avoidance of over-fertilizing with nitrogen lessens the danger of infection.

The antibiotic streptomycin gives good control of fire blight. It is used as a spray applied 3-5 times during the period of early and full bloom but not after petal fall.

Gray Mold Blight or Botrytis Blight (Botrytis cinerea). This is a common fungus disease of many kinds of plants and flowers both outdoors and in greenhouses. Vegetables and soft ripe fruits are susceptible. At times this is serious on African Violets, Begonias, Calendulas, Chrysanthemums, Dahlias, Geraniums, Gladioli, Lilies, Peonies, Primroses, Roses, Sweet Peas, Zinnias, Dogwoods and many other plants. This disease shows itself as a gray mold which covers affected parts and is accompanied by a rotting of the tissues.

Gray mold blight damages both flowers and leaves of Flowering Dogwood, Cornus florida.

Pick off and burn blighted flower and leaf parts. Avoid overcrowding and overhead watering. Provide good ventilation in greenhouses and cold frames. Spray with zineb.

Large numbers of small spots on the foliage are a characteristic symptom of Hawthorn leaf blight.

Hawthorn Leaf Blight (Fabraea maculata). This fungus leaf blight is common on English Hawthorn and occurs also on Pears, Quinces, Amelanchiers and some other botanically related plants. Affected Hawthorns may be defoliated by late summer. The disease first appears as small reddish brown spots; it also causes bark cankers. It is especially prevalent in wet seasons.

Spray with lime sulphur when tree is dormant. When leaves unfurl spray with Zineb and repeat 2 weeks later. Organic mercury and Acti-dione are also effective. Rake and burn fallen leaves.

Lawn Grass Blights. A number of blights affect grass turf and are especially likely to be prevalent during hot, humid weather. Frequent watering during such times favors the growth of the fungi that cause these diseases.

There has been much confusion in the identification of lawn diseases. However, the diseases that affect home lawns are often different from those that are most troublesome on golf putting greens. Brown patch, dollar spot and copper spot diseases (which see under Rots—Lawn Grass Rots, below) are known to be particularly likely to affect Bent Grasses and hence are common on putting greens; but, as Bent Grasses are less common in home lawns, the diseases mentioned are less prevalent there also.

Exact identifications of turf diseases are not easy for the amateur to make and it is usually advisable to send samples of affected grass to a State Agricultural Experiment Station or other competent authority for microscopic examination and diagnosis. The inexperienced are even likely to confuse with diseases the damage due to mowing too closely, chinch bugs, drought, improper fertilization and other causes. Some of the most serious blights of turf grasses are those we shall now discuss.

Bluegrass blight or going-out disease (Helminthosporium vagans) chiefly affects Kentucky Bluegrass (its variety, Merion Bluegrass, is comparatively immune), Canada Bluegrass and Rough-stalked Bluegrass. The disease develops early in the season, even before the grass is mowed for the first time. Purple spots appear on the leaves and these enlarge and become straw colored at their centers. Eventually the entire leaf turns brown and dies and the stems, rhizomes and roots are killed. This disease may be controlled by treatment with a Captan or Acti-dione RZ fungicide or a fungicide containing cadmium.

Curvularia blight or fading-out disease (caused by species of Curvularia) destroys a wide variety of turf grasses. It is prevalent during periods of high temperatures, particularly following rain or heavy watering. The grass assumes an indefinite yellow and green dappling and dies out in patches. Control of this disease may be obtained by the use of Acti-dione RZ, Tersan OM or fungicides containing cadmium.

Melting-out disease (caused by species of Helminthosporium) affects Bent Grasses, Fescues and Bluegrasses. The symptom is dying of the grass in rather definite patches. At first, affected leaves assume a smoky blue appearance, then they turn successively yellow, brown and almost black. This disease develops during periods of high humidity and high temperatures. Control may be had by using Captan or Acti-dione RZ fungicide or a fungicide containing cadmium.

Lilac Phytophthora Blight (Phytophthora Cactorum). The flowers and the growing tips of Lilac shoots often turn brown and die back in wet springs, and sucker shoots may be severely killed back by this fungus disease. Specimens that are in shaded locations and those that are overcrowded are especially liable to attack. The fungus that causes this disease is also responsible for canker and dieback disease of Rhododendrons and other plants.

To control this disease, keep Lilac and Rhododendron plants apart. Prune out weak and crowded growths of Lilacs and thin out sucker growths so that there is adequate air circulation between them. Spray Lilacs with Bordeaux mixture when leaves unfold and repeat once or twice at 2-week intervals.

Lily Botrytis Blight (Botrytis elliptica). This fungus blight is especially serious on the Madonna Lily, but all kinds are more or less susceptible. The first symptoms are usually orange or reddish spots on the lower leaves. The spotting spreads upward until all the leaves may become blackened and limp and the buds and flowers rotted or distorted.

Avoid planting in shady and low-lying areas where air circulation is poor. Spray with

Peony flower buds, the one at the right affected by gray mold blight.

Bordeaux mixture when the stems are about 6 in. high and repeat this every 10-14 days until flowering. Burn all old stems and foliage trash.

London Plane Blight. See Plane Canker Stain under Cankers and Diebacks, below.

Pachysandra Blight (Volutella Pachysandrae). In recent years Pachysandra plantings in some places have been disfigured by brown or blackish blotches on their leaves caused by this fungus disease. This is especially likely to occur if the stems have been broken by being walked upon or by other causes, or if masses of wet leaves are allowed to lie on the Pachysandra plants.

Remove and burn the badly affected plants and spray once or twice with Bordeaux mixture.

A partly opened flower of Peony rotted as a result of infection with gray mold blight.

Peony Botrytis Blight (Botrytis Paeoniae). This is a very common fungus disease of Peonies. It causes blasting (withering without opening) of the flower buds and spotting of the leaves, flowers and stems. Young shoots are likely to rot off at their bases.

When the new shoots which appear in spring are 8-9 in. high, spray the plants with ferbam (1 oz. to 4 gallons of water) or Bordeaux mixture or apply ferbam dust. Repeat this treatment 3 or 4 times at 10-day intervals. Promptly remove blasted buds and any badly affected foliage and burn them. Cut the old stems off just below the ground line and burn them after the fall frost has brought an end to the season's growth.

Poppy Bacterial Blight (Xanthomonas Papavericola). This disease affects Poppies of all kinds but is perhaps most serious on the Oriental varieties. It shows as small black spots on the leaves, flowers and pods, and as long black lesions on the stems. Gum is exuded from the spots and lesions.

The best control measure is to remove and destroy infected plants and choose another location for new plants.

Potato and Tomato Early Blight (Alternaria Solani). This fungus disease is common on Potatoes and Tomatoes and occurs sometimes on Eggplants and Peppers. Dark brown spots, round or elliptic in shape and marked with a target-like pattern of concentric rings, first appear on the lower leaves and later on the foliage above. The spots grow together to form large diseased areas. A rot of the lower stems of seedlings, stem cankers and dropping of flowers may also affect Tomatoes as a result of infection. This disease is most serious when the weather is humid and warm.

To control this blight, avoid growing Potatoes, Tomatoes, Eggplants and Peppers for three years on ground where an infected crop has been. Spray with zineb or ziram. Use seed that has been treated with hot water.

Potato and Tomato Late Blight (Phytophthora infestans). This serious fungus disease has been long known to be most destructive to Potatoes and more recently has infected Tomatoes over wide areas. It spreads rapidly in wet seasons but may not be evident in dry years. On Potatoes the symptoms of this disease are large, dark green water-soaked spots that appear on the foliage in wet weather. The spots enlarge and their centers dry and become dark brown. A whitish, downy growth appears on the undersides of the leaves and lesions occur on the stems. The tubers are discolored and are affected by a red-brown dry rot. Affected plants give off a distinct and characteristic odor.

Tomatoes are usually not attacked until about the time their fruit is ripening. Their leaves first show dark green water-soaked spots, then suddenly turn brown and hang lifeless. Rot quickly spoils the fruit.

To control, spray Tomatoes with zineb or nabam, or apply a copper dust especially prepared for Tomatoes.

Plant only certified sets (seed tubers) of disease-resistant varieties of Potatoes. Spray the crop several times with zineb during the growing season.

Southern Blight. See Crown Rot, under Rots, below.

Tulip Botrytis Blight or Tulip Fire (Botrytis Tulipae). This serious fungus disease of Tulips first shows as a malformation of the young leaves. Often the foliage looks as though frost had injured it. Soon a gray mold appears on the surfaces of affected leaves and the buds and flowers become spotted and develop the characteristic mold.

Spray or dust early in the season with ferbam and repeat at 10-day intervals. Dig up and burn badly diseased plants. Cut fading flowers and pick up fallen petals promptly and burn them. Cut and burn all foliage after it has withered. Inspect all bulbs before planting and discard any showing circular, slightly depressed, yellow or brown lesions just under the outer skin in the white tissue of the bulb or that have tiny, shining black bodies (sclerotia or reproductive phase of the fungus) on their surfaces.

Dust discolored bulbs with sulphur before planting.

Willow Blight. See Willow Black Canker under Cankers and Diebacks, below.

Blotches. Blotch diseases are typically caused by fungi and are characterized by irregular dead

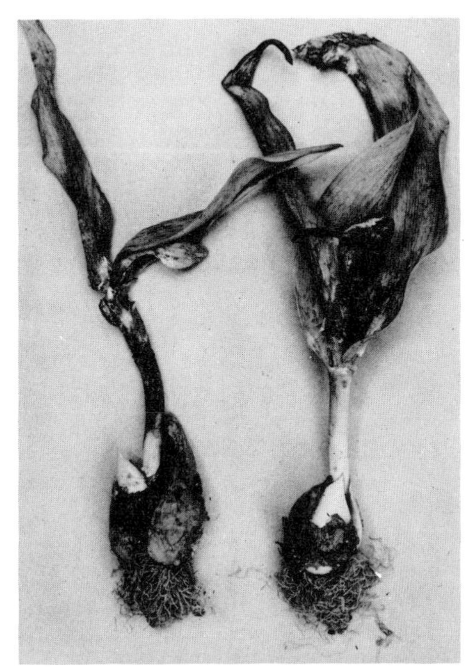

The foliage, flowers and bulbs of Tulips are seriously damaged by Tulip botrytis blight.

areas on the surfaces of leaves or fruits. The dead areas are less clearly defined than in leaf spot diseases. No very clear line of separation exists between blotches and blights. Among the most familiar blotch diseases are the following:

Amaryllis Red Blotch. See Narcissus Leaf Scorch, under Leaf Scorches, below.

Avocado Blotch (Cercospora purpurea). This fungus causes the leaves to be marked with tiny angular brown spots which may be numerous enough to join and form irregular patches. Larger brown sunken spots occur on the fruits.

Control is had by spraying three times with Bordeaux mixture or other copper spray, applying the first spray during the first half of May, the second 4 or 5 weeks later and the last 4 or 5 weeks after the second.

Horse-Chestnut Leaf Blotch (Guignardia Aesculi). In rainy seasons Horse Chestnut trees are made unsightly by large reddish-brown blotches on their leaves caused by this fungus disease. The same disease also attacks other species of Aesculus, especially A. glabra, the Ohio Buckeye. Considerable loss of leaves commonly follows the blotching of the leaves.

Spraying with Bordeaux mixture, zineb or

Puratized Agricultural Spray is the best control. This should begin when the buds open, and be repeated 2 or 3 times at 2-week intervals. Fallen leaves should be raked up and burned. Effects similar to those caused by this disease may result from drought but the scorched areas then do not have tiny black dots (spore-producing organs) of the fungus on affected leaves. Thorough watering and not spraying is the remedy for scorching caused by drought.

Peony Leaf Blotch, Red Spot or Measles (Cladosporium Paeoniae). This common disease first makes its presence known by the appearance of tiny, circular, purplish or brownish red spots on the foliage and flowers and reddish-brown streaks on the stems. The spots join to form conspicuous blotches.

Control is had by cutting off close to the ground and destroying the tops of Peony plants after fall frost has damaged the foliage, and by spraying repeatedly with Bordeaux mixture at 10-day intervals from the time the young shoots are a few inches high in spring until the flowers begin to open.

Cankers and Diebacks. A canker is usually a clearly visible and well-defined diseased area or lesion on a woody stem, and it may develop into an open wound or enlarge until the stem is girdled. Often the stem above the infected portion is killed because the canker prevents water and nutrients from passing to it. This results in a dieback effect similar to that produced by certain dieback disease organisms which work directly in the tip areas of stems. Many woody plants are liable to canker injury, including Conifers, Apples, Dogwoods, Maples, Oaks, Poplars, Willows and Roses. Various fungi are responsible for these troubles.

The principal control measures are the cutting out of diseased parts with tools that are sterilized by wiping with denatured alcohol or a 5 per cent solution of formaldehyde between cuts. Unnecessary wounds should be avoided, and fertilizer applied if the trees or shrubs lack vigor. Poorly drained soil often tends to encourage cankers.

Some of the commonest canker and dieback diseases that affect garden plants are the following:

Apple Blister Canker (Nummularia discreta). This serious fungus disease affects Pears and Mountain Ash as well as Apples and Crabapples. The cankers are often of large size with patches of living wood interspersed among the dead tissue and with numerous nail-head-like fungus bodies sprinkled over the surface. Several other cankers infect Apples, including bleeding canker (which see, below), black rot or New York Apple tree canker (Physalospora obtusa), which causes cankers on the twigs and Apple bitter rot disease (see under Rots, below), which causes cankers on the branches.

Bleeding Canker (Phytophthora Cactorum). This disease is caused by the same fungus that is responsible for trunk canker of Apples, Apricots and some other fruits; crown canker of Dogwood; a dieback disease of Rhododendrons; phytophthora blight of Lilacs; and stem rots and root rots of Peonies, Tomatoes, Tulips and some other plants. Bleeding canker is so called because a light brown or reddish sap oozes in conspicuous amounts from cracks in the bark and dries to blood color. The foliage wilts and has a blighted appearance, and a serious dieback of affected branches results. The sunken, furrowed cankers are more easily seen on young branches than on old trunks.

The fungus enters through the roots. Trees sometimes recover but there is no reliable cure.

Blueberry Cane Canker (Physalospora corticis). This fungus disease causes reddish swellings on the stems which enlarge into rough black cankers and cause the death of the branches above the point of infection. Certain varieties of Blueberries are much more resistant than others to this disease. Consult State Agricultural Experiment Stations for recommended varieties.

Boxwood Nectria Canker (Volutella Buxi). The fungus that causes this canker is also responsible for a blight of Boxwood leaves. The cankers kill the twigs, branches and trunks and on affected ones salmon-pink spore pustules appear. The blight comes in summer, especially in moist weather, and causes the leaves to become straw-colored. Affected leaves bear small pink pustules on their undersides.

For control, cut out and burn all affected branches and dead leaves that collect in the interior of the bushes, and spray the interior with a 1 to 50 dilution of lime-sulphur.

Butternut Melanconis Dieback (Melanconis Juglandis). Butternuts and Walnuts suffer from this fungus disease, which brings about their eventual death. Trees weakened by drought or other causes are destroyed much more rapidly than those which are in vigorous condition when attacked and are sustained by adequate fertilizing and by watering in periods of drought. The symptoms are the gradual dying back of twigs and branches. The cankers have on their surfaces tiny, black, wartlike protuberances.

Once the disease reaches the main trunk there is no hope of saving an infected tree. Such trees should be removed and burned promptly.

Camellia Canker or Dieback (Glomerella cingulata). This fungus, in addition to causing a widespread canker disease of Camellias and of some other plants such as Azaleas, Blackberries, Roses, Raspberries, Mountain Ash and English Ivy, is responsible for the disease called bitter rot in Apples and for anthracnose diseases of Sweet Peas and many other kinds of plants. The cankers are elliptical and are formed on the older branches. A dieback of the branch tips of Camellias which is commonly associated with infection by this canker disease is believed to be caused by the same fungus.

In addition to cutting out diseased parts, spraying with a copper fungicide, such as Bordeaux mixture, is recommended.

Currant Canker or Currant Cane Blight (Botryosphaeria Ribis) . This serious fungus disease of Currants also causes cankers or dieback in a wide variety of other plants, including Apples, Avocados, Figs, Gooseberries, Hickories, Pecans, Pyracantha, Quinces, Rhododendrons, Roses and Willows. On Currants and Gooseberries the leaves yellow and the stems die back about the time the fruits ripen; on Roses the stems are cankered, the leaves wilt and the shoots die back above the affected part. Redbuds are damaged by a slow girdling and killing of the twigs above the cankers. Rhododendrons develop leaf spots and the twigs die back. Willows are likely to be killed within a few years.

Douglas Fir and Pine Canker (Dasyscypha Ellisiana). This is one of several fungus-produced cankers that affect Douglas Firs and Pines. It causes a free flow of resinous sap from the trunks and lower branches but does not cause the death of vigorous trees.

Gardenia Canker or Stem Gall (Phomopsis gardeniae). This is a common fungus disease of Gardenias grown in greenhouses. It makes its presence known by the appearance of brown lesions low down on the stems. The affected areas enlarge and crack, and the stem just above assumes a bright yellow hue. Eventually the cankers girdle the stems, the foliage wilts and the branches die.

Destroy affected plants. Propagate from disease-free stock and insert the cuttings in a sterile rooting medium.

Grape Dead Arm Disease (Cryptosporella Viticola). Infection with this fungus disease causes small, angular, dark-centered, yellow-margined spots on the leaves and canes and on the stems of the leaves and those of the clusters of flowers. The buds on the canes are killed and the fruit may be caused to rot. As the disease progresses the spots are likely to coalesce and form large brown areas marked with darker spots. The arms or branches of the vines are often killed.

Nectria or Trunk Canker (Nectria Galligena). Common on Apples, Aspens, Beeches, Birches, Elms, Hickories, Maples, Oaks, Pears, Quinces and many other nonconiferous trees, this fungus disease causes small, dark-colored, sunken cankers which, as they get older, somewhat resemble targets in appearance because of the concentric rings of callus tissue they show. Near the edges of the infected areas tiny red spore-bearing bodies (perithecia) are likely to be found.

Oak Sphaeropsis Canker and Dieback (Physalospora glandicola). This is a serious fungus disease of Oaks that often results in their death. Branches and twigs are killed and leaves wither and die. Bark on affected stems is sunken and wrinkled and studded with small, black spore-bearing organs. Ridges of callus growth develop around the larger cankers and the sapwood beneath is discolored and has black streaks through it. Young shoots grow in profusion from below the dead crown of an affected tree.

Because trees weakened by drought, insect

attack or other cause are most likely to be harmed, a program of fertilizing, watering during dry weather, and insect eradication is helpful.

Plane Canker Stain or London Plane Blight (Ceratocystis fimbriata platani). Symptoms of this serious fungus disease are long, sunken cankers on branches and trunks and sparse foliage. The cankers gradually broaden and eventually girdle the limb and kill it. A bluish-black or reddish discoloration of the wood beneath the cankers is evident. London Planes and the native American Sycamore or Buttonwood are affected.

If only a branch or two are affected they may be removed, but any seriously infected tree should be promptly destroyed.

Poplar Canker (Dothichiza Populea). Although most common on Lombardy Poplars, this fungus disease also infects other kinds of Poplars and Cottonwoods. It is especially likely to attack young trees growing in nurseries. The lesions are mostly near the bases of twigs and branches and at first are simply sunken, discolored areas. Completely girdled stems are killed; in some cases the cankers swell and increase in size and kill the branches or the tree later.

When their leaves are expanding, spray young trees with Bordeaux mixture and repeat this after each rain.

Poplar and Willow Cytospora Canker (Cytospora chrysosperma). Although Poplars, Cottonwoods, Willows and Aspens are most subject to this fungus disease, it occasionally attacks Cherries, Elderberries, Maples and Mountain Ash. Trees that are not favorably located or that are not growing vigorously are especially liable to infection. The cankers are formed on the trunks and larger branches, and in old cankers layers of callus tissue encircle exposed wood.

Rose Cankers. Several distinct canker diseases affect Roses. The commonest are Rose canker or dieback (Griphosphaeria corticola), stem canker or common canker (Leptosphaeria coniothyrium), brown canker (Cryptosporella umbrina) and brand canker (Coniothyrium Wernsdorffiae). All of these form obvious discolored cankers on the canes.

Rose canker or dieback forms cankers near the bottoms of the stems; the others, at various points on the stems. The cankers of the Rose canker or dieback are often freely spotted with shining black or nearly black pustules.

Stem canker is particularly likely to affect stubs of stems that have been cut back, but not close to a bud; however, it also attacks all other parts of the plant. The diseased areas begin as small red or yellow spots which enlarge to form dry, brown withered areas.

Brown canker first becomes noticeable as a result of small purplish spots which appear on the canes. These soon become white at their centers and reddish purple at their margins. Often the spots are grouped to form quite large lesions. This is particularly likely to occur on parts of the cane that have been covered with earth during the winter. On leaves and petals the canker fungus forms small spots, cinnamon-buff colored, those on the leaves with a purplish border.

Brand canker begins as dark reddish spots, which, as they increase in size, develop definite purple or reddish brown margins. The cankers usually form under the soil that is heaped around the bushes to provide winter protection.

The best control for cankers on outdoor Roses is provided by the prompt removal of all affected stems, especially during spring pruning, the application of a dormant-strength lime-sulphur spray immediately following spring pruning, the cutting of stems close to buds without leaving stubs, and the avoidance of using water-holding materials such as wet manure or leaves for winter covering.

A disease that seems to be confined to greenhouses is crown canker (Cylindrocladium scoparium). The part most commonly attacked is the portion of the plant just above the graft union. The canes are rarely killed but both quantity and quality of the blooms of affected plants are reduced. The fungus lives in the soil. Sterilization of the soil and benches that hold it or the provision of fresh soil in newly sterilized benches is the recommended control.

Twig Canker, Coral Spot or Dieback (Nectria cinnabarina). This fungus disease affects many kinds of nonconiferous trees and shrubs. It is closely related to the Nectria or trunk canker. The twig canker commonly grows as a saprophyte on dead wood but it functions also as a weak

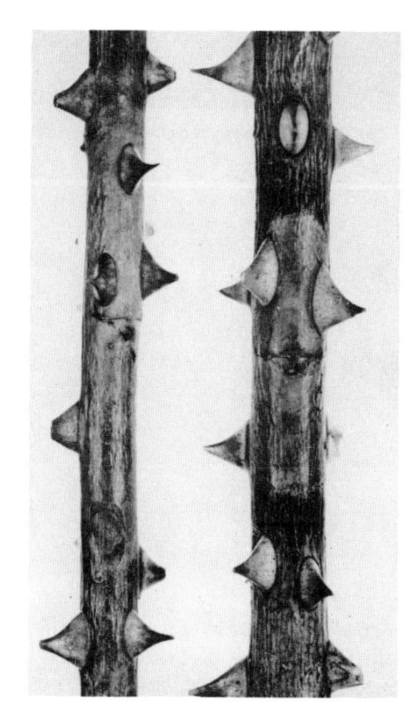

Rose canes, showing lesions caused by brown canker disease.

parasite and causes cankers and dieback, particularly on Maples. It is especially liable to infect recently pruned trees and those weakened by any cause. The diseased areas bear conspicuous coral-pink pustule-like spore-bearing organs.

Willow Black Canker (Physalospora Miyabeana). This fungus disease causes cankers on the larger stems and premature leaf dropping. Together with the black scab disease it is responsible for the condition called Willow blight in eastern North America. Masses of pinkish spores may be seen on the cankers and dead twigs that this disease causes.

In addition to pruning out and destroying dead twigs, it is recommended that three applications of Bordeaux mixture be made at about 10-day intervals, beginning when the leaves start to unfold in spring. For another canker that attacks Willows, see Poplar and Willow canker, above.

Chlorosis. See Physiological Diseases, below.

Club Root. This disease (Plasmodiophora Brassicae) is sometimes known as finger-and-toe disease. It is common on Cabbages and other vegetables, flowers and weeds that belong in the Mustard family (Cruciferae). Affected plants wilt on hot days and are stunted. Their root systems are scabby and much swollen and become rotten and evil-smelling. The spores of this parasite survive in the soil for several years and can be transferred from place to place on tools and shoes and in manure and compost. The organism causing this disease is not a true fungus but belongs to a group called slime fungi.

Liming the soil about 6 weeks before planting to bring its *p*H reaction to 7.2 or higher is effective in controlling this disease. Crop rotation is a helpful preventative. Seeds of plants likely to be affected should be sown in sterilized soil. When setting the young plants out, water each plant with ⅓ pint of Terraclor solution. This solution is prepared by mixing 3 lb. of Terraclor in 50 gallons of water.

Damping Off. Damping off is the most serious trouble afflicting seedlings of most garden plants, especially those raised in flats or pots. The delicate seedlings are easily infected by various fungi commonly present in soils, especially if the conditions are too wet or too sour for the healthy growth of plants. The fungi grow into the tissues of the stems and weaken the latter so that the seedlings topple and usually die. The commonest causes of this trouble are the fungi Pythium

Club root disease causes the roots of the plants attacked to become swollen and contorted.

Two flats of seedlings. Many seedlings in the flat at the right (growing in unsterilized soil) have been killed by the damping-off disease. Those in the flat at the left, growing in sterilized soil, are not affected.

debaryanum and Rhizoctonia solani but other species also cause damping off.

The surest way of preventing damping off is to provide a sterile medium in which to sow the seeds, and environmental conditions that do not include overwatering or an excessively humid atmosphere.

Vermiculite and sifted sphagnum moss are excellent sterile media in which to sow seeds; so is soil that has been sterilized by steam or with formaldehyde, chloropicrin or other chemical sterilizing agents. A simple method is to mix 2½ tablespoonfuls of commercial 40 per cent formaldehyde in 1 cup of water and sprinkle this over 1 bushel of soil and mix thoroughly. Then fill clean flats or pots with the treated soil and cover with moist paper. After 24 hours, sow the seeds and water them in. Another method is to water after sowing the seed, and again a week after the seedlings are up, with oxyquinoline benzoate (sold as Anti-damp), 1 part to 100 parts of water.

A number of commercial preparations to treat seeds with before sowing, such as Arasan, Cuprocide and Spergon, are sold as protections against damping off and are generally excellent. The manufacturers' directions should be carefully followed.

Thin sowing, careful attention to watering and ventilation and early transplanting are good protective aids against damping off.

Diebacks. See Cankers and Diebacks, above.

Fruit Spots. Fruits may be spotted unnaturally as a result of various causes, including insect injury, spray injury and infection with certain rot and leaf spot diseases. In addition to these causes of blemished fruits there are a few diseases specifically known as fruit spots or fruit specks. It is with these latter that we are concerned here; for the other causes, see Leaf Spots, Rots, and also Physiological Diseases, below.

Brooks Fruit Spot (Mycosphaerella Pomi). This fungus disease of Apples causes the skin to be marked with red or black spots on places where it is red, and with green spots where the skin is yellow. The spots are slightly depressed, irregular in shape, less than ¼ in. in diameter and most numerous at the end of the fruit not attached to the stalk.

Spraying during the summer with a sulphur spray provides control.

Fly Speck (Leptothyrium Pomi). A common disease of Apples which also affects Blackberries, Citrus fruits, Grapes, Japanese Persimmons, Pears, Plums, Raspberries and Quinces, this

[45]
Physiological disease,
Winter Injury of Boxwood

[46]
Physiological Leaf Scorch
of Horsechestnut (Aesculus)

[47]
Chlorosis of Mountain Laurel
(Kalmia)

[48]
Injury of Pelargonium caused by
manufactured gas

[49]
Rose Foliage eaten by Japanese Beetle

[50]
Damage caused by European Pine Shoot Moth

[51]
Beans Damaged by Mexican Bean Beetle

[52]
Insect Leaf Galls on Leaves

fungus causes dark "fly specks" to mar the fruits. No serious harm results but the effect is disfiguring.

Sulphur sprays applied during the summer give control.

Galls. When plants develop abnormally and produce tumor-like growths, such growths are called galls. Galls vary greatly in size and different kinds occur on various parts of plants; thus we have root galls, stem galls, leaf galls and other kinds.

Many kinds of galls are caused by insects, mites and nematodes; these are discussed under Insects, above. Yet other galls, including some of the most serious plant diseases, are the result of infection with bacteria and fungi; it is these with which we are concerned here.

Azalea Leaf Gall (Exobasidium Vaccinii). This fungus disease is the principal cause of galls on deciduous (leaf-losing) and evergreen Rhododendrons, Blueberries and related plants. On most susceptible kinds the galls are conspicuous swollen enlargements of all or parts of the leaf, white or pinkish and soft at first but later turning brown and hard. On Cranberries and Huckleberries the galls are small, round red blisters.

This disease is not serious and usually can be controlled by picking off the infected leaves.

A large gall caused by a fungus on the trunk of an Oak.

These large, soft, pinkish growths on Azaleas are caused by the Azalea leaf gall fungus.

Camellia Leaf Gall (Exobasidium Camelliae). This fungus disease causes infected leaves of Camellias to become very much enlarged, thick and succulent with a thin white membrane covering their undersides. Some of the young shoots may also be thicker than normal.

Prompt removal of affected parts is the best control measure.

Crown Gall (Erwinia tumefaciens). This deadly bacterial disease is contracted by plants from soil in which the organism is present. Large round, roughened swellings or galls may occur at the base of the stock in a large number of fruit trees and in various places on a large variety of plants.

Apple tree roots attacked by crown gall.

These galls are produced by the bacteria stimulating the plant cells to divide. The bacteria appear to be able to enter the tissues only through wounds.

Besides the Apple, the following fruit trees may be attacked: Pears, Plums, Quinces, Cherries, Apricots and Peaches, and the disease is quite common on Roses. Crown gall may also occur on the parts of the stem above ground in Raspberries, Loganberries, and Blackberries, and on some species of Chrysanthemum (for example, C. frutescens or Marguerite). Certain kinds of Apple stocks are particularly susceptible.

There is no sure cure for attacked plants; the disease can be prevented by selecting varieties of less susceptible kinds, planting in fresh, clean soil, and taking care to avoid wounds. Dipping affected plants in a solution containing streptomycin before replanting them in uninfected soil is a recommended procedure.

Hairy Root. This is a disease of Apples, Cotoneasters, Elaeagnus, Gleditsia, Loniceras, Mulberries, Peaches, Quinces, Roses, Spiraeas, Tomatoes and many other plants, caused by the bacterium Erwinia rhizogenes. It is characterized by the development of a large number of fine roots directly from the stems or roots or from hard swellings that form on them. Control measures are the same as for crown gall disease. See Crown Gall.

Leaf Blisters and Leaf Curls. These are diseases characterized by the production on the leaves of blister-like developments and by puckering and curling, often accompanied by discoloration and by dropping of the leaves. Among the commonest of these diseases are the following:

Oak Leaf Blister (Taphrina caerulescens). This fungus disease is especially damaging in the South but occurs in other sections also, especially on Red Oaks. The blisters are yellowish and raised (convex) on the upper leaf surfaces and on the under surfaces are blackish or gray. As a result of infection the leaves curl and drop off.

To control this disease, spray with dormant-strength lime-sulphur just before the leaf buds open in spring. An alternate control that is reported to give good results is spraying with Puratized Agricultural Spray when the leaves are developing.

Peach Leaf Curl (Taphrina deformans). This fungus disease is common on Peaches and also affects Apricots and Nectarines. It causes the young foliage to become reddish and curled or puckered. Often the leaves drop prematurely and the young fruits are cracked or misshapen.

Control is had by applying a dormant-strength (1 to 15 dilution) lime-sulphur spray either in fall or before the leaf buds open in spring.

Leaf Curls. See under Leaf Blisters and Leaf Curls, above.

Leaf Scorches. Here are considered certain fungus diseases that produce a scorched appearance of the foliage. True scorching of foliage, caused by excessive heat and certain other unfavorable environmental conditions, also occurs, and is discussed under Physiological Diseases, below.

Azalea Leaf Scorch (Septoria Azaleae). This fungus disease, sometimes called Azalea leaf spot, causes most harm in greenhouses and during periods when the atmospheric humidity is high. The foliage is marred by small spots, which gradually enlarge and turn reddish brown and dark brown at their centers.

Control is by spraying with Bordeaux mixture.

Black Scorch (Ceratostomella paradoxa). Palms of various kinds, including the Coconut Palm and Date Palm, are affected by this disease, which causes the leaf and fruit stalks to be blackened and roughened as though they had been burned, and the young leaves to be of subnormal size and to dry and turn black. The interiors of the trunks rot.

Prompt destruction of infected parts is the only control.

Narcissus Leaf Scorch or Amaryllis Red Blotch (Stagonospora Curtisii). A most serious fungus disease of a number of bulbous plants including Crinums, Eucharis, Hippeastrum (Amaryllis), Hymenocallis, Leucojums, Nerines, Sternbergias, Vallotas and Zephranthes, this is sometimes called red fire disease and red leaf spot disease. The symptoms on Hippeastrums (Amaryllis) are deformed foliage and flower stalks and red or purplish spots on the leaves, stalks and flowers. Infected Narcissus foliage appears as though the upper 2-3 inches had been frosted; the lower portions of the leaves are marred with tiny

The same parasitic fungus causes Narcissus leaf scorch disease and Amaryllis red blotch disease. This is an affected Amaryllis (Hippeastrum).

water-soaked spots or scabby reddish-brown areas. The foliage dies prematurely. The flower stalks and blooms may be marked with brown spots. Symptoms on the other plants affected resemble either those that appear on Hippeastrum or those that appear on Narcissi.

Control measures consist of discarding very badly infected bulbs and from others removing infected leaves and bulb scales, avoiding syringing in greenhouses and excessive watering, and by dipping the bulbs, after first soaking them for 1 hour in water, in a 1 to 750 dilution of mercuric chloride or in a 1 to 100 solution of formalin. Spraying with Bordeaux mixture while the plants are in leaf is also helpful.

Opuntia Scorch or Sunscald (Hendersonia Opuntiae). Opuntias (Prickly Pears) are commonly infected with this fungus disease, which causes the stems or pads to turn reddish brown and die. The central portions of the diseased areas become cracked and grayish brown as the infection progresses.

No control is known other than cutting out and destroying affected portions.

Strawberry Leaf Scorch (Diplocarpon Earliana). Characterized by dark purplish spots (without white centers), measuring about ½ in. across, this fungus disease is serious on Strawberries. The spots are numerous on the leaves and lesions occur on stems, flower stalks and runners. Sometimes the flowers and young fruits are killed as a result of girdling of the fruit stalks.

To gain control, spray with Bordeaux mixture at 10-day intervals beginning when growth starts in spring and continuing until the flowers open. Some varieties of Strawberries are somewhat resistant to this disease.

Leaf Spots. Leaf spot diseases are very numerous and affect a great variety of plants. Many of these diseases are not particularly harmful, but some, such as black spot disease of Roses, are among the most serious afflictions of plants. The majority of leaf spots are caused by fungi and bacteria and are likely to be most prevalent in rainy seasons. Leaf spots caused by bacteria often have a water-soaked appearance; those caused by fungi usually develop tiny black fruiting bodies which appear as small dark dots near the centers of the spots.

Leaf spot diseases are characterized by the appearance, on the foliage, of well-defined discolored spots of dead tissue. The spots may be small or fairly large and often have margins differing in color from their centers. Leaf spot diseases differ from anthracnose, blight, blotch and scorch in that the dead portions are quite precisely delimited instead of being large and indefinite.

The prompt removal and destruction of infected leaves and spraying with fungicides are the chief control measures used in combatting leaf spot diseases. In addition, the avoidance of excessive humidity (in greenhouses) and of wetting foliage at times when it will not dry quickly is helpful. The following are some of the more common of the many leaf spot diseases that may affect garden plants.

Begonia Bacteriosis (Xanthomonas Begoniae). This common disease affects all kinds of Begonias. Round, blister-like spots of dead tissue mar the leaves. The spots are brown with translucent margins. The stems may also be affected and become watery and soft. Frequently the leaves fall off.

To prevent this disease, avoid crowding the plants, avoid syringing and wetting the foliage unnecessarily. Spray with Bordeaux mixture.

Boston Ivy Leaf Spot (Guignardia Bidwelli Parthenocissi). Leaves of Boston Ivy and Virginia Creeper are often disfigured by reddish-brown spots that may cause premature loss of leaves in this fungus disease.

Spray with ferbam or nabam as the leaves develop, and repeat 2 or 3 times at 2-week intervals. This gives fair control.

Chrysanthemum Leaf Spot (Septoria Chrysanthemi). This is a common fungus disease of Chrysanthemums which is sometimes mistaken for nematode injury. Its symptoms differ from nematode injury in that they begin as definite small spots which change from yellow to nearly black and may later join to form blotches; nematode injury appears as wedge-shaped brown areas between the veins.

Characteristic symptoms of Chrysanthemum leaf spot disease.

Avoid overhead watering, and dust or spray with ferbam.

Clematis Leaf and Stem Spot (Ascochyta Clematidina). This serious fungus disease of Clematis often girdles the stems near the ground and causes the portions above the point of attack to wither and die. In addition, the leaves may be disfigured with small water-soaked spots which become buff-colored with reddish margins.

The best methods of control are to cut off and burn infected leaves and stems promptly, and to spray or dust repeatedly with sulphur.

Cucurbit Septoria Leaf Spot (Septoria Cucurbitacearum). This fungus disease causes circular gray spots, each usually bordered with a yellow zone, to appear on the foliage of Cucumbers, Melons, Squash and Watermelons.

The recommended control is to clean up and burn all infected plants at the end of the harvesting season.

Currant Leaf Spot (Mycosphaerella Ribis). This fungus disease often causes partial or total loss of leaves in Currants and Gooseberries. If experience indicates that frequent serious attacks may be expected, the bushes should be sprayed with a 3-3-100 Bordeaux mixture, the first application being given immediately after blooming and a second one 2-3 weeks later. Ferbam also controls this disease.

Delphinium Black Spot (Pseudomonas Delphinii). This is a common bacterial disease of Aconitums and Delphiniums that forms irregular tarlike black spots on the leaves, stems and flower buds. It causes some distortion but much less than the Cyclamen mite does.

Control measures consist of picking off diseased leaves and spraying all above-ground parts with Bordeaux mixture. Old stalks and leaves should be burned at the end of the season.

English Ivy Bacterial Leaf Spot (Xanthomonas Hederae). This disease causes spots, at first water-soaked in appearance and later with dark brown or black centers, to appear on the leaves. The foliage becomes yellowish and the plants lack vigor.

As a preventative, avoid wetting the leaves unnecessarily and do not crowd the plants. Spray with Bordeaux mixture.

Geranium Bacterial Leaf Spot (Xanthomonas

Bacterial leaf spot disease on English Ivy.

. Pelargonii). Fairly common on Geraniums (Pelargoniums), this disease first makes its presence known by small water-soaked spots on the under surfaces of the leaves. These enlarge, become brown, dry and brittle. Eventually the whole leaves turn yellow or brown and shrivel.

To bring the disease under control, pick off and burn infected leaves, provide ample ventilation so that a free circulation of air is assured, avoid wetting the leaves unnecessarily and spray with Bordeaux mixture.

Gladiolus Leaf and Flower Spot (Curvularia lunata). This fungus disease is most serious in the South, where it causes heavy losses. Small oval, tan to dark brown spots appear on both sides of the leaves and brownish spots and blotches on the petals. The disease spreads rapidly in warm moist weather and the flowers may fail to open. Some varieties of Gladioli are much more resistant than others.

Spray with zineb weekly after growth starts and every 3 or 4 days after the flower spikes show, if the weather is moist.

Holly Tar Spot (Phacidium Curtisii). This fungus disease of American Holly (Ilex opaca) and English Holly (Ilex aquifolium) and their varieties. is unsightly but does no very serious harm. In summer small yellow spots appear. Later these turn reddish brown and eventually black. Occasionally the dead areas drop out, leaving holes in the leaves.

Rake up and burn promptly all fallen leaves. Spraying with Bordeaux mixture is effective but may cause some injury to the foliage.

Hydrangea Leaf Spot (Phyllosticta Hydrangeae). Circular brown spots which occur mostly near the leaf margins and may be numerous enough to cause premature loss of foliage are produced by this fungus disease.

Spray with zineb when the leaves are developing, and repeat 2 or 3 times at 10-day intervals for the best control.

Iris Leaf Spot (Didymellina macrospora). This fungus disease is widespread on bulbous and rhizomatous Irises in wet seasons. The oval spots it causes vary from dark brown to tan or yellow-brown and are mostly on the upper halves of the leaves.

Clean up and burn all old foliage in the fall. Cut off badly spotted leaf ends in midsummer. Spray weekly in the early part of the season with zineb. Apply lime to the soil if it is distinctly acid.

Lawn Grass Leaf Spots (various species of fungi). Turf grasses are subject to several leaf spot diseases. The spots are usually straw colored, reddish or brown, sometimes with darker borders.

Foliage of Geranium (Pelargonium) infected with bacterial leaf spot disease.

To minimize infection with zonate leaf spot (Helminthosporium giganteum), which causes straw-colored spots 1/8 in. or less in diameter, plant only resistant strains of Bent Grass such as Washington and Metropolitan. In most cases help is obtained by spraying areas that are affected with leaf spots, using Captan, Acti-dione RZ, or Kromad.

Maple Tar Spots (Rhytisma Acerinum and R. punctatum). The first of these fungi is common in the East, the second in the West. Apart from being disfiguring, they do no great harm, although some loss of foliage may result from severe infections. R. Acerinum causes raised spots to bespeckle the upper surface of foliage. They resemble spots of tar and may measure up to 1/2 in. in diameter. R. punctatum, called the speckled tar spot, produces pinhead-sized spots, arranged in groups and bespeckling yellowish-green areas on the upper surfaces of the leaves.

These diseases are best controlled by raking up and burning all leaves that fall. With young trees it is practicable to spray with Bordeaux mixture, but this is scarcely worthwhile with large specimens.

Mountain Laurel Leaf Spot (Phyllosticta Kalmicola). Foliage of Mountain Laurel is often disfigured with the purplish-bordered circular grayish spots of this fungus disease. This is especially true of plants subject to the drip from trees.

Spraying with ferbam, 2 or 3 times at 2-week intervals, when the new leaves are appearing, is the recommended control.

Plum and Apricot Leaf Spot (Coccomyces Prunophorae). This shot-hole disease, which attacks Plums and Apricots, is similar in its effects to the Cherry Leaf Spot, which see, above. It requires the same treatment.

Raspberry Leaf and Cane Spot (Mycosphaerella Rubi). This fungus disease is common on Raspberries and also infects Blackberries, Boysenberries, Dewberries, Loganberries and Youngberries. Small circular spots, at first reddish, but becoming gray and with black spots at their centers, appear on the leaves and stems late in the season. Leaves may fall prematurely as a result of infection.

This disease is controlled by spraying with Bordeaux mixture 4-4-50 just before the fall rains begin and again just after the first leaves are fully developed in spring.

Rhododendron Leaf Spots (various species of fungi). Rhododendrons are subject to a number of leaf spot diseases which cause spots of various sizes. These may be at the margins of the leaves, at their tips or towards the centers. Often they are pale tan or gray and in some cases have prominent red margins. Sometimes, after the tissue dies, it falls out and leaves conspicuous holes. Plants in poor health and those growing in unfavorable locations are much more susceptible to attack than others.

Spraying three times at 10-day intervals with Bordeaux mixture, beginning when the new leaves are half grown, gives good control. Any measures to improve the health of the bushes, such as mulching, watering thoroughly during dry weather and so forth, are helpful.

Ring Spot. See Virus Diseases and Physiological Diseases, below.

Rose Black Spot (Diplocarpon Rosae). This is a most serious fungus disease of Roses. It occurs in most areas where they are grown but is less harmful in semi-arid regions than in moist climates. A symptom of the disease is the appearance, on the foliage, of black spots with fringed margins. The spots measure up to 1/2 in. in diameter. Small black areas also develop along the stems. The fungus winters over on infected stems and on fallen leaves that are allowed to remain on the ground.

Some varieties of Roses are more susceptible than others. Those with yellow and coppery colored flowers, or flowers that are blends of

A Rose leaflet attacked by black spot disease.

these colors, are likely to be especially susceptible. Black spot disease causes the leaves to drop off prematurely. Seriously infected plants may be almost completely defoliated by midsummer. Such plants put out new leaves which in turn are likely to be infected with the disease and, as a result, the plants are partly defoliated again. The premature loss of leaves has a weakening effect on the Rose plants and shortens their lives.

Clean up and burn all fallen Rose leaves in the fall. Spray the plants with lime-sulphur, 1 part to 9 parts of water, just before new growth starts in spring. Spray or dust at about weekly intervals throughout the growing season. In rainy weather, applications of spray or dust should be made oftener than once a week; in dry weather every 8-9 days may be often enough. Dusting sulphur, copper sprays and dusts and ferbam give good results in controlling black spot of Roses. Nabam, Phaltan and ferbam are also satisfactory controls. Copper-containing fungicides may cause some foliage injury in cool, dull weather; sulphur may cause burning of the foliage in very hot weather.

Many excellent dusts and sprays for the control of black spot of Roses are sold under trade names. Apply these strictly according to manufacturers' directions. Combination sprays which control insects as well as fungus diseases are also available and are generally satisfactory. Whichever spray or dust is used, it is very essential to cover both surfaces of the leaves with an even coating.

Strawberry Leaf Spot (Mycosphaerella Fragariae). This causes purple-bordered gray spots on Strawberry leaves. Most present-day Strawberry varieties are so resistant that the disease is not often serious in the North. Providing good air circulation and allowing the bed to bear fruit only one year are measures that tend to reduce injury from this fungus leaf spot. Southern growers may use Bordeaux mixture at frequent intervals to control it if necessary.

Stone Fruits Bacterial Spot (Xanthomonas Pruni). This disease causes small reddish spots to appear on the leaves. These spots join and their centers die and drop out to produce a shot-hole effect. Spots, fissures and cracks appear on the fruit, and cankers form on the twigs. In severe cases serious loss of leaves takes place. Vigorous trees are injured less than weak trees.

Several applications of a zinc sulphate spray give at least partial control. Keep the trees in good health by careful pruning, fertilizing and other good cultural practices.

Tomato Nailhead Spot (Alternaria Tomato). This fungus disease affects the foliage in the same manner as Potato and Tomato early blight (see Blights, above) but the spots it causes on the fruits are distinctive. They are 1/8 in. or less in diameter, tan-colored at first, becoming slightly sunken and grayish brown at their centers, with darker borders.

Control is had by purchasing seed that has been treated to free it of infection, by using resistant varieties, by burning or otherwise destroying all Tomato tops at the end of the season and by rotating the Tomato crop so that it is not grown in the same place more than one year in each three or four.

Tomato Septoria Leaf Spot (Septoria Lycopersici). This fungus disease of Tomatoes is especially common in the East and Midwest, where, especially in wet seasons, it does considerable harm. It is sometimes called Tomato blight but is quite distinct from other blight diseases of Tomatoes (see Blights, above). Septoria leaf spot infects Tomato plants at any stage of growth but most commonly after the fruits are in evidence. At first the spots, which are not more than 1/8 in. in diameter, appear on the lower leaves. They have a water-soaked appearance and are circular; later they become gray with a dark border. As the disease progresses, leaves higher up on the stems are affected, and badly infected ones may be killed.

The best control is had by burning the tops of infected plants at the end of the season, by eliminating all weeds, especially those that belong to the Nightshade family (Solanaceae), by spraying with a fixed copper spray or with a copper dust fungicide and by rotating crops so that Tomatoes are not planted in the same place oftener than every 3-4 years.

Viburnum Leaf Spot (Pseudomonas Viburni). This bacterial leaf spot occurs on many kinds of Viburnums and is especially damaging to Viburnum Carlesii. It shows as black angular spots on the leaves and in a wet season may cause premature loss of leaves.

Spray with Bordeaux mixture or ammoniacal copper carbonate early in the season and repeat 3 or 4 times at weekly intervals. Use a somewhat weaker solution than recommended if the weather is cool. Mistakes have been made by using sulphur, which is injurious to this plant. Promptly rake up and burn fallen leaves.

Willow Tar Spot (Rhytisma Salicinum). This fungus disease causes black, tarlike spots about 1/4 in. in diameter to bespeckle the leaves. Apart from being disfiguring, it does no very serious harm.

The best control is to rake up and burn all fallen leaves.

Mildews. The fungi known to gardeners as mildews include the true mildews or powdery mildews and the false mildews or downy mildews The term black mildew is sometimes applied to the sooty mold fungi (see under Molds, below).

Powdery mildews or true mildews grow on the surfaces of affected plants, not inside their tissues and buds. They form whitish (occasionally blackish) felty coatings on leaves, stems and buds, more especially on those that are young, vigorous and succulent.

The powdery mildews are a clearly defined fungus group and different species attack many kinds of plants all over the world. All powdery mildews are parasitic. They obtain their nourishment through tiny suckers which penetrate the epidermal cells of the host plants; the main body or mycelium of the fungus is always entirely outside the host. Powdery mildews thrive when the atmosphere is humid but not during rainy weather, because their spores do not germinate in free water. Cool nights following warm days favor the growth of these fungi. When plants are crowded together or there are other impediments to free air circulation, powdery mildews are encouraged. Sulphur sprays and dusts, copper sprays and Mildex or Karathane give good control. Susceptible plants should be planted only where free air circulation is assured.

Downy mildews or false mildews are parasitic fungi, the spores of which are visible as white, gray or purplish patches of downy appearance, usually on the under surfaces of affected leaves,

Powdery mildew on Pansy.

but the main body of the fungus is always inside the tissues of the host plant.

Downy mildews thrive in wet weather. Spraying with zineb is effective against most downy mildews. Bordeaux mixture is also recommended as a control.

Apple Powdery Mildew (Podosphaera leucotricha). This is a common disease of Apples, Pears, Quinces and some other trees and shrubs belonging to the botanical family Rosaceae. It causes crinkling or other distortion of the leaves and patches of a white felty coating, which later turns brown, to mar the foliage and young shoots.

It is important to cut out all mildewed twigs when pruning during the dormant season (winter or early spring). For effective control, spray with lime-sulphur, 1 to 50 or 1 to 100 dilution, before the flowers open, and later several times with wettable sulphur.

Crape Myrtle Powdery Mildew (Erysiphe Lagerstroemeriae). This most important disease of Crape Myrtles appears early on the young shoots and forms a conspicuous white covering. The leaves become thickened and fail to attain normal size. The shoots remain stunted and the flower buds may fail to open. Finally, affected leaves and buds drop off.

Control is obtained by spraying with

lime-sulphur, 1 to 80 dilution, when the buds start into new growth in spring and repeating this spray two weeks later. Good results are also obtained by spraying with Acti-dione, with wettable sulphur or with a copper fungicide such as Bordeaux mixture after growth is more advanced.

Cucurbit Downy Mildew (Pseudoperonospora cubensis). This is common on Cucumbers, Gourds, Melons, Pumpkins and Squash in wet seasons. It shows itself as irregular yellow spots on the upper surfaces of the leaves and brown to purple patches on their undersides. The leaves may die and the fruits fail to develop to normal size. This disease does not show in the North until about midsummer or later but appears earlier in the South.

Spraying with zineb, ziram or nabam gives the most satisfactory control.

Cucurbit Powdery Mildew. See Phlox Powdery Mildew, below.

Euonymus Powdery Mildew (Oidium Euonymus-japonici). Euonymus japonicus and its varieties are subject to this disease, which forms a conspicuous covering on the leaves and may result in some dropping of the foliage.

Dusting or spraying with sulphur is effective. Spraying forcibly with water from a hose washes the foliage clean and helps to prevent serious infection.

Grape Downy Mildew (Plasmopara Viticola). This is most destructive on varieties of the vinifera or European Grapes but other kinds may be affected. Yellow, usually circular spots, which later turn brown, appear on the upper surfaces of the leaves and a white downy coating develops on their undersides. Young shoots and leafstalks may be infected also. Affected berries harden and may be covered with a grayish fungus growth.

A spray of Bordeaux mixture applied when the shoots are 6-8 in. long, again after the petals have fallen, and once or twice more before the berries color, gives control. Fallen leaves should be raked up and burned.

Legume Powdery Mildew (Erysiphe Polygoni). Beans, Lupines, Peas, Sweet Peas and other plants belonging to the botanical family Leguminosae, as well as many plants belonging to other families, such as Anemones, Calendulas, China Asters, Clematis, Dahlias, Delphiniums, Gardenias, Hydrangeas and Peonies, are affected by this fungous disease.

Dusting or spraying with sulphur gives effective control. Mildex or Karathane are also effective. Some varieties of susceptible vegetables are more resistant to mildew than others.

Lilac Powdery Mildew (Microsphaera Alni). This disease is prevalent on Lilacs in late summer and is common on many other shrubs and trees, especially Alders, Azaleas, Blueberries, Euonymus, Privets and Viburnums. It is unsightly but does no great harm to the plants it infects.

An application of sulphur dust, a sulphur spray or Mildex, applied about midsummer or at first sign of the foliage whitening, usually gives good control. Repeat applications may be necessary.

Lima Bean Downy Mildew (Phytophthora Phaseoli). This is a serious disease in wet seasons but does little harm in dry ones. At its worst it may practically destroy the Lima Bean crop. The fungus shows as conspicuous patches of white, downy growth on the pods and in severe cases may cover them. Eventually the pods turn black. On the foliage the fungous growth is less noticeable but the veins of the leaves may be twisted or otherwise distorted and they often assume a purplish hue.

A spray made of nabam and zinc sulphate gives control.

Onion Downy Mildew (Peronospora destructor). This is a serious disease of Onions and Garlic in cool wet seasons. As a result of infection the leaves turn yellow and wither prematurely.

Dusting early with ferbam or zineb gives control. Clean up and burn all dead leaves. Practice crop rotation.

Peach Powdery Mildew (Sphaerotheca pannosa Persicae). This mildew infects Peaches, Nectarines, Apricots, Almonds and some other kinds of plants. The foliage is marred by dense patches of white mycelium, and brown patches or blotches are found on the fruits, which are usually malformed and scabby.

Control is obtained by spraying with lime-sulphur at 1 to 100 dilution.

Phlox Powdery Mildew (Erysiphe Cichoracearum). This disease occurs on Phlox and many other garden plants towards the end of summer. It especially attacks Asters, Chrysanthemums,

Dahlias, Delphiniums, Rudbeckias and Zinnias. It also is a serious disease of Melons, Cucumbers, Squash and other Cucurbits (plants belonging to the botanical family Cucurbitaceae), for which reason it is also known as the Cucurbit powdery mildew.

Sulphur dust gives good control of this disease but copper fungicides, such as Bordeaux mixture, are safer to use on Cucurbits. Mildex or Karathane is also effective.

Rose foliage infected with powdery mildew.

Rose Powdery Mildew (Sphaerotheca pannosa Rosae). This is a common disease of Roses both in greenhouses and outdoors. It causes curling of the leaves and forms a white coating on buds, leaves and stems. It is especially likely to attack young, succulent shoots and leaves.

Recommended controls are sulphur dusts, sulphur sprays, Mildex or Karathane, and Phaltan.

Molds. The term mold as it refers to plant diseases is applied loosely. Usually it is limited to certain fungi that produce on the surfaces of leaves, stems, flowers, fruits and other parts a profuse and easily visible growth of mycelium (fungous growth). But not all fungi that do this are named molds; many are classified as blights, mildews, rots and smuts. Not all molds are harmful to living plants; many grow and feed on dead organic matter (that is, they are saprophytes rather than parasites). These are often found on decaying leaves, manure and similar materials. Important diseases known as molds are:

Gray Mold Blight. See under Blights, above.

Pink Snow Mold (Calonectria nivale). This disease of turf and lawn grasses, like ordinary snow mold, causes more or less circular patches of dead grass to show about the time the snow disappears in spring. The fungous growth is whitish gray but often assumes a pinkish tinge because of the slimy pink spore masses it produces. It is likely to be more prevalent when snow falls before the soil freezes.

Control is had by applying in fall either bichloride of mercury or calomel or a mixture of both at the rate of 3 oz. to 1,000 sq. ft. of surface or Panogen Turf Spray as recommended by the manufacturer.

Snow Mold (species of Typhula). These fungi cause conspicuous, roundish, white felty patches of fungous growth to develop on lawns and other turf areas at the time the snow melts in

Flowering shoots of Rose infected with powdery mildew.

late winter or spring. The grass in the affected areas becomes light brown but the roots are usually not killed and natural recovery almost invariably takes place. If desired, the areas may be treated in the same way as recommended above for pink snow mold.

Sooty Molds (species of Capnodium). The sooty molds can scarcely be regarded as diseases. They are not parasites on plants but live, rather, on honeydew deposits (excretions of aphids, scales and mealybugs) that occur on leaves and stems. They do, of course, interfere somewhat with the functions of the leaf by blocking light and in other ways, and they are unsightly. They are sometimes called black mildew.

Control of sooty molds is had by eliminating the insects that produce the honeydew.

Tomato Leaf Mold (Cladosporium fulvum). This is common on Tomatoes grown in greenhouses and may be harmful in wet seasons to outdoor Tomatoes, chiefly in the South. Symptoms are whitish spots on the upper surfaces of the leaves and velvety areas of olive-brown on the under surfaces. The leaves enlarge and become yellow. Excessive atmospheric humidity is necessary for this disease to flourish.

In greenhouses control is had by growing resistant varieties, giving free ventilation and by operating the heating apparatus at night during cool spring and fall weather. For outdoor Tomatoes, spraying with ziram is the preferred control.

Needle Casts (caused by various fungi, including species of Adelopus, Bifusella, Hypoderma, Hypodermella, Lophodermum and others). These diseases of Pines, Spruces, Firs, Douglas Firs, Hemlocks, Larches and other conifers are usually characterized by an abundant shedding of the needles (leaves). In a few cases the needles simply die, turn brown and remain hanging on the branches. The term needle blight is sometimes used instead of needle cast.

No entirely satisfactory control methods are known. Recommended measures are: raking up and burning all fallen leaves in spring before the new leaves appear, and spraying with Bordeaux mixture, when the new leaves are developing. Attention to all cultural details that promote healthy growth, such as watering and fertilizing, is helpful.

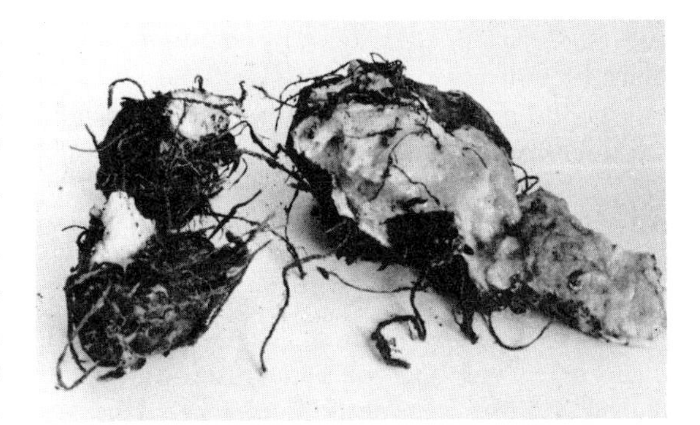

The tuber of a Caladium destroyed by a rot-causing fungus.

Oedema. See Moisture Excesses and Deficiencies under Physiological Diseases, below.

Powdery Mildews. See Mildews.

Ring Spot. See under Virus Diseases and under Physiological Diseases, below.

Rots. Diseases known as rots are characterized by the death and decay of portions of the plant

A Cactus destroyed at its base by rot caused by a fungus.

tissues. Affected parts usually become brown, black or otherwise markedly discolored and may be wet and mushy or dry. In some cases they give off an offensive odor. Rots affect various parts of plants, most commonly roots, rhizomes, bulbs, stems, trunks, fruits, buds and flowers. Leaves are also attacked but rots affecting leaves are most often called leaf spots or blights.

Rots are caused by fungi, bacteria and some other organisms and, in some cases, by physiological conditions (see Physiological Diseases, below). Tubers, bulbs, fruits and other parts of plants or plants in storage are very likely to be infected if the storage conditions are not ideal, particularly if ventilation is insufficient or if the plants are too moist. Poor soil drainage commonly favors the rotting of roots and other underground plant parts. Storm damage and other mechanical injury and poor pruning (particularly leaving stubs instead of cutting close to a main trunk, branch or bud from which a new shoot will develop) encourage the development of trunk and stem rots.

Control of rots mostly depends upon providing favorable growing and storage conditions, careful pruning, the prompt cutting out of affected parts (or in extreme cases the destruction of the plant or plant part affected), dusting or spraying with a fungicide to check reinfection and, in the case of soil-borne kinds, soil sterilization. Among the most common rots of garden plants are the following:

Apple Bitter Rot (Glomerella cingulata). This fungus disease is a major trouble of Apples in the hotter, more humid Apple-growing regions south of the latitude of southern New York. Infection is most apt to occur during hot, damp weather as the fruit approaches maturity, from mid-July to early September. Small, light brown spots appear on the fruits and enlarge but remain circular. The rotted areas beneath the spots are firm, but become shrunken and form saucer-shaped depressions. Eventually the fruits shrivel and become mummies. This disease also causes rough cankers on large branches. The same fungus causes anthracnose, rots, dieback disease and canker of a wide variety of trees, shrubs and vines, including Sweet Peas, Cranberries, Grapes and Camellias.

Control measures include frequent and thorough use of copper fungicides such as Bordeaux mixture.

Blossom End Rot. See Physiological Diseases, below.

Blueberry Mummyberry (Monilinia urnula). This serious disease of Highbush Blueberries is caused by a fungus which infects the shoot tips and blossoms in early spring, and later the young fruits. The infected berries turn cream or tan and drop off shortly before the normal berries ripen. In some seasons the crop may be reduced considerably.

Control consists of cultivation and raking or sweeping the soil to disturb the overwintering mummified berries before they discharge their spores in the spring. This disease is also called brown rot and twig blight.

Brown Rot of Stone Fruits (Monilinia fructicola). This fungus disease is common on Cherries, Peaches, Plums and other stone fruits; it occasionally occurs on Apples, Quinces and Pears. It is most familiar on Peaches. Spores are carried over on mummied fruits. Infection starts at blossom time and the disease develops as the fruits grow. On the fruits it first shows as a small, round brown spot; this spreads quickly and eventually covers the fruits, which become shrunken, brown and mummified. Moist, warm weather favors the development of the rot. Sometimes cankers appear on the branches, and gummy sap is exuded.

Collect and destroy all mummied fruit in the fall. Spray with wettable sulphur, 3 lb. to 50 gallons of water, when the flowers are at the pink bud stage, again when the petals and shucks have fallen, yet again 2-3 weeks later and finally about 3 weeks before the fruit ripens. Ferbam, maneb and Phygon have been used with good results for the last 2 or 3 sprays.

Calla Root Rot (Phytophthora Richardiae). This rot disease, which destroys the feeder roots, beginning at their tip ends and working backwards along them, is the result of infection by a fungus. About the time the plants begin to show flower buds the outer leaves turn yellowish in a more or less streaked pattern, then wilt and eventually become brown and die. Any flowers that develop are likely to be misshapen. The interior structure of affected roots is often completely destroyed and only a sheath of epidermis remains. The rhizomes are sometimes affected.

Control measures consist of cutting out any rotted spots from the rhizomes and cutting off all affected roots, then soaking the rhizomes for one hour in a 1 to 50 solution of formaldehyde or a 1 to 1,000 solution of mercuric chloride. Soil in which affected plants have been grown should not be used for growing Callas again unless it is first sterilized.

Calla Soft Rot (Pectobacterium carotovorum Aroidae). This common Calla Lily disease is caused by bacterial infection. A soft, white, slimy decay sets in, all parts being attacked, including rhizomes, leaves and flower stalks. There may also be indefinite dark spots on the leaves and flowers. The slimy decayed parts often have a very unpleasant smell. The disease is contracted from the soil and can be very destructive. The bacterium which produces it can attack a large number of other plants, including Beets, Cabbage, Cauliflowers, Eggplants, Geraniums, Iris, Potatoes, Tomatoes and Turnips.

The disease in Calla Lilies is readily controlled by the following treatment: After the plants have dried off, shake the rhizomes or rootstocks out of the pots, scrub thoroughly with a hard brush and scrape away all the diseased parts. Then steep them in formalin for 2 hours, using a 2 per cent solution (1 part commercial formalin added to 49 parts of water). Afterwards, pot in fresh soil in sterilized pots and stand the pots on tiles previously sterilized by baking them or by soaking them in formalin solution.

If fresh soil is not available the old soil may be used if it is first sterilized. To sterilize the soil with formalin, use the same strength as above and soak thoroughly. The Calla Lilies should not be potted until about 3 weeks after the soil has been treated.

Canna Bud Rot (Xanthomonas Cannae). Plants infected with this bacterial disease show yellow to brown irregular water-soaked areas on the leaves, the stalks may be gummy and exhibit blackened areas and the flowers are spoiled by infection or rot.

To control this disease, destroy all badly affected plants. Soak dormant rootstocks (roots)

Healthy roots of Calla Lily (Zantedeschia).

Calla Lily (Zantedeschia) roots damaged by root rot disease.

for 2 hours in a 1 to 1,000 bichloride of mercury solution (1 tablet to 1 pint of water). Avoid splashing the plants with water.

Crown Rot or Southern Blight (Pellicularia Rolfsii and Sclerotium Delphinii). This widespread fungus disease is sometimes known as Mustard seed fungus because the sclerotia (tiny, hard reproductive bodies) resemble light-brown Mustard seeds. Some authorities regard the fungus S. Delphinii, which is responsible for crown rot in the North, to be merely a form of P. Rolfsii, which causes Southern blight in the South; others consider them to be two closely related but distinct organisms.

Be that as it may, the symptoms produced by these fungi are the same in a great variety of vegetables and herbaceous plants, including Aconites, Ajugas, Beets, Carrots, Delphiniums, Onions, Irises, Narcissi and Phlox. The first sign of infection is the formation in humid weather of white webs of mycelium at the bases of the stems and sometimes on the nearby ground. The stems of such plants as Delphiniums, Aconites and Phlox bend or break near the ground. Ajuga and other plants quickly rot away.

Dig up affected plants together with the surrounding soil and burn them. Drench the holes with a 1 to 1,000 bichloride of mercury solution (1 tablet to 1 pint of water) and pour some of the solution over the crowns of surrounding plants. Dusting with sulphur slows the growth of the mycelium but does not kill the sclerotia, which can live in the soil for more than a year. Soil in which no plants are growing may be disinfected with chloropicrin, or with a formaldehyde solution, 1 part of formalin to 100 parts water, applied at 3 gallons per square foot.

Gladiolus Fusarium Rot (Fusarium oxysporum Gladioli). This fungus disease causes serious decay of Gladioli corms (bulbs) in storage. The decay first appears as small reddish-brown surface lesions, usually on the lower parts of the corms. These enlarge and become brown, and eventually the entire corm may become hard, dry, brownish-black and shriveled.

Control measures consist of promptly discarding all corms that show evidence of infection and soaking the corms for 3 hours in a solution of 4 tablespoons of Lysol in 3 gallons of water immediately before they are planted.

Grape Black Rot (Guignardia Bidwellii). The first noticeable symptoms of this fungus disease are the rotting of the half-grown berries. Light spots appear and enlarge rapidly until the berry becomes a hard, shriveled mummy, the surface of which is covered with minute, black, pimple-like bodies which contain the spores. On the leaves, the disease produces small, circular reddish-brown spots.

Ferbam at the rate of 1½ lb. in 100 gallons of water is the most effective fungicide for black rot on Concord Grapes. The first application is just before bloom, the second just after bloom, and the third 7 to 10 days later. On Catawba, Niagara and Fredonia varieties, which are susceptible to downy mildew, Bordeaux mixture or a fixed copper spray is used.

Heart Rot. See Physiological Diseases, below.

Lawn Grass Rots. Many different diseases affect grass turf; in addition to the rots described here others are described under Blights and under Leaf Spots, above, and under Molds, above.

Brown patch (Pellicularia filamentosa), which chiefly infects Bent Grasses (and thus is prevalent on putting greens), also attacks other kinds, including Bluegrasses and Bermuda Grass. Infected areas are usually roundish and may vary from a few inches to several feet across. The grass in them first assumes a dark hue and later becomes tan colored. The margins of the patch form a darker ring of recently attacked and wilted grass. Brown patch develops only during periods of high temperatures and high humidities. It may be controlled by spraying with calomel or corrosive sublimate, alone or in combination, or by using phenyl mercury acetate.

Copper spot disease (Ramulispora Sorghi) affects Bent Grasses and develops after rainy periods in spring. The symptoms are round patches of turf, 3 in. or less in diameter, which assume an orange or coppery color. The grass leaves are covered with salmon-colored spore masses.

Control is effected by the use of fungicides containing cadmium and by the use of phenyl mercury acetate fungicides. This disease is much more serious on soils that are distinctly acid.

Dollar spot disease (Sclerotinia homoeocarpa) attacks Bent Grasses, Fescues and Bluegrasses. It produces spots that are not more than 2 in. in diameter (although they may merge to produce much larger browned areas). At first they are brown but later they become straw colored. Often a fine cobwebby fungus growth may be seen in the early mornings before the dew is dispersed on affected lawn areas.

The best controls for dollar spot are fungicides that contain cadmium. Applications at monthly intervals through the growing season are recommended.

Stem rot of Geranium (Pelargonium).

Lily Fusarium Rot (Fusarium oxysporum Lilii). This fungus causes rotting of Lilies, Crocuses, Freesias and some Cacti. It affects bulbs, roots and stems.

Control may be had by disinfecting the soil, before planting, with formaldehyde or chloropicrin or in some other effective manner and by soaking the bulbs in a 1 to 50 solution of formalin and water before planting.

Mushroom Root Rot (Armillaria mellea) is known also as Armillaria root rot; as honey Mushroom fungus because of the color of the toadstools it produces, which grow in clumps at the bases of infected trees; and as shoestring fungus, because of the black strands of mycelium which grow out from infected roots. It is common throughout North America on many kinds of evergreen and leaf-losing (deciduous) trees and shrubs. In the West, on land recently cleared of Oaks, it has been very destructive to Citrus and other fruit trees. This fungus causes the roots to decay, with consequent dwarfing and premature dropping of the foliage and general loss of vigor of infected plants. A similar root rot (Clitocybe tabescens) is equally destructive in Florida to Citrus trees and a great variety of ornamental trees and shrubs.

The toadstools should be removed promptly. Individual trees may be aided by excavating around the root crown and removing diseased parts of the bark and roots. Paint all wounds with a solution made of one 7-grain tablet of mercuric chloride dissolved in a mixture of 1½ cups of water and ½ cup of denatured alcohol. This mixture should not be put in a metal container. Leave the treated parts exposed until cold weather.

Disinfecting the soil with carbon bisulphide is

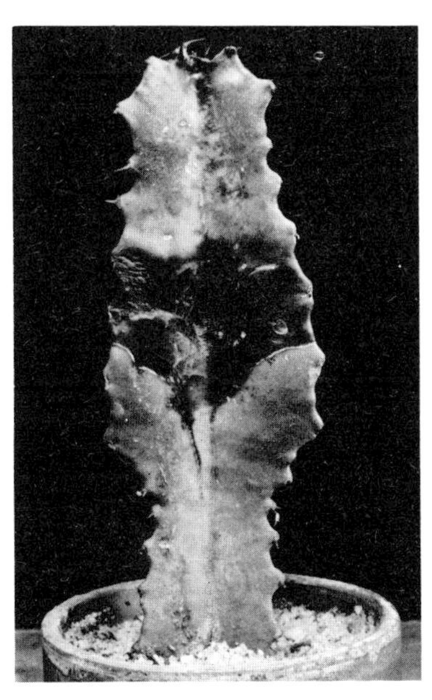
Stem rot infection of Euphorbia.

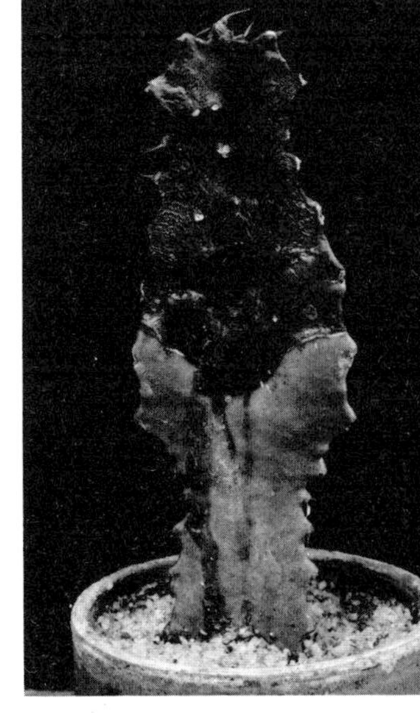
The same Euphorbia one week later.

Toadstools of Mushroom root rot disease in characteristic clumps near the base of a tree.

recommended before replanting where plants have died of the disease. Holes 6 to 7 in. deep and 18 in. apart are made. Into each are injected 2 oz. by weight of carbon bisulphide and the holes are closed immediately with soil. After 60 days the land may be prepared for planting.

Narcissus Basal Rot (Fusarium oxysporum Narcissi). This is a common fungus disease of Narcissi. It causes the interiors of the bulbs to degenerate into a spongy brown or purplish-brown mass. The rot begins at the base of the bulbs and gradually spreads upwards and inwards. Growth from infected bulbs is stunted and poor, or there is none at all.

Only sound bulbs should be planted. Dusting the bulbs with Arasan or Spergon before planting is helpful. Dipping the bulbs before planting in formaldehyde, 1 to 100 dilution, is also recommended.

Pea Root Rot (Aphanomyces). This fungus disease destroys the roots and lower stems of Peas, Sweet Peas and perennial Peas (Lathyrus latifolius). Plants infected while young wilt and die, older specimens that become infected grow poorly and their foliage gradually dries from the base of the plant upwards. Poor drainage and excessive moisture are the causal conditions. The application of a nitrogenous fertilizer reduces the occurrence of this disease.

Phytophthora Root Rots or Stem Rots (various varieties of Phytophthora Cactorum). These fungi cause root and stem rots of Marigolds, Peonies, Rhododendrons, Tomatoes, Tulips, Zinnias and a great variety of other plants, as well as collar rots of Apples, Dogwoods, Walnuts, Pears and other trees.

Whenever possible, avoid planting susceptible plants on land infested with the fungus or sterilize the soil before planting. Prune out all affected parts. Spray repeatedly with Bordeaux mixture.

Soft Rot (Pectobacterium carotovorum). This is a serious bacterial disease of Irises and of a number of other ornamentals. It also attacks many vegetables both in the garden and in storage, causing an evil-smelling slimy, wet rot. The bacteria enter through wounds and a wet rot quickly follows, especially where there is poor ventilation.

This is the most serious disease of rhizome-forming Irises. It causes the leaves to turn yellow and wither, and reduces the rhizomes to a soft pulp. Affected rhizomes should be cut off and burned. Deep planting and damp shady sites should be avoided.

Cut surfaces should be dusted with a copper-lime dust. It is a good plan to lift and divide Irises every 3-4 years. At that time cut out all rotted portions and soak the parts to be replanted in a 1 to 1,000 mercuric chloride solution (1 tablet to 1 pint of water) for 30 minutes; allow them to dry in the sun for a day or two before replanting. Clean all old foliage away in fall. Do everything possible to control the Iris borer, which spreads this disease. Store vegetables in a cool, well-ventilated place.

Stem Rot and Leaf Rot (Sclerotinia sclerotiorum). Many vegetables and garden flowers, including Aconites, Beans, Calendulas, Celery, Chrysanthemums, Dahlias, Delphiniums, Lettuce, Lilacs, Peonies, Peppers, Snapdragons, Tomatoes and Zinnias, are subject to this fungus. It causes a wet or cottony rot of the stems and shows as a white cottony mold in which are embedded the black sclerotia (fungus reproductive bodies), which range up to the size of peas and vary in shape.

Cut out and burn affected parts. Dust with sulphur. Practice crop rotation.

[53]
Cabbage eaten by Caterpillars

[54]
Grapes damaged by Yellow Jacket Wasps

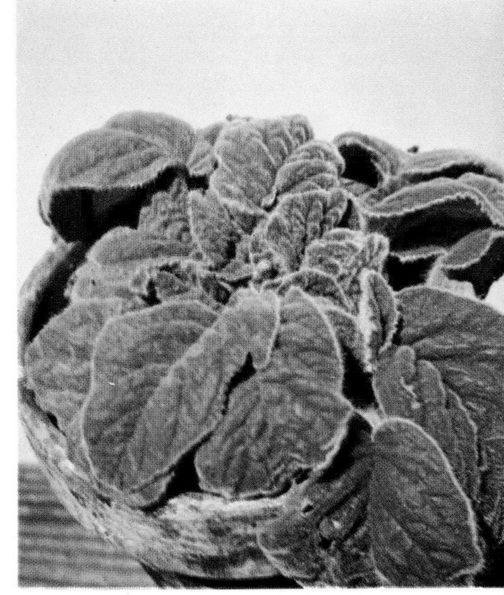

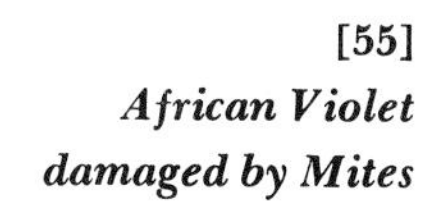

[55]
African Violet damaged by Mites

[56]
Damage caused by Cooley Spruce Gall Aphid

[57]
Injury by Lacebugs on Pieris

[58]
Yew foliage eaten by Black Vine Weevil

[59]
Broccoli affected by Club Root Disease

[60]
Roots of Broccoli contorted by Club Root Disease

Strawberry Red Stele Disease (Phytophthora Fragariae). This fungus invades and destroys the roots of Strawberries. Symptoms are the drying up of the previous year's leaves and the production of undersized, short-stalked leaves of bluish appearance in spring instead of normal large, healthy, green ones. Little fruit is produced and the plants are likely to die in dry weather.

Cold, wet soils favor the development of this disease. Do not plant Strawberries for at least four years on land where infected plants have been cultivated. Only purchase plants that are certified as disease free. Check with your State Agricultural Experiment Station about resistant varieties.

Tulip Gray Bulb Rot (Rhizocotonia Tuliparum). This fungus rots the bulbs and as a result bare patches appear in plantings of Tulips where foliage and flowers should be. Masses of felt-like mycelium (fungous growth) are to be found between the scales of the bulbs.

In soil in which infected bulbs have been growing, new bulbs should not be planted for at least 3 years after the old bulbs are removed unless the soil is first sterilized with formaldehyde.

Wood Rots. Some fungi are very destructive to trees. They infect the trunks and branches and are commonly known as heartwood rots and sapwood rots. These fungi are mostly species of Fomes and Polyporus and are commonly known as bracket fungi because of the large, bracket-like fruiting bodies (toadstools) which develop from affected trunks and branches. The brackets of Fomes continue to increase in size and last for years; those of Polyporus rarely last more than one season.

Wood rot fungi enter the living tissues through unprotected wounds left by bad pruning, storm damage and damage to the bark by various causes. The best prevention is to keep trees in vigorous condition by feeding and watering, careful pruning and prompt removal of dead wood. The protection of exposed wood surfaces with tree-wound paint is a good measure.

Rusts. Gardeners sometimes misapply the term rust by using it to describe reddish or rusty appearances of foliage not caused by rust fungi; for example, Bean anthracnose disease is sometimes called Bean rust. Properly applied, the term rusts refers to a well-defined group of microscopic fungi which live all over the world and are parasitic on a great variety of plants. Some do very great damage to crops. The most famous example of these is the stem rust of grains and grasses, or Wheat stem rust, as it is often called. The white rusts are distinct; see White Rusts, below.

There are many different species of rusts, all very similar in general character. They are remarkable in that they form different kinds of spores at different stages in their life history, and frequently the different spore forms grow on different host plants.

Rust fungi are not able to live except as parasites on living plants and are usually restricted to one, or to a few, species of plants.

Rusts have been familiar from the earliest times. The Romans held the festival of Robigalia on April 25th to propitiate the rust god Robigus. Theophrastus (307 B.C.) said Barley was most susceptible, and the rust was most severe on lands which were low-lying and sheltered.

There were, of course, no clear ideas of the true nature of rusts until recent times. A writer in 1620 suggested that the dew which supposedly brought the rust should be warded off by covering fields with a cloud of smoke. The agriculturist Jethro Tull thought in 1773 that Wheat rust was insect excreta.

In spite of ignorance, it is remarkable that as early as 1660 the growth of Wheat stem rust on Barberry bushes in the spring was realized to be connected with its occurrence on cereals in the summer. Laws were passed in several countries in the seventeenth and eighteenth centuries (in 1600 in France, in 1726 in Connecticut, in 1755 in Massachusetts), making compulsory the eradication of the Barberry near fields of grain. The Italian scientist Fontana first proved a rust was a fungus in 1767.

The life story of the stem rust of grains and grasses (Wheat stem rust) may be briefly described to illustrate that of rusts in general. On the underside of Barberry leaves in spring, bright orange cluster cups appear, which contain spring spores or aeciospores. These cannot reinfect Barberry leaves but grow readily on certain grasses and cereals. In early summer small specks, which soon become yellow or orange masses of spores, appear on the leaves of infected grasses and cereals. These summer spores or urediospores are produced in enormous quantities and they infect other cereal and grass plants and so spread the disease in summer. The urediospores cannot infect Barberry, which is free from rust.

At the end of the summer another kind of spore is developed which causes black streaks and spots to appear on infected plants. These are winter spores or teliospores. Many teliospores are left in the stubble after harvest and many other spores fall on the ground. The winter spores are very thick-walled and adapted to resist extreme conditions. They are, in fact, able to germinate only after exposure to frost. Germination takes place in the spring to form minute spores (basidiospores) which infect young Barberry leaves; they cannot infect grass or cereal leaves. The cycle is now complete.

There are two important points to note in this life history. The alternate host, the Barberry, is essential where the summer spores are unable to survive the winter; therefore destruction of the Barberry would eliminate the stem rust of grains and grasses (Wheat stem rust). The second point is that the seriousness of an epidemic is governed by the production of summer spores. If these are produced in large quantities the epidemic will be bad. This is to a large extent governed by the weather, which also determines how long the summer spores will survive.

In southern Texas, Mexico and some other warm regions the summer type of spores is produced throughout the winter. Because of this, the rust disease can persist even though the alternate host, the Barberry, does not grow nearby. It is possible for infections to start in northern states from summer spores arriving from the South.

When eradication of the alternate host is ineffective, or impracticable, the control measures available for combatting rust diseases are spraying or dusting and the growing of resistant varieties. Rust spores are long-lived and difficult to kill. Because of this and because the main fungous body grows inside the host plant, spraying or dusting has to be repeated many times and success is rarely complete.

Sulphur sprays and dusts are fairly effective in controling many rust diseases; success is reported in some instances from the use of ferbam and of zineb. In some cases prompt destruction of infected plants is the only wise course.

Of the many rust diseases that affect plants the following are most likely to trouble the gardener:

Asparagus Rust (Puccinia Asparagi). This serious fungus disease is common wherever susceptible varieties of Asparagus are grown. Affected plants are weakened and after a few years fail to produce shoots of culinary quality or may even be killed. The rust disease causes the stems and leaves to assume a reddish or brownish appearance and, when these are brushed against or similarly disturbed, a dust-like cloud of spores arises from them. This rust has only one host, the Asparagus. The rust winters over as teliospores on old shoots.

The best preventative is the planting of resistant varieties, such as Mary Washington and Martha Washington. It is important to destroy all chance seedlings of Asparagus that spring up in or near Asparagus beds. Spraying with zineb and dusting with sulphur give some control.

Bean Rust (Uromyces Phaseoli typica). This is common on Snap Beans, especially Kentucky Wonder Pole Bean. The reddish-brown spore pustules occur in groups on leaves (especially the undersides), stems and pods, and may be numerous enough to cause premature loss of foliage and consequent reduction in crop yield. This disease is quite distinct from Bean anthracnose, which is often wrongly called rust.

Dusting with sulphur checks the spread of this disease. Varieties that are somewhat resistant to this disease are offered in seedsmen's catalogues.

Beet Rust (Uromyces Betae). This is common on Beets, Sugar Beets and Swiss Chard but rarely does serious harm.

Destruction of badly diseased plants usually gives adequate control; spraying or dusting is rarely worth while, although a dust composed of ferbam and sulphur is effective.

Blackberry Orange Rust (Gymnoconia Peckiana). This fungus disease of Blackberries, Black Raspberries and Dewberries is serious only when control measures are neglected. The symptoms are that the undersides of the leaves are covered in spring with orange-colored pustules, which discharge numerous spores. These spores spread the disease to other plants.

Diseased plants should be dug promptly and burned because the fungus lives in all parts of the plant and no infected plant ever recovers. Wild Blackberries are likely to harbor the disease; any in the vicinity of garden plantings should be destroyed. Blackberry varieties Eldorado and Snyder are resistant to Orange rust disease.

Carnation Rust (Uromyces Caryophyllinus). This fungus disease of Carnations, Sweet Williams and other kinds of Dianthus is very troublesome on Carnations grown in greenhouses. In greenhouses the summer-type spores persist all the year round. Both summer and winter spores are chocolate brown and occur on both sides of the leaves and on the buds and stems.

The best control measures are the selection of resistant varieties, good cultivation and adequate ventilation. Spraying or dusting with ferbam or sulphur also helps.

Cedar-Apple Rust (Gymnosporangium Juniperi-virginianae). This serious disease infects Red Cedar (Juniperus virginiana) and sometimes other Junipers, including Juniperus horizontalis and Juniperus scopulorum. Its alternate hosts are Apples and Crab Apples. Serious harm is not usually done to the Junipers but great damage may result to the alternate hosts. Bechtel's Crab is notoriously susceptible. Oriental species of Crab Apples are resistant. Closely related diseases, which also affect Junipers, are Hawthorn rust and Quince rust, both described below.

A gall of the Cedar-Apple rust disease, showing the characteristic protruding horns.

On the Junipers galls are produced. These are more or less rounded growths that vary in size from very small up to about 2 in. in diameter. The galls at first are green; later they become chocolate brown and at maturity in spring are covered with conspicuous, protruding orange-colored gelatinous horns from which spores are released. These spores are carried by the wind; if they alight on the foliage of Apples or Crab Apples they infect these hosts and soon produce on the upper surfaces of the leaves yellow spots which become orange-red, with a circle of black dots in the center of each. On the under leaf surfaces, circles of tiny brown cup-shaped bodies appear. Loss of foliage may take place and often the fruits of Apples and Crab Apples are deformed or dwarfed. In late summer spores formed on the alternate hosts are blown back to the Junipers and reinfect them.

The best control is had by taking care that Red Cedars and other susceptible Junipers are not planted within several hundred yards of Apples or Crab Apples. The galls should be picked off the Junipers before they develop horns in the spring. Effective measures are: spraying Junipers with wettable sulphur in early spring, and Apples and the alternate hosts with a mixture of ferbam and sulphur or with Actidione several times in spring and early summer.

Chrysanthemum Rust (Puccinia Chrysanthemi). This fungus disease of Chrysanthemums is rare on outdoor plantings, much more common in greenhouses. It causes pinhead-sized blisters to form chiefly on the undersides of the leaves but occasionally on their upper surfaces. The blisters burst open when mature and release vast numbers of brown summer-type spores which are the means by which the infection is propagated. Winter-type spores are not produced in America

Underside of a Chrysanthemum leaf infected with rust disease.

although they are in Japan, but summer-type spores live over the winter successfully in greenhouses.

The best control is had by avoiding syringing (which distributes the spores from plant to plant), spacing the plants so that air circulates freely between them and prevents the foliage from lying wet for long periods, avoiding wetting the leaves unnecessarily, and cutting off and destroying all stems and foliage as soon as flowering is through. Spraying with ferbam and dusting with sulphur are also helpful in reducing the damage done by this disease.

Hawthorn Rust (Gymnosporangium globosum). This produces effects similar to those of the Cedar-Apple Rust (which see, above) but the galls produced on the Red Cedar (Juniperus virginiana) and other Junipers it affects are smaller, rarely more than ½ in. in diameter, and of a more mahogany-red color. The alternate host is most usually Hawthorn, but Apples, Crab Apples, Mountain Ash and Pears may also be infected.

Orange-brown pustules of Hollyhock rust on the underside of a leaf.

Control measures are the same as for Cedar-Apple Rust.

Hollyhock Rust (Puccinia Malvacearum). This disease is common and troublesome and seriously limits the cultivation of Hollyhocks; it also attacks Mallows and Lavateria. It produces only one kind of spore, the winter-type spore, which is formed from April to November.

This disease shows itself as small, pinhead-sized, orange-brown (or sometimes gray) spots on the undersides of the leaves and as rather larger spots of yellow or orange color with brown centers on the upper sides; it also occurs as spots on the bracts and as elongated lesions on the stems. In severe cases the spots run together to form larger discolored areas and the leaves may dry and droop on the stems. The fungus winters over on old leaves and stems.

In fall, clean up and burn all old stems and leaves and any green leaves that show infection. In spring, as soon as new leaves show, begin spraying or dusting with sulphur or zineb (Parzate or Dithane Z 78) and repeat this every 7-10 days until the flowers open. Repeat this treatment throughout the late summer and fall.

Mint Rust (Puccinia Menthae). This is a common and troublesome disease. It affects Mint and a number of botanically related plants, including Bee Balm, Dittany and Germander. All spore forms occur on Mint but only the winter spores survive the winter. Symptoms of infection are yellow or brown raised spots that appear in spring on deformed stems and leafstalks, and golden-yellow to chocolate-colored spots which are in evidence in late summer and fall.

The best method of control is to establish a new bed with healthy roots; if possible, a resistant strain of Mint should be obtained. Dusting with sulphur gives some control.

Quince Rust (Gymnosporangium clavipes). This produces on Red Cedar (Juniperus virginiana) and certain other Junipers slight swellings of the twigs and branches and often causes the death of infected twigs. Black, rough patches

Rose leaf rust disease is especially prevalent on the Pacific Coast in the Southwest.

mark infected areas on the trunks. On the alternate hosts, which are Amelanchiers, Apples, Chokeberry, Crab Apples, Hawthorns, Mountain Ash, Quinces and Pears, distortion of the fruits, twigs and buds is apparent. Premature leaf dropping often occurs. On English Hawthorn the disease is especially conspicuous; the fruits are covered with bright orange spore clusters surrounded by long white projections.

The only reliable control is to make sure that susceptible Junipers are not permitted to grow within several hundred yards of plants of the alternate hosts.

Rose Leaf Rust (Phragmidium disciflorum). This is more prevalent on the Pacific Coast and in the Southwest than in the East. In spring tiny spots appear; these are yellow on the upper leaf surface and bright orange on the lower leaf surface. In its summer stage reddish-orange spores occur in small spots on the undersides of the leaves. The spores germinate and infection occurs only when the leaves are constantly wet for a few hours.

Spraying or dusting with ferbam or zineb is the best control, but neither is completely reliable.

Snapdragon Rust (Puccinia Antirrhini). The pustules of this disease are dark brown and appear on the undersides of the leaves and on the stems. This disease is less troublesome than it was before the introduction of rust-resistant strains of Snapdragons.

The selection of rust-resistant varieties is the best control. Spraying with zineb is recommended if the disease appears.

White Pine Blister Rust (Cronartium ribicola). This most destructive disease of certain Pines needs Currants or Gooseberries as alternate host plants. It affects White Pine (Pinus Strobus), Western White Pine (P. monticola) and Sugar Pine (P. Lambertiana). On the Pines it first shows as small golden-yellow or reddish-brown spots on the leaves. Within a year or two of infection the bark assumes a yellowish appearance and blisters, exuding a sweetish, yellowish liquid. Later, pustules of orange-yellow spores develop on the bark; after the spores from these are freed and have blown away, the bark dries, cracks and dies. The wood beneath also dies. When the wood is killed or severely damaged, the foliage dies and remains hanging on the trees as red-brown "flags."

The spores produced by fungus on Pines cannot infect other Pines; instead, they develop on Currants and Gooseberries (species of Ribes). Infected Ribes bear clusters of tiny blisters on areas of the leaf turned yellow as a result of the infection. These blisters break and discharge summer-type spores, which infect other Ribes, and this process is repeated several times. At the end of summer, winter-type spores are produced on the Ribes; these cannot infect other Ribes, but if they are blown onto the leaves of susceptible Pines infection of the Pines will result.

Because alternate hosts are necessary for the survival of this fungus, the elimination of one or the other of the hosts gives most effective control. In practice the Ribes host is the one ordinarily eliminated. Black Currants, being the most susceptible of the Ribes group, should not be grown at all in regions where susceptible kinds of Pines occur, and Red Currants, White Currants and Gooseberries should not be planted within 300 or more feet (depending upon state regulations) of such Pines. Wild Gooseberries and wild Currants should be eliminated from the neighborhood of susceptible Pines.

Cankers on valuable trees should be cut out

and the area painted with Acti-dione BR, as directed by the manufacturer.

Scabs. Scab diseases are those that show on leaves, tubers, fruits or other parts as more or less corky spots consisting of an overgrowth of the plant tissues. Many different kinds of plants are affected by scab diseases. Sulphur, Bordeaux mixture and carbamate fungicides are used in control.

Apple Scab (Venturia inaequalis). This is the commonest and most destructive fungus disease of Apples in the northern states. In the South it is of less importance. Unless it is controlled the fruit is rendered nearly worthless and the foliage may be injured sufficiently to devitalize the trees and make them susceptible to winter injury as well as likely to bear only light crops or no crops at all. The Apple scab fungus also infects Crab Apples, Hawthorns and Mountain Ash. A closely related fungus attacks Pears (see Pear Scab, below).

Apple scab lesions on the leaves are circular, olive-colored spots that are without well-defined margins. The spots may increase in size and join each other until much of the leaf is involved. Similar spots occur on the fruits, appearing first near the calyx ends. In years that are favorable to the development of scab fungus—that is to say, in wet seasons—enough lesions occur to cause cracking of the fruit. Premature dropping of leaves and young fruits often accompanies severe infections.

Satisfactory control of Apple scab is usually possible with the use of sulphur sprays, but they must be applied at the right times and coverage must be thorough. Because the spray schedule for this disease must be varied for different localities and seasons, it is important to seek the advice of the local County Agricultural Agent or the State Agricultural Experiment Station with regard to the number and timing of the spray applications. In wet seasons 12 or more applications may be needed, in dry seasons not less than 5. In addition to sulphur sprays, dinitro compounds, ferbam, Phygon, Bordeaux mixture and Puratized Agricultural Spray are used to control Apple scab.

Citrus Scab (Elsinoe Fawcettii). Common on all Citrus fruits except the Sweet Orange, this fungus disease produces spores which are spread mostly by wind and rain. They infect the young tender shoots and fruits. As a result of infection the foliage may be distorted and stunted and bear slightly raised scabs with corky crests which at first are light yellow or pinkish and later a greenish drab color. On the fruits, raised corky scabs are formed, and these may join together to form patches of considerable size. The fruits are often distorted and stunted.

Spraying with Bordeaux mixture or other copper spray just before spring growth starts and again when most of the blossoms have fallen is the best control.

Gladiolus Scab (Pseudomonas marginata). This is a widespread bacterial disease of Gladioli. On the corms (bulbs) it shows as water-soaked circular spots which change from pale yellow to dark brown and in time become sunken, with raised, hard margins. These lesions may exude a sticky sap. On the leaves the same disease appears as tiny reddish spots which amalgamate into large areas and appear rotted. The bacteria overwinter on the corms.

To gain control, dip the corms for 1 minute in a calomel solution (3 oz. in 1 gallon of water) or dust the corms with Arasan.

Peach Scab (Cladosporium carpophilum). This fungus produces small, round olive-black spots on the fruits about 6 weeks after the petals fall; if the spots are numerous, the fruits may crack. The leaves are marred by brown spots from which the tissue falls out, leaving slot holes. On the twigs, which may be killed by the disease, circular yellowish spots with bluish borders appear. The disease affects Peaches, Almonds, Apricots, Cherries, Nectarines and Plums.

Control is obtained by using the sprays recommended for the control of brown rot disease. See under Rots, above.

Pear Scab (Venturia Pyrina). This fungus disease produces dark moldy patches on the fruit and leaves of Pears and Quinces. Loss of foliage occurs, which reduces the vigor of affected trees. Scabby fruits are undesirable. The Pear varieties Flemish Beauty, Winter Nelis and Easter Beurre are very susceptible to scab; occasionally other varieties are troubled. Pear scab is very closely related to Apple scab but does not attack Apples; neither does Apple scab attack Pears.

(Left) Pear fruit blackened and split by scab disease. *(Right)* The flowers of Pear at the petal-fall stage, which is an important time in the spray schedule.

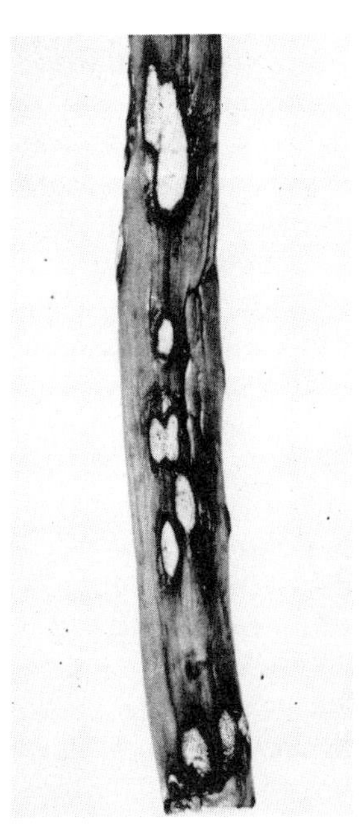

The stem of a Poinsettia showing marked symptoms of scab disease.

Sulphur sprays are effective in controlling Pear scab.

Potato Scab (Streptomyces scabies). This common Potato disease often causes heavy market losses. It is widespread also on Beets and may affect other root vegetables. On Potatoes the lesions (scabs) on the tubers are first seen as tiny brown spots. These grow into warty or corky growths which may be depressed or raised and may crack open. On Beets the lesions are more bulging but otherwise similar.

As a control measure, Potato sets may be dipped for 2 hours in a solution of 1 pint of formalin to 30 gallons of water, but it is better to plant disease-free sets if these are procurable. Avoid the use of lime, fresh manure and wood ashes on the Potato plot because these increase soil alkalinity and this favors scab disease.

Violet Scab (Sphaceloma Violae). This serious disease of Violets and Pansies causes the leaves and stems to be marred by white-centered, reddish spots which later become irregular raised scabby lesions. The foliage may be markedly distorted.

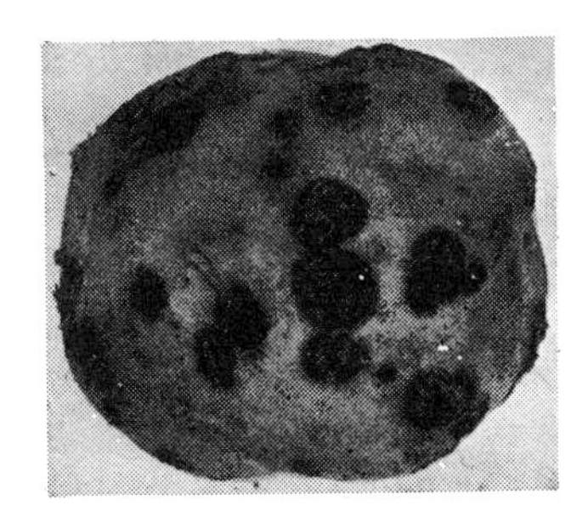

A Potato tuber infected with scab disease.

The best methods of control are the prompt picking off and burning of affected leaves and repeated spraying with Bordeaux mixture or ferbam.

Scurf (Monilochaetes infuscans). This fungus disease of Sweet Potato is also sometimes called soil stain. It causes the tubers to be marked with brown or nearly black spots or patches, followed by shrinking in storage. This disease affects the tubers in the ground. It does not spread to non-infected tubers in storage. It is more destructive in heavy soils than sandy ones. The fungus persists in affected soil for several years even though no Sweet Potatoes are grown.

Control is had by planting disease-free sprouts. It is advisable to treat the sprouts with ferbam before they are planted.

Smuts. Smut fungi are characterized by the production of masses of black spores. Not many kinds affect garden ornamental plants; most of those that trouble gardeners and farmers are diseases of cereals, grasses and vegetables. The commonest kinds in gardens are the following:

Corn Smut (Ustilago Zeae). This infects all

kinds of Corn and is especially harmful to Sweet Corn. Large boil-like developments appear on the stalks, tassels, husks and ears. These boils are covered with thin, greenish-white skins which rupture, displaying large masses of black or nearly black spores. Affected plants are often distorted. Corn smut thrives in hot weather. Under conditions especially favorable to its development, it may affect every Corn plant in a planting. The disease winters over in soil, manure and on old Corn stalks. The spores retain their ability to grow and infect Corn plants for 5-7 years.

The most important control measure is sanitation. In home gardens it is important to cut off and burn the boils before they break open and discharge their spores. Controlling Corn borers also seems to reduce the danger of infection with Corn smut disease. After harvest, all Corn stalks should be cleaned up and burned.

Onion Smut (Urocystis Cepulae). This disease is much more likely to be troublesome on Onions grown from seeds than on those grown from sets, and in regions where fairly cool summers prevail. The leaves of affected plants are marked with elongated, black spore-bearing pustules; brown or black pustules mar the bulbs. Young plants may be killed and those that survive are likely to be stunted. The fungus spores remain alive in the soil for several years but only very young Onion plants can be infected. After they are about two weeks old (counting from the time the young Onion leaves push through the ground) they are safe from being infected, but Onion plants infected before this time remain infected.

The best control measure is to grow Onions from sets or, if the soil is infected, to sow Onion seeds in disease-free soil and transplant the young plants later. Treating the seed with Arasan is recommended.

White Rusts. These are distinct from true rusts. They are characterized by whitish blisters just beneath the outer skin or epidermis of the plant attacked. There are no practical controls other than the prompt removal of affected parts, the destruction of badly infected plants and, in some cases, changing the location of new plantings that are made the following year.

Beet White Rust (Albugo Bliti). This causes the appearance of small blisters, which at first are white but later turn brown, on Beets, Amaranths and Globe Amaranths. Distortion of stems and flowers occurs. Do not use seed from infected plants because the fungus winters on the seeds.

Crucifer White Rust (Albugo candida). This fungus affects Arabis, Cabbages, Candytufts, Drabas, Horse-Radish, Mustard, Radishes, Stocks, Sweet Alyssum, Water Cress, Wallflowers and other members of the botanical family Cruciferae. It produces blisters of varying size on leaves, stems and flowers and swellings on the stems as well as considerable deformation of the stems and other parts.

Portulaca White Rust (Albugo Portulacae). This disease of Portulaca produces small blisters and deformed and thickened stems.

Salsify White Rust (Albugo Tragopogonis). A common trouble of Salsify, this disease also affects a number of other plants in the Daisy family, the Compositae, including Antennarias, Artemisias, Centaureas, Chrysanthemums, Matricarias, Senecios and Sunflowers. Pale yellow areas appear on the leaves, and then raised white blisters. Affected plants are often stunted.

Spinach White Rust (Albugo occidentalis). Small white blisters appear on the leaves of Spinach, chiefly on their undersides.

Sweet Potato White Rust (Albugo Ipomoeae-panduratae). A common disease of Sweet Potatoes, this also affects Morning Glories, Moonflowers and botanically related plants. White blisters are produced on the undersides of the leaves and irregular, yellowish areas on the upper surfaces.

Wilts. Wilting, or "flagging," as gardeners sometimes call it, means that a plant becomes flaccid and droops as the result of an excessive loss of moisture from the tissues. Only the softer parts of plants, such as leaves and petals, wilt; firmer tissues, such as woody stems, dry or shrivel when deprived of moisture.

Wilting may occur because there is not sufficient water in the soil or because the plants, even though healthy and with sound root systems, are not able to take up enough moisture to replace that lost by transpiration from their above-ground parts. Plants wilted from these causes normally recover when water is supplied to the soil or when the conditions that cause too-rapid transpiration, such as strong sunshine or wind, are modified, provided the necessary corrections are made before permanent damage is done.

Wilting can also result from mechanical damage to roots that occurs in transplanting, cultivating and similar operations and from damage that results from poor drainage, overwatering, excessive applications of fertilizer and similar causes (see Physiological Diseases, below).

In addition to the above, many fungus, bacterial and virus infections cause plants to wilt. The term "wilt disease," however, is usually reserved for a specific group of diseases that produce no visible, external decay of the host plants; the major symptom is permanent wilting, often accompanied by a change of foliage color.

The organisms causing wilt diseases normally affect the roots or the water-conducting tissues of the stems. They are difficult to control effectively.

Aster Wilt (Fusarium oxysporum Callistephi). As a result of this fungus disease, China Asters quickly wilt and die. If they are first infected when nearly full grown, their flower heads may droop suddenly. Older plants are sometimes stunted and one-sided.

The best control is obtained by planting wilt-resistant strains of seed and by promptly uprooting and destroying every affected plant.

Cabbage Yellows or Fusarium Wilt (Fusarium oxysporum conglutinans). This is a common and serious disease of Cabbage, Collards and Kohlrabi and also infects Brussels Sprouts, Broccoli and Cauliflower. The symptoms are stunting, dull yellowish-green foliage, distortion and dropping of the lower leaves and a dark, water-soaked appearance of the woody stem tissues.

The only control is to avoid, for several years, planting susceptible plants in soil that has been infected. Resistant varieties are available and should be selected for planting.

Carnation Bacterial Wilt (Pseudomonas Caryophylli). This disease is more likely to be found in greenhouses than outdoors. Infected plants become grayish, wilt, turn yellow and die. The roots die and diseased tissue is sticky, which distinguishes this disease from the fungus-produced Fusarium wilt disease.

To secure control, destroy infected plants. Take cuttings only from healthy ones. If diseased plants have been near apparently healthy ones from which cuttings are taken, place the cuttings in a solution of potassium permanganate (1 oz. to 5 gallons of water) for about 20 minutes, then set them in sterilized sand.

Carnation Fusarium Wilt (Fusarium oxysporum Dianthi). Carnations infected with this disease are likely to wilt, especially during the heat of the day; their foliage becomes pale green or yellow and withers, and the plants are stunted. Part only of an infected plant may show the symptoms or the entire plant may be infected. Brownish streaks mark the insides of the stems.

Control measures consist of using only disease-free plants for propagating purposes, the prompt destruction of diseased plants and the sterilization of the soil.

Celery Wilt or Yellows (Fusarium oxysporum Apii). This fungus disease causes yellowness of the foliage, stunting and the development of a bitter taste in Celery.

Control measures consist of planting resistant varieties and rotating the crop so that it is not planted on the same ground oftener than once every 4-5 years.

Corn Wilt or Stewart's Disease (Bacterium Stewartii). This is chiefly a disease of Sweet Corn. The bacteria that cause it are spread by flea beetles and by infected seeds and, occasionally, by infected soil. Affected plants are stunted, the stems become brown at the nodes, streaks appear on the leaves and the plants wilt and die. This disease is most prevalent after mild winters.

The best control measure is to plant resistant varieties. Golden Bantam is particularly susceptible.

Cucurbit Wilt (Erwinia tracheiphila). This is often serious on Cucumbers and Muskmelons, less so on Pumpkins and Squash. The bacteria that cause it winter inside Cucumber beetles and the plants are infected as a result of the beetles' feeding and through the stomata (pores) in the leaves. The foliage develops dull, soft patches and sudden wilting of the leaves follows. Viscous material oozes from cut or broken stems.

Control may be had by protecting the plants from infestation by Cucumber beetles, by keeping the plants covered with hotkaps or fine wire screening in their early stages and by dusting repeatedly later with rotenone.

Dutch Elm Disease (Ceratocystis Ulmi). This devastating disease has killed thousands of elms in the eastern and central United States since 1930. Trees may suddenly show all-over wilting of the foliage in early summer, or a branch or two only with yellowing leaves may indicate infection. When infection by the disease is rapid the leaves wither and fall while still green; in other cases deterioration is more gradual. The disease organisms cause a dark discoloration of the water-conducting tissues of the sapwood.

Only by laboratory diagnosis can this disease be distinguished from Elm Dothiorella wilt and verticillium wilt diseases, which see below. Bark beetles spread the disease; it is also transmitted by natural root grafts when trees grow close to each other.

Dead trees and limbs should be removed and burned in spring before the beetles emerge. Trees should be given every care in such cultural matters as fertilizing, watering and spraying to control bark beetles and other insects. Spray with a dormant-strength DDT spray before the leaves extend and with a regular-strength DDT spray when the trees are in leaf.

Elm Dothiorella or Cephalosporum Wilt (Deuterophoma Ulmi). Only by laboratory diagnosis can this fungus disease be distinguished from Dutch Elm disease (which see, above). The symptoms are wilting and yellowing of the foliage, gradual dying back of the branches and discoloration of the outer layers of the wood. Trees may die within a few years of infection, may linger longer or may ultimately recover.

Prune out infected branches at least 1 ft. below the point where they exhibit symptoms. Apply a combination insecticide and fungicide to lessen the danger of the infection spreading.

Gladiolus Fusarium Yellows (Fusarium orthoceras Gladioli). When infected with this fungus disease, the foliage of susceptible varieties of Gladioli becomes yellow, turns brown and dies. The centers of the corms (bulbs) develop a brown discoloration. The disease is most destructive in hot, dry seasons.

The best protection is to plant resistant varieties, to rotate plantings of Gladioli so that they are grown in the same place only every 4-5 years and to treat the corms each year with a fungicide.

Oak Wilt (Ceratocystis Fagacearum). This disease has spread rapidly in recent years. Leaves of infected trees first become crinkled and pale in color. This is followed by a browning of the foliage, which spreads inwards from the leaf margins. All kinds of Oaks are susceptible but Red Oaks die most quickly, often within a month or two of infection. White Oaks may survive for several years.

No method of control is known. Diseased trees should be destroyed.

Pea Fusarium Wilt (Fusarium oxysporum Pisi). Infected Pea plants wilt and die sooner than they should, their growth is stunted and their foliage light green in color. Usually the stems are thickened near their bases and the leaves curl downwards.

Control measures consist of planting resistant varieties and of rotating the Pea crops so that they are not planted in the same place oftener than once every 4-5 years.

Sweet Potato Wilt (Fusarium oxysporum Batatas). A serious disease of Sweet Potatoes, this fungus causes the plants to turn yellowish, the leaves to droop and drop and the lower parts of the stems to turn brown or blackish.

Plant Sweet Potatoes in the same place not oftener than once every 3-4 years. Select varieties that are somewhat resistant to the disease. Be sure that propagating stock is free from the disease. Dip cuttings and sprouts in Spergon or ferbam.

Tomato Fusarium Wilt (Fusarium oxysporum Lycopersici). This, one of the most serious of Tomato diseases, affects both plants grown outdoors and those cultivated in greenhouses, with the result that they crop poorly or die. Leaves of young plants first curve downwards and those of older ones turn yellow, often one side of the leaf or one side of the plant being affected before the other. The insides of the stems turn dark brown. Infection is almost entirely from the soil.

The best control is had by rotating the Tomato crops so that they are not grown in the same place oftener than one year in four, by making sure that the seeds are sown and the young plants are grown in uninfected soil and by planting wilt-resistant varieties.

Verticillium Wilt (Verticillium albo-atrum). This wilt is widespread in North America. A wide variety of plants may be affected, including Elms, Maples and other trees and shrubs, fruit trees, Raspberries and other bush fruit, Strawberries, Roses, Eggplants, Tomatoes, Aconites, Chrysanthemums, Dahlias and many other perennials. The symptoms include yellowing and drooping of the leaves from the lower parts of the plant gradually upwards; this is followed by loss of foliage, and the internodes (lengths of stem between successive leaves) are shorter than normal, the plants are stunted and the wood of the stems is discolored internally. Sometimes one side only of a plant is affected.

In Elms it is not possible to distinguish this from Dutch Elm disease (which see, above) without a laboratory diagnosis. When verticillium wilt infects Raspberries it is sometimes known as bluestem disease because it causes broad blue stripes to develop on the sides of the new canes. Infected Strawberries wilt and die about the time that the fruits begin to turn red and ripen.

Verticillium wilt is a soil-borne disease but soil disinfectants do not give effective control. Herbaceous plants that are infected should be immediately destroyed and great care should be taken not to transplant plants from infected to clean soil. Infected branches of trees should be pruned out close to the trunk and burned. Tools used for cutting diseased branches should be sterilized by washing them in denatured alcohol or a 5 per cent formalin solution before they are used on healthy trees. Avoid planting Raspberries, Blackberries or Strawberries on ground that has been planted to those crops or to Potatoes, Tomatoes, Peppers or Eggplants for the preceding 3 years.

Watermelon Wilt (Fusarium oxysporum niveum). Watermelons, Pumpkins, Squash and Cucumbers are affected by this fungus disease, which causes the plants to become yellow and wilt and their stems to show dark streaks.

The only control is to use wilt-resistant varieties. The fungus that causes the disease may remain alive in the soil for nearly twenty years, even though crops that are susceptible to it are not grown in this soil.

VIRUS DISEASES

The nature and causes of plant virus diseases are still imperfectly understood. The infective entities of viruses are known to consist of extremely minute particles, ultra-microscopic and capable of passing through the finest filters. They are infectious and may be transmitted from diseased to healthy plants by budding, grafting or contact with the infected sap, but are mainly spread by sucking insects, known as vectors, which visit healthy plants after having fed on diseased plants. The virus is carried in their saliva.

Virus diseases are systemic and, once present in the sap, pass to all parts of the plant even, in some instances, to the seeds. There is no practical cure. The only remedy lies in the early destruction of infected plants before they become a source of infection to other healthy plants. The symptoms vary according to the virus involved.

When foliage shows a more or less even yellowing and loss of green coloring the disease is called virus yellows. When foliage is mottled more or less evenly with green and yellow the virus causing the condition is called a mosaic virus. Yellow rings on foliage are caused by ringspot viruses. Other common viruses cause distortion of foliage, stunting of growth, warty or gall-like growths and the development of witches'-brooms.

Probably the ultimate solution to the virus problem lies in the breeding of virus-immune plants. At present, however, control lies primarily in the planting of healthy, virus-free stock, good cultivation and control of insect vectors (virus carriers), with the prompt destruction of infected plants.

The common virus diseases encountered in gardens are those described here.

Aster Yellows. This is a common disease of China Asters and of a wide variety of other

Yellowing of the young foliage is a typical symptom of the virus disease called Aster yellows.

plants, including Anemones, Calendulas, Carrots, Coreopsis, Cosmos, Delphiniums, Endive, Marigolds, Parsley, Petunias, Phlox, Scabious, Spinach and Strawflowers. A special strain which occurs in the West also infects Celery and Zinnias. Symptoms of the infection are: yellowing of the young leaves; the appearance of many new side shoots that are stunted, erect and stiffish and of a greenish coloring; dwarfing and distortion of the flowers.

Transmission of Aster yellow virus is most commonly effected by leaf hoppers. Susceptible plants are sometimes grown in special houses made of a stout, cheesecloth-like material called Aster cloth. Aster cloth is woven fine enough to prevent the entry of leaf hoppers.

Bean Viruses. Beans are subject to several virus diseases. Bean mosaic virus 4, which is transmitted through the seeds, causes a yellowish mottling of the foliage, dark green or shiny areas on the pods and some distortion of the pods. Another Bean mosaic virus causes the early leaves to be crinkled, stiff and yellow and later mottled yellow. The edges of the leaves often curl downwards. This virus is transmitted in the seeds and also by aphids.

Bean yellow mosaic virus causes a coarse yellow mottling of the leaves together with stunting, distortion and a great reduction of the crop, the maturing of which is delayed. Bean yellow mosaic virus also infects Clover, Freesias, Gladioli, Peas and Sweet Peas. Sugar Beet curly-top virus (see Beet Viruses, below) also infects Beans.

Beet Viruses. Sugar Beet mosaic virus causes Beets to develop distinct yellowish lesions and yellowish mottling of the foliage and the ends of the leaves to curl backwards. The same virus infects Spinach, with the result that the leaves die from the tips downwards and the young leaves are flecked with yellow. Aphids transmit this virus. The Beet-Savoy virus, transmitted by the tingid bug, causes the roots to die, the leaves to curl downwards and be dwarfed and the small veins of the leaves to thicken. Sugar Beet curly-top virus (which see, below) also infects Beets.

Blueberry Stunt. This virus disease can be serious if uncontrolled. Symptoms are dwarfing of the bushes, brilliant reddening of the leaves in late summer, the reddening appearing first on the margins. The use of virus-free planting stock that has been certified as healthy by a state agricultural inspection service and the prompt removal of diseased plants usually prevent serious losses from stunt.

Carnation Viruses. Carnation mosaic virus and Carnation streak virus, when present together, produce a condition in Carnations called yellows, in which the foliage is conspicuously spotted with yellow. Carnation mosaic virus itself causes the leaves to be mottled with pale green, and colored flowers to be marked with lighter streaks. This virus is transmitted by knives and other tools and in similar contacts made in cultural practices. Symptoms of Carnation streak virus include yellowish or reddish spots and streaks on the foliage and, often, the death of the lower leaves. Sugar Beet curly-top virus (which see, below) also infects Carnations.

Cauliflower Mosaic Virus. This disease affects Broccoli, Brussels Sprouts, Cabbage, Cauliflower and Kale, causing stunting of the plants and a light yellowish mottling of the foliage and some distortion of the leaves. Transmission is by aphids.

Celery Viruses. Celery calico virus causes the leaf veins to lose their coloring, the leaves to be deformed and yellow, and green zigzag bands to mark the leaflets. This disease, which also infects Cucumbers, Delphiniums, Larkspurs, Squash and Tomatoes, is transmitted by aphids.

Celery mosaic virus occurs in the West on Celery, Celeriac and Carrots. It causes yellow mottling, twisting and cupping of the leaves and stunting. Transmission is by aphids. Celery may also be infected with Aster yellows virus (see above) and Sugar Beet curly-top virus (which see, below).

Cherry Viruses. In the West, mottle-leaf disease of Sweet Cherries, which is transmitted by budding, causes the foliage to be puckered and distorted and the fruits to be dwarfed, hard and insipid. Affected trees are stunted.

Cherry vein-clearing virus infects Sweet Cherries in the West and causes the leaf veins to lose their color, the leaves to be narrow and perforated, the upper sides of the leaves to be silvery and the veins on the lower surfaces to be blistered. The leaves wilt and drop, the blossoms are abundant but the fruit crop is reduced. The method of transmission is not known.

Cherry banded-chlorosis virus affects flowering Cherries and the Mazzard Cherry in the Northwest. On the former, yellowish bands surround discolored leaf areas. Mazzard Cherries are dwarfed and the leaves are marked with yellow bands. Transmission is by budding.

Chrysanthemum Viruses. Chrysanthemums are subject to the spotted wilt virus disease (see below). Another serious virus disease of Chrysanthemums is Chrysanthemum stunt, which causes a reduction of the sizes of foliage and flowers, a more upright growth of the shoots, a distinct dwarfing of the plants and a paling of the blooms in pink- and bronze-flowered varieties. Transmission may be by aphids and by handling infected tools and plants.

Citrus Psorosis Virus. This disease is common on Grapefruits, Oranges and Lemons. The young leaves are flecked with longish pale spots and are sometimes distorted. Yellowish patterns are evident on older leaves. The bark becomes deformed and the outer layers flake off. Transmission is by budding and root grafting.

Cranberry False Blossom Virus. This virus causes the fruits of infected plants to be undersized and irregular in appearance. Other symptoms are distortion of the flowers so that they are erect instead of drooping, abnormally formed stamens and pistils, short petals marked with red and green streaks, and enlarged calyx lobes. Lateral growth of much-crowded erect shoots form characteristic witches'-brooms. This virus is transmitted by the blunt-nosed Cranberry leaf hopper. Control measures consist of planting resistant varieties and, to kill the leaf hoppers, dusting with pyrethrum and flooding the Cranberry bogs with water late in June.

Cucumber Viruses. The principal virus disease affecting Cucumbers (also Squash, Melons and many other plants) is Cucumber mosaic. Infected plants of Cucumbers, Squash and Melons show a yellow mottling of the foliage; the leaves are distorted and smaller than normal, the plants are dwarfed and the fruits are mottled and deformed. Transmission is by aphids. Some varieties of susceptible plants are resistant to this disease and are listed as resistant in seedsmen's catalogues.

Other viruses that affect Cucumbers include Celery calico virus (see Celery Viruses, above) and Sugar Beet curly-top virus (which see, below).

Dahlia Viruses. A characteristic symptom of Dahlia mosaic virus disease is mottling of the foliage. The mottling is inconspicuous in varieties that are tolerant to the disease, but intolerant varieties yellow. This symptom is accompanied by distortion of the foliage and dwarfing of the plants. Transmission is by aphids. Dahlias are also susceptible to spotted wilt virus (which see, below).

Dahlia mosaic virus disease is also known as Dahlia stunt disease.

The Dahlia mosaic virus causes a mottling and distortion of the foliage and dwarfing or stunting of the plant.

Elm Phloem Necrosis. This virus disease has killed a great many American Elms in several central states. Trees may wilt and die within a few weeks or linger for a year or more. When the bark is scraped off, the wood beneath shows a butterscotch yellow color and there is an odor of wintergreen. The virus is spread by leaf hoppers.

Gladiolus Viruses. A most serious condition that affects Gladioli is the Gladiolus white-break mosaic disease. It causes the leaves to be streaked or spotted much as if they were infested with thrips. On the flowers yellowish green or grayish spots develop and sometimes the flowers are paler in color than is normal. The corms (bulbs) are likely to be deformed. Although this condition is believed to be caused by a virus, this has not been absolutely proved.

Gladioli may also be infected with the Bean yellow mosaic virus disease. This causes the flowers to be flecked or striped and the young leaves to be mottled. It is advisable not to plant Gladioli near Beans.

Grape Virus. The virus known as Pierce's Disease is widely distributed and may be very destructive to varieties of the European Grapes. It causes leaf mottling and dwarfing of the new shoots in early summer and drying of the leaves, premature coloring of the fruit and uneven maturity of the canes. Diseased vines soon die. Transmission is caused by grafting and by leaf hoppers.

Iris Virus. The Iris mosaic virus disease affects bulbous Irises and also Babianas. It causes a yellow mottling of the foliage and dwarfing of the plants. Transmission is by aphids.

Lettuce Viruses. Lettuce mosaic virus causes the leaves to lose color along their veins and yellow mottling to appear on the foliage. Sometimes the margins of the leaves are scorched in appearance and the centers of the plants are distorted. Transmission is by aphids and by seeds. In addition Lettuce may be infected with spotted wilt virus disease (which see, below).

Lily Viruses. Latent mosaic virus disease of Lilies affects nearly all kinds of Lilies and also Tulips. In the latter the foliage is mottled with yellowish markings and the flowers, according to variety, either lose some of their color or have their color intensified. Lilies may show yellowish mottling, or show no very evident symptoms and yet have the disease (and thus be unsuspected sources of infection to other plants). Transmission of the disease is by aphids.

Lily rosette or yellow flat virus disease affects Lilium longiflorum and causes the plants to be dwarfed, the leaves to curl downwards and to be yellowish and the plants to die down earlier than normal.

Lily symptomless virus disease affects Lilium longiflorum but shows no symptoms unless Cucumber mosaic virus is also present, in which case small dead flecks mark the plants. Lily symptomless virus is transmitted by aphids.

Cucumber mosaic virus infects Lilies and produces a marked yellowish mottling of the foliage.

Loganberry Virus. The disease of Loganberries called Loganberry dwarf virus occurs in the West and causes the new canes to be short and thin and the leaves small. The leaves may be crinkled and killed along the veins, and the finer veins may be yellow. The fruits do not ripen uniformly, and easily fall apart. Transmission is by aphids.

Narcissus Viruses. A virus known as Narcissus mosaic, yellow stripe and gray disease causes infected plants to be dwarfed and the flowers to be small, of poor quality and often streaked. The foliage is marked with streaks of yellow, light green or grayish coloring. Transmission is by aphids.

Narcissus white streak disease is caused by a virus which shows its presence by narrow, dark green streaks in the leaves. These streaks become white, yellowish or gray after the blooming season. The plants die down and go dormant earlier than usual.

Onion Virus. The yellow-dwarf virus of Onions causes flattening, yellowing and crinkling of the young leaves and a general dwarfing of the plants. The virus is transmitted by aphids.

Peach Viruses. Peaches are subject to several virus diseases, some of which have caused severe losses in the past and, unless suitable precautions are taken, can again be destructive. Generally, these precautions include the use of virus-free propagating wood, the detection and prompt removal of virus-infected trees, and the elimination of nearby host plants that serve as sources of infection for the Peach trees. Among these virus carriers are wild and cultivated Plums of several species, wild and cultivated Cherries and Choke Cherries.

The principal virus disease of Peaches is Peach yellows, which causes the trees to produce slender, erect shoots having small, yellowish leaves and brings about premature ripening of the fruit and early death of the trees. Japanese Plums become infected with this virus but show no obvious symptoms; most other kinds of Prunus can be infected. Transmission is by leaf hoppers and by budding.

Peach X-disease is a serious threat to Peach production in many parts of the country. By early summer the foliage of affected trees is light yellowish green marked with red and yellow spots. Parts of the leaves may drop out, leaving ragged foliage. The fruits shrivel and fall or ripen early and have a bitter taste. Young trees are often killed. This disease also affects the Choke Cherry; trees of this kind that are near cultivated Peach trees should be eliminated. Transmission is by budding.

Peach phony disease is troublesome in the Southeast. It causes the trees to be dwarfed, the foliage deeper green than normal and the fruits to be undersized. It is transmitted by leaf hoppers.

Peach rosette virus disease causes infected trees to wilt and die suddenly or to produce short shoots with small leaves which have thickened veins lacking normal coloring; early death of the tree follows. This disease, which is troublesome in the Southeast, also infects Plums. Transmission is by budding.

Peach mosaic virus disease affects Peaches and Nectarines. Early in the year yellow mottling of the foliage occurs, but disappears as the season advances; distortion of the leaves and a shortening of the distances between leaves on the shoots are also symptoms. The fruits of affected trees are small and uneven. Transmission is by budding.

Peach wart virus disease occurs in the West, causing the fruits to be blistered and later covered with discolored warty growths. Transmission is by budding.

Peach asteroid virus disease occurs in California. It is characterized by distinct yellow lesions which form star-shaped markings along the veins. Transmission is by budding.

Prunus line-pattern virus disease infects Peaches, Japanese Plums and Mahalab Cherries. Peach and Cherry foliage is marked with light-colored lines or faint yellow mottling. Transmission is by budding.

Pear Stony Pit Virus. In the West this virus affects Pears, causing the fruits to be deformed and pitted. The bark of affected trees is much cracked and the foliage is reduced and sometimes shows yellowish veinlets. Transmission is by grafting.

Pea Viruses. Peas are subject to infection with a number of virus diseases. The most important is Pea mosaic virus disease, which also infects Sweet Peas, Clover and Broad Beans. It causes stunting of the vines and yellowish mottling of the foliage. The flowers of Sweet Peas show mottling of the color. Transmission of the disease is by aphids.

Pea-enation mosaic virus, which also infects Sweet Peas and Broad Beans, causes the veins to lose their normal color and yellowish areas to develop. These become translucent and soft and are surrounded on the undersides of the leaves with an unnatural growth of leaf tissue. Pods may be blistered, misshapen and mottled. Transmission is by aphids.

Pea streak virus disease causes the leaves to curl downwards and the stem tips to be twisted and crowded with leaves. Transmission is by aphids.

Peas may also be infected with Bean yellow mosaic disease, which in them causes the veins to become yellow.

Pelargonium Leaf-Curl Virus. This disease is common on Geraniums. It first shows as small yellowish spots with brown centers. The leaves may turn yellow and be crinkled and distorted and are often undersized. On the leaf stalks and stems raised corky streaks appear and the upper parts of the plants may die. The symptoms are most conspicuous in spring.

Peperomia Ring Spot. This virus causes distortion of the foliage of Peperomias and the development of yellowish or brownish ringlike markings on it. Affected plants are stunted and unhealthy in appearance. There is no cure.

Potato Viruses. Leaf roll disease is common.

Potato leaf curl disease caused by a virus. The leaf at left is unaffected.

The symptoms are an upward and inward rolling of the leaves starting with the older leaves and progressing through the plant, resulting in dry, crisp foliage and stunted growth, with reduced yield. The disease is transmitted by aphids.

Mosaic virus disease shows in a mottling of the foliage, accompanied by a puckering or crinkling of the leaflets and, when severe, a dwarfing of the plant. Potato aucuba mosaic is similar, but the mottling shows as bright yellow spots or patches against the dark green of the leaf.

Spotted wilt virus, which see, below, infects Potatoes.

Several other virus infections affect Potatoes and result in dwarfed and degenerating plants. In all cases, infected plants should be lifted and destroyed. New virus-free certified seed Potatoes should be obtained the following year, and precautionary spraying should be done against aphids and leaf hoppers.

Raspberry shoot, showing mottling and crinkling caused by mosaic disease.

Raspberry Viruses. Three virus infections of Raspberries—mosaic disease, leaf curl disease and streak disease—are similar in that affected plants are greatly reduced in vigor and never recover; some varieties may be killed.

Raspberry mosaic disease causes a distinct yellow mottling of the foliage; the berries are small and seedy. Red Raspberry varieties differ in their resistance to mosaic. Milton and Indian Summer usually escape infection. Newburgh is partially resistant where aphids are not very numerous. Latham is tolerant of the virus and continues to grow with fair vigor even though infected. No Black Raspberry variety is mosaic resistant, and unusual vigilance is often necessary to maintain the plants virus-free for several years. Very often the duration of the planting is determined by its virus content.

Raspberry leaf curl causes the leaves to crinkle, curl and become dark green and dry. The fruits are of poor quality and undersized. Following infection with Raspberry streak virus, the plants are much dwarfed, on young canes bluish-violet spots show, the leaves are usually curled and close together and may be twisted upside down. Infected plants die within 2-3 years.

These viruses are transmitted by aphids. Practicable control, however, has not resulted from attempts to eliminate the aphids. Control of Raspberry viruses is obtained by planting certified virus-free plants several hundred feet away from any suspected diseased plants and by removing and destroying all virus-infected plants. All wild Raspberries and run-out cultivated plantings within 500 ft. of disease-free plants should be eradicated.

States in which Raspberry plants are grown in quantities for sale require that the plants be inspected during the growing season and certified as nearly free from disease.

Ring Spot. See Tomato Viruses, below, and Peperomia Ring Spot, above. See also Ring Spot under Physiological Diseases, below.

Rose Viruses. In the East, Rose streak virus causes the leaves and stems to be marked with brownish or reddish ringlike patterns. Dead areas appear on the stems near the budding union and girdling of the stems occurs, with consequent wilting of foliage. On the West Coast, Rose mosaic virus causes yellowish areas to branch out from the leaf midveins and some distortion of the leaves to occur. The same virus infects greenhouse Roses everywhere.

Both of the above viruses are transmitted by budding and grafting.

Spotted Wilt Virus. This is a very serious disease that affects many different kinds of plants. In the East it is most common in greenhouses; in the West it occurs on crops grown outdoors. Among plants affected are Begonias, Calendulas, Calla Lilies, Chrysanthemums, Dahlias, Delphiniums, Fuchsias, Gloxinias, Hippeastrums, Lettuce, Nasturtiums, Peas, Potatoes, Primulas, Petunias, Salvias, Stocks, Tomatoes, Verbenas and Zinnias. The symptoms vary somewhat on different host plants.

Calla Lilies show whitish spots and streaks that later turn brown. Affected Dahlias show yellow ring spots on the foliage. Lettuce is stunted and yellowed and has parchment-like spots with brown margins on the leaves. Peas and Sweet Peas develop purplish spots or streaks on their stems and leaves and the foliage yellows. Potatoes develop streaks on their stems and dead spots on their upper leaves; the tops of the stems wilt and collapse.

Tomatoes are stunted, show leaf distortion and a yellowish mosaic and have bronzy ringlike lesions on the foliage; the fruits are spotted.

Strawberry Viruses. Virus diseases are widely distributed in Strawberry varieties. They reduce the vigor and productivity of the plants but do not kill them. Recently, virus-free plants of a number of varieties have been located and made available to nurseries. If these are available in your locality, you should use them in preference to plants of unknown health.

Yellow-edge disease shows as dwarfing of the youngest leaves, with a yellowing localized around the margins, most noticeable in the latter half of the season; the crop is reduced and the berries are smaller than normal.

Strawberry crinkle disease differs in that the yellowing occurs in spots over the leaf blade as well as at the edges and the leaves become wrinkled or cupped.

Strawberry stunt disease causes the plants to be dwarfed, the foliage dull and the leafstalks very short. The fruit crop is poor.

Virus-infected Strawberries should be removed and burned.

Sugar Beet Curly-Top Virus. This virus affects a great variety of plants, including Beans, Beets, Carnations, Carrots, Celery, Cabbage and related plants, Cucumbers and related plants, Delphiniums, Eggplants, New Zealand Spinach, Pansies, Petunias, Poppies, Strawflowers, Tomatoes and Zinnias.

The symptoms in Beets include leaf curling, loss of color from the veins, an increase in the number of rootlets and the appearance of sharp protuberances on the undersides of the leaves.

Cucumbers, Melons and Squash show excessive dark green in the leaves and at the tips of their stems and a turning upwards of the stem tips. Tomatoes, especially seedlings, become yellow and die. Most other plants become stunted and deformed and have their leaves mottled as the result of infection. This disease is transmitted by leaf hoppers.

Tomato Viruses. Tomato mosaic or, as it is also called, Tobacco mosaic virus, is common. On infected plants the leaves have mottled light and dark green areas and are usually somewhat deformed. A particular strain of this virus, sometimes called aucuba mosaic, shows as bright yellow blotches on the leaves.

Streak disease is believed to be the work of more than one virus. The symptoms are brown spots or flecks on the leaves, brown dead streaks on the stems and brown, sunken pits on the fruits.

Shoestring disease is produced by the same virus as Cucumber mosaic disease. It causes Tomato leaves to become twisted, narrow and like tendrils.

Tomato ring-spot disease and Tobacco ring-spot disease (which also affects Tomatoes) cause the leaves to be marked with ring-shaped markings and the plants to be stunted. Tobacco ring spot may be transmitted by means of infected Petunia seeds.

Tomatoes are also subject to spotted wilt

virus, which is discussed at greater length above.

Special care should be taken to disinfect tools used in tending Tomatoes, and to control aphids, whiteflies, red spider mites and other insects. Smokers of tobacco should wash their hands very thoroughly, as it is possible to transmit a virus to Tomatoes from virus-infected Tobacco. Do not mulch Tomatoes with Tobacco stems.

Tulip Viruses. Tulip color-adding virus disease scarcely interferes with the growth of the plants or the appearance of the leaves but it causes the flowers to develop dark stripes. It is transmitted by aphids.

Tulips also are affected by Lily latent mosaic virus. It is unwise to plant Lilies and Tulips in close proximity to each other.

PHYSIOLOGICAL DISEASES

These are troubles not traceable to the effects of living organisms but which arise from adverse environmental conditions or errors of cultivation. For example, soil that is acid is harmful to Cabbages, Cauliflowers and many other members of the Mustard family (Cruciferae); alkaline soil is deadly to most plants belonging to the Heath family (Ericaceae).

Moisture Excesses and Deficiencies. Poor subsurface drainage of the soil is often responsible for damage, and plants are especially likely to die in winter as a result of this. Overwatering of plants grown in pots and other containers is another frequent cause of trouble. Poor growth, wilting foliage that does not recover when the soil is watered, and rotting of the roots are common symptoms.

Some plants develop a "dropsical" condition called oedema as a result of overwatering and being grown in an excessively humid atmosphere. Small wartlike growths, sometimes corky in character, appear on the undersides of the leaves. Oedema sometimes occurs outdoors but it is far more frequent on plants grown indoors. Kinds of plants especially likely to develop these symptoms include Begonias, Cabbages, Camellias, Geraniums and Peperomias.

The roots of this Begonia have rotted as a result of poor drainage and too frequent watering.

Excessive dryness of the soil is often responsible for unsatisfactory growth. If it occurs in late summer and fall it is likely to cause serious injury to Rhododendrons and many other evergreens, and this manifests itself in winter and spring by a scorching or drying of the foliage.

Similar scorching of tree foliage often occurs in summer, especially when a hot, dry period follows a cooler, moister one. Horse Chestnuts and Maples are especially susceptible and may show symptoms even before a period of drought.

The same conditions that cause physiological leaf scorch of Horse Chestnuts, Maples and other trees are contributing factors of the trouble called blossom end rot of Tomatoes, Peppers, Squash and Watermelons. This condition shows itself as dark-colored, shrunken blotches or spots at the end of the fruits, opposite the stalks, with rotting of the underlying tissues. Recent research shows that calcium deficiency is also a cause of blossom end rot of Tomatoes.

Blossom end rot is most common when drought follows a period of ample moisture. Prevention may largely be had by preparing the soil deeply, by fertilizing fairly generously, by watering thoroughly in dry weather and by mulching to conserve moisture in the ground.

Insufficient supplies of soil moisture often cause stunted growth. Provided the tissues have not actually been killed, most plants that have wilted as a result of lack of water recover soon after water is supplied. Wilting is harmful, however, in that it adversely affects the plants' ability to function properly for a considerable time after the wilting has ceased.

Bitter pit or stippen of Apples and some other fruits is characterized by sunken, round, or angular spots on the surface of the fruits, with the flesh underneath brown, spongy and bitter in taste. It usually develops after harvest, but is caused earlier. A fluctuating moisture supply seems to be responsible in part for this disease. Young trees bearing overgrown fruits, trees that are thinned excessively, trees that are overpruned or fertilized heavily with nitrogen fertilizers are most susceptible to bitter pit. Avoiding these conditions is about all that can be done to control this disorder.

Water core of Apples occurs in most Apple-growing regions but is most severe where temperatures and light intensities are high. The flesh has a water-soaked, glassy appearance near the core and is firmer. The cause of the trouble is not known. Fruits should be harvested before they are overripe, and excessive thinning should not be practiced.

Grading operations often result in trees becoming unhealthy and their lives being shortened. Any change of grade which markedly raises or lowers the soil level over tree roots is likely to be harmful. Roots buried too deeply, especially if the soil above them is clayey, suffer from lack of sufficient oxygen. Roots exposed or nearly exposed by grading operations are likely to suffer from drying.

Soil placed above tree roots should be of a decidedly porous nature and a well (of sufficient diameter to allow for the growth of the trunk) should be built around the trunk to keep the soil from being in contact with the bark.

If the fill above the roots must exceed a few inches in depth the best procedure is to lay, on the soil surface, agricultural tile drains, in a pattern like the spokes of a wheel, from the well to beyond the outmost spread of the branches and then to connect the tips of the spokes with a circular row of drains just beyond the branch spread. Over this drain system course gravel, crushed stone, rough cinders or similar very porous material should be placed to within 6-8 in. of the finish grade, then porous topsoil is filled in to the required level.

Spraying and dusting may cause damage to foliage and flowers. Bordeaux mixture and other copper sprays are likely to be disfiguring when cool, moist weather follows their application. The damage takes the form of numerous small reddish or brown spots and in some cases the leaves later turn yellow and drop. Stunting of Cucumbers, Melons and related plants as well as some others may take place as a result of copper spray injury, and the flowers of Tomatoes may drop off before fruit forms.

Sulphur sprays and dusts are apt to damage foliage and flowers when the temperature is 90 degrees F. or more. The damage takes the form of scorching of the affected parts, especially at the tips and margins of leaves and petals. The application of lime-sulphur may cause the foliage of some plants to assume a rusty brown appearance and to cause the fruits of Apples to drop.

Arsenate of lead is likely to harm Peaches, Apricots, Cherries and other stone fruits. It may cause spotting or burning of their foliage if they are sprayed without the addition to the spray of lime or zinc sulphate.

DDT sprays and dusts may cause injury to the foliage of Cucumbers, Melons and related plants, and to Roses, Camellias and some other plants. The harm done is a stunting of growth and a yellowing of the foliage. Roots may be damaged as a result of accumulations in the soil of DDT from repeated spraying.

Selective weed killers, such as 2,4-D and 2,4,5-T, may cause serious harm to plants other than those they are intended to kill. If mists of these sprays drift on to plants of almost any kind other than Grasses, they are likely to cause distortion of the foliage and perhaps death. Such weed killers should always be applied with great care in calm weather, and containers and sprays used for them should be reserved for their use or should be most thoroughly cleansed before being used for other purposes.

Manufactured gas leaking into the ground or into the atmosphere indoors may cause very serious damage to plants. The effect may be a slow deterioration or almost sudden death. Jerusalem Cherries drop their fruits and African Violets fail to bloom when small amounts of gas are present in the air. Tomato plants are extremely sensitive and may be used for testing purposes. A small amount of manufactured gas causes their leaves to bend downwards. Location of and prompt repair of the leaking main or fixture is the answer to this trouble.

Burning gas in the home does not harm plants; it is unconsumed, escaped, manufactured gas that is harmful. Burners should not be turned on until a match or other igniter is lighted above them. Natural gas does not contain materials that are toxic to plants, but injury may result from natural gas leaking into the ground, replacing the air in the soil, and thus cutting off the supply of oxygen needed by the roots.

Smoke and other atmospheric impurities may cause serious dwarfing and discoloration of foliage as well as dropping of leaves. In smoke the chief harmful ingredient is sulphur dioxide. Atmospheric conditions play a large part in modifying the damage that is likely to be done. In breezy, dry weather the harmful impurities are likely to be carried away; in moist and still weather poisonous substances accumulate and serious harm is likely to result, as so often happens in smogs.

Accumulations of soot, a residue from smoke, deprives leaves, particularly those of evergreens, of needed light. Spraying with soapy water or with water containing a detergent and then rinsing with clear water will help to remove soot.

Salt-Water Damage. Salt spray from the sea may cause injury to the foliage of a great variety of plants many miles inland when the winds are inshore and strong. As a result, many coniferous evergreen trees appear as though scorched by fire, the foliage turning a conspicuous yellow or orange color.

When salt water inundates the land many plants are likely to suffer root injury. To minimize damage, prompt applications of gypsum to the soil and thorough drenchings with fresh water, to leach out the salt, should be given. Sea sand that has not been thoroughly washed free of salt will harm the roots of plants if it is used in seed sowing and potting-soil mixtures.

Sun Scald results when the trunks or branches of thin-barked trees such as Beeches, that have previously been shaded, are suddenly exposed to strong sun. This most usually happens when a tree is transplanted to a new location, when a neighboring tree or other source of shade is removed and when pruning is so severe that it exposes the branches.

Newly transplanted trees may be protected by having their trunks wrapped in burlap or special paper made for the purpose, for a few months following transplanting. Pruning should be done gradually over a period of two or three years rather than all at once.

Fruits may also be damaged by sun scald. It is likely to affect Tomato fruits if there is a reduction of their foliage as a result of pruning or of other causes, and may affect Grapes and some other fruits under similar circumstances.

Sun Scorch. See Leaf Scorch, under Some Specific Physiological Diseases, below.

Graft incompatibility is sometimes responsible for lack of vigor and other troubles. If the understock on which a plant is grafted is not quite suited to it, or if the graft union is not well made and established, failure or partial failure results. Such troubles are not well understood but it seems that in many cases the plant's ability to transport water and nutrients through its tissues is reduced. Lilacs, Walnuts, Japanese Maples and some other kinds of plants often give poor results because of graft incompatibility.

Deficiency Diseases. For growth, plants need carbon dioxide, taken from the atmosphere through the leaves, and water plus mineral nutrients, taken from the soil through the roots. Carbon dioxide and water make up 80 to 90 per cent of the weight of most growing plants, while the mineral nutrients contribute 5 to 15 per cent of their dry matter or ash content. Nevertheless, certain mineral elements are essential to the healthy growth of plants. When the supply is insufficient, symptoms of deficiency diseases become apparent.

Major Elements. Some elements are needed in relatively larger quantities and are termed major elements; others are required only in very small quantities and are termed trace or minor elements. The major elements are nitrogen, phosphorus, potassium, calcium, magnesium, and sulphur; the trace elements are manganese, boron, copper, zinc and molybdenum. Other elements such as sodium, chlorine, aluminum and silicon do not seem to be absolutely essential to plant growth.

The deficiency of an essential element causes characteristic symptoms to appear in the growth and appearance of a plant. Care, however, is needed in reading the symptoms, since they may also be produced by weather conditions such as low temperatures, drought, or wind; by soil conditions such as waterlogging, lack of humus, weediness and subsoil pan; by pests, by fungal and bacterial disease or virus infection. Such factors should be borne in mind when diagnosing deficiency diseases.

Nitrogen Deficiency. Nitrogen is needed in connection with all growth processes in plants, since it forms part of the protoplasm of plant cells and of chlorophyll. The chief symptoms of deficiency in all plants are: restricted root and top growth; stunted, thin shoots; upright spindly growth; small leaves, usually pale, yellowish-green at first, developing highly colored tints of yellow, orange and red later; premature leaf fall, beginning with the older leaves; and poor lateral growth development.

These symptoms are common among Brassicas (Cabbage, Cauliflower, Brussels Sprouts, Rutabagas, etc.) and Beets. Potatoes are stunted and the number of tubers much reduced. All tree and bush fruits show short, thin shoot growth, sparse foliage, small, yellowish leaves becoming highly orange, red or purple-tinted; fruit buds and blossoms are few, and fruits small and highly colored. In Strawberries there are few crowns. Tomatoes are dwarfed, thin and erect, with leaves small, pale green, tinted yellow or purple, and old leaves dying off early.

Correction lies in the application of nitrogenous fertilizers and manures such as sulphate of ammonia, dried blood and sodium nitrate and animal manure. (See Fertilizers.)

Phosphorus Deficiency. Phosphorus, like nitrogen, is intimately concerned with vital plant growth processes, and is specially important to root development, and the maturing of seeds and fruits. The symptoms of deficiency are apt to appear on poor clay soils and alkaline or limestone soils. These symptoms are in many ways similar to those of nitrogen deficiency—restricted root and top growth; short, thin shoots; a spindly uprightness of leaves, etc.; small leaves, falling prematurely, the oldest first; poor blossoming and reduced yields. Leaf color is usually a dull bluish-green, developing purplish tints or a bronzing with purple or brown spotting.

On Apples, the foliage is sparse with small, dull green leaves becoming purple- or bronze-tinted and falling prematurely; fruits are small with variable color. Pear leaves tend to be bronzed. In Raspberries, canes are thin and the leaves dull-purple. In Strawberries, crown growth is poor and the leaves dull green, turning purple and falling early.

Brassicas are thin and stunted, with leaves dull and purple tinted. In Potatoes, the leaves roll upwards and the margins show scorching. In Tomatoes, the leaves are bluish-green, with tints of purple.

Phosphorus deficiency can be corrected by the use of quick-acting superphosphate or bone flour, or by adding to the soil bone meal or basic slag.

Potassium Deficiency. Potassium is present in all parts of plants, particularly in the leaves and at growing points. It is an essential catalyst, and seems necessary to the formation of proteins and carbohydrates, the regulation of water balance, transpiration and photosynthesis, and the resistance of plants to disease. The symptoms of potassium deficiency vary according to its extent, but appear more markedly in growing points and leaf margins. Growth may be stunted, and shoot and root growth poor, and there is either a browning of the tips or margins or a brown spotting of leaves, but many plants show specific characteristics.

In Apples, the shoots are thin, leaves bluish-green with marginal browning and sometimes intervenal paleness, and fruits small and immature. In Pears, the leaves have a dark brown marginal scorch. Marginal scorching also develops in the bush fruits, Raspberries and Strawberries, usually with poor growth. In Brassicas and broad-leaved plants, the leaves are dull dark green, with marginal and intervenal browning. In Potatoes, growth is stunted, leaves a dull green, with marginal browning and premature falling. In Tomatoes the leaves develop a pale grayishness at the margins and between veins, later becoming browned, and fruits ripen unevenly. In Beans, growth is stunted and the marginal scorch is dark brown or blackish, while in String Beans and Peas there is a yellowing of the leaves between the veins and at the edges.

Correction of potassium deficiency may be accomplished with sulphate of potash, muriate of potash, or unleached wood ashes, or by adding organic manure or compost to the soil.

Calcium Deficiency. Calcium is found chiefly in the leaves of plants as a constituent of cell walls. It also plays a part in neutralizing organic acids and in the development of growing points. A deficiency results in poor roots, and the young leaves become distorted, with possible die-back. In Brassicas, the symptoms are narrowly whitened or ragged, scorched leaf margins which roll upwards, and similar symptoms may be observed in calcium-starved Rutabagas, Beets and Potatoes. In Apples, tips of shoots may die back, but it is in the lime-loving plants that the symptoms are most likely to occur.

Adequate liming of the soil with one or another form of lime prevents calcium deficiency from developing in plants.

Magnesium Deficiency. Magnesium is a constituent of the green pigment, chlorophyll. When a plant is deficient in this mineral, the general symptoms are those of chlorosis, beginning with the oldest leaves and progressing to the youngest. Deficiency is apt to provoke marked symptoms in various species. In Brassicas, the older leaves become marbled with pale areas and often highly tinted with orange, red and purple. In Beets, the intervenal chlorosis is accompanied by high red tints. In Apples and Pears, the leaves become brown and dead between the veins and the leaves fall from the base of shoots upwards. In Raspberries, the leaves develop yellow and red tinting at the centers and margins, and Strawberries exhibit similar symptoms. In Tomatoes, the old leaves pale and yellow quickly, and soon hang and die, with the symptoms progressing up the plant.

Magnesium deficiency tends to appear on long-cultivated soils. It is readily corrected by the application of magnesium sulphate (Epsom Salts) to the soil.

Leaves of Mountain Laurel, Kalmia latifolia, showing chlorosis caused by iron deficiency, a result of an excessively alkaline soil.

Iron Deficiency. Iron is essential to chlorophyll formation, though not part of it. Any deficiency is reflected in a paleness or chlorosis of the foliage. This is most likely to develop on alkaline soils. In many tree fruits and bush fruits, the tip leaves of shoots show chlorosis first, and shoots may die back. Raspberries and Strawberries are often severely affected. In Brassicas, the whole of the foliage becomes chlorotic.

Rhododendrons, Mountain Laurels and other plants belonging in the botanical family Ericaceae often suffer from iron deficiency when grown in soil that is not sufficiently acid for their needs. Their leaves become yellow, with the veins remaining typically green.

The correction of an iron deficiency lies in applying iron sulphate or chelated iron and in decreasing the alkalinity of the soil by the use of organic manures. The grassing-over of the roots of fruit trees also makes more iron available.

Manganese Deficiency. Manganese is looked upon as a catalyst, and as being closely associated with iron in function. It is apt to become deficient on wet soils and soils with a high organic matter content. The symptoms of a manganese deficiency are very similar to those of a lack of iron—chlorosis of the leaves—and, consequently, care is needed in diagnosis. In Apples, the chlorosis begins near the margins of leaves, extending inwards, and does not affect strongly growing young shoots. In Pears, the chlorosis is similar but fainter than that of iron deficiency. Plums and other stone fruits are affected similarly to Apples.

Among vegetables, Peas show the deficiency in a condition of the seed known as Marsh Spot. Beets show a rather faded reddening, and in Brassicas and other leafy crops the leaves may be pale or bleached except for the veins.

Manganese deficiency may be avoided by the application of manganese sulphate to the soil.

Boron Deficiency. A deficiency of this element may occur on dry, well-drained soils, or through overliming. The role of boron in plant nutrition is imperfectly understood, but a deficiency produces some definite symptoms. In Cauliflowers, it causes the curd to turn brown or fail to develop; in Kale, the stem becomes hollow; in Cabbage, the pith in the stem becomes hollow at the head; in Beets, there is canker, with a rotting of the crown; and in Celery the stems may be split longitudinally, with the young leaves drying.

Boron deficiency causes a condition known as heart rot, brown heart or black heart in Sugar Beets, Turnips and Rutabagas. The symptoms are twisting and stunting of the foliage and a darkening or blackening of the interior of the roots, with a water-soaked appearance of the tissues.

Correction lies in the application of small amounts of granulated borax, roughly at a rate of 1 oz. per 20 sq. yds.

Zinc Deficiency. An insufficiency of available zinc in the soil is a cause of the disease known as little leaf (see below) of Apples, Apricots, Grapes, Peaches, Plums and some other fruits and of a condition of Citrus called mottle leaf (see below). It also is responsible for rosette disease (see below) of Pecans and Walnuts.

Zinc deficiency is corrected by spraying Almond, Apple, Apricot, Grape, Peach and Plum trees with zinc sulphate at the rate of 5 lb. to 10 gallons of water the first year and 2½ lb. to 10 gallons the second year. Grapes are treated by wetting the vines, including pruning cuts, immediately after pruning, with a solution of 2 lb. of zinc sulphate to 1 gallon of water. Mottle leaf of Citrus is controlled by spraying the trees with 5 lb. of zinc sulphate and 2½ lb. of hydrated lime in 50 gallons of water. Pecans and Walnuts are treated by spreading zinc sulphate on the soil beneath the trees in winter at the rate of about 5 lb. for a mature tree.

Deficiencies of other elements such as sulphur, copper, and molybdenum are sometimes of practical interest.

State agricultural experiment stations and county agricultural agents are equipped to give advice as to deficiencies that are likely to occur locally in soils and to make soil tests. Gardeners who suspect troubles of these kinds should consult these agencies. See State Agricultural Experiment Stations.

Some Specific Physiological Diseases. The following are specific physiological diseases of importance to the gardener:

Bitter Pit. This affects Apples (on this host it is often called Stippen), Pears and Olives. It causes Apples and Pears to develop small, slightly depressed spots on the fruit and these increase during storage, especially if the temperature is comparatively high; it causes a dry rot of the fruits of Olives. It seems to occur on Apples and Pears when there is a deficiency or widely fluctuating supply of available soil moisture. With Olives it seems to be caused by excessive fertilization.

Blossom End Rot of Tomatoes, Peppers, Squash and Watermelon. This trouble most often occurs when dry conditions follow a period

Tomatoes spoiled by blossom end rot.

during which ample moisture is available to the roots (see Moisture Excesses and Deficiencies, above), but other factors that limit root development, such as shallow soil, improper soil drainage, deep surface cultivation, as well as excessive fertilization with nitrogen and deficiency of calcium may be contributory causes.

Chlorosis. A term used to describe the insufficient development of chlorophyll (the green coloring matter in leaves) that occurs as a result of a deficiency of one or more essential nutrient elements or of some other unfavorable circumstance. In chlorotic plants the foliage is yellowish in parts or all over, and has a generally unhealthy appearance.

One of the most common causes of chlorosis is iron deficiency, which may result from lack of iron in the soil; often, too, on alkaline soils the iron that is there is held in a form unavailable to the plants. Deficiencies of nitrogen, manganese and boron also bring about chlorosis. Yet another common cause of this condition is an insufficient supply of oxygen to the roots of plants growing in poorly drained and waterlogged soils.

When poor drainage is the cause of chlorosis, you can remedy the condition by draining the soil or by moving the affected plants to a more favorable location. When chlorosis is caused by lack of a necessary element, the condition can be corrected by applying the deficient item, either to the soil or in the form of a spray to the foliage. Often applications of exceedingly small amounts of the deficient element are all that is necessary. See Deficiency Diseases, above.

Foliage of Clivia severely damaged by physiological leaf scorch as a result of excessive exposure to strong sun.

The damage suffered by the leaves of this Orchid is leaf scorch, caused by keeping the plant too close to an electric light bulb.

If chlorosis occurs and the gardener is not certain of its cause, the wise plan is to send samples of the affected foliage and samples of the soil in which the plant is growing to the State Agricultural Experiment Station for diagnosis and recommendations.

Leaf of a Ficus partly killed by physiological leaf scorch as a result of insufficient atmospheric humidity.

Gummosis. The symptom of this condition is an exudation of a gumlike substance by the bark of trees, chiefly fruit trees. It is caused by some fungus cankers and rot diseases, by injury by borers and sometimes by mechanical injury, but in other cases it results from unsuitable environmental conditions, especially improper soil and poor drainage.

Heart Rot, Black Heart or Brown Heart. This disorder occurs in Beets, Potatoes, Turnips and other root crops. See Boron Deficiency, under Deficiency Diseases, above.

Leaf Scorch. Leaf scorch caused by organisms is discussed under Bacterial and Fungus Diseases, above. Physiological leaf scorch may be caused by excessively high temperatures, by limited supplies of moisture and especially by a combination of these factors. Exposure to excessive sunlight or wind may also be responsible, as may a too low relative humidity of the atmosphere. Physiological leaf scorch is also called sun scorch. See Moisture Excesses and Deficiencies, above.

Little Leaf. This is a condition that affects Almonds, Apples, Apricots, Grapes, Peaches and some other fruit trees. Characteristic symptoms are reduced size and often an unnatural narrowness of the leaves, and a crowding together of the foliage in a rosette-like manner. Often the leaves of the tips of the shoots are yellow. It is caused by a deficiency of zinc in the soil. See Zinc Deficiency, above.

Mottle Leaf of Citrus. The cause is deficiency of zinc. Symptoms are a reduction in the size of the leaves and a distinct, contracting coloring of dark green along the midrib and main veins and of yellow or yellow green between the veins. See Zinc Deficiency, above.

African Violet, Saintpaulia, suffering from physiological ring spot disease.

Oedema. See Moisture Excesses and Deficiencies, above.

Ring Spot. This condition shows as yellowish or pale colored ringlike markings on the foliage of African Violets and some related plants. It is supposed to be caused by wetting the leaves with cold water. Other ring-spot diseases are caused by viruses.

Rosette. This term is applied to a condition in which the internodes (length of stem between leaves) are unnaturally short, with the result that the leaves are crowded together in a rosette-like manner and are reduced in size. It is essentially the same as little leaf disease, above. See also Zinc Deficiency, above.

Sun Scorch. See Leaf Scorch.

INSECTICIDES AND MITICIDES

The term insecticide is usually employed to include all materials used to kill the smaller garden pests and is not limited to those that eradicate insects only. Because many insecticides have little or no adverse effect on mites (which are not true insects) and there are a group of materials such as Azobenzene, Aramite, Dimite and Ovex that are especially effective against such pests, these materials are often known as miticides.

The primary purpose of insecticides and miticides is to control and destroy pests which infest garden plants, but they must do this without serious risk of harm to human beings and animals, without damaging the plant hosts and, if possible, without adversely affecting insects which are beneficial by reason of their pollinating or pest-destroying activities. Insecticides and miticides usually destroy pests either by contact or when eaten.

Great advances have been made in recent years,

so that not only has the range of effective insecticides and miticides been increased, but their modes of application have been improved in many cases. The commonest forms are still sprays and dusts, but newer methods are available, especially for confined spaces such as greenhouses, where insecticides and miticides can be effectively employed as aerosols. The following insecticides and miticides are those most useful to the modern gardener.

Insecticides and miticides are only effective if they are used properly. When applying sprays and dusts, it is essential that all surfaces of the affected plants be covered with a thin coating of the material being used. Inexperienced and careless gardeners often miss the undersides of the leaves, the interior parts of plants and the sides of the plants opposite to where they stand.

A good-quality duster or sprayer is a wise investment; cheap models are often wasteful and unsatisfactory. Sprinkler-can types of dusters are almost useless. The objective is to apply the spray or dust in the form of an extremely fine mist or cloud and to get complete coverage with the minimum use of material; spray that drenches the ground and dust that falls in little heaps is mostly wasted. To get the best results, keep the spray nozzle or the end of the dust gun moving back and forth and approach the plant with it from several directions. By spraying mostly from underneath you make sure that both the tops and bottoms of the leaves are protected.

Aldrin. This is a synthetic insecticide effective against grasshoppers, leaf miners, grubs and many other pests. It is available as a 25 per cent wettable powder, a 25 per cent emulsion and a 1-2 per cent dust. This insecticide may be used together with alkaline materials such as lime. Use it according to the manufacturers directions.

Aramite. This miticide does not kill insects but is very effective against mites. It is generally used as a 15 per cent wettable powder at the rate of 1 tablespoonful to 1 gallon of water. It is a constituent of some brand-name insecticides. It is relatively non-poisonous to man and animals and is remarkably effective against mites. Aramite is not compatible with Bordeaux mixture, lime-sulphur and other alkaline materials or with dinitro compounds, and it is usually considered wise not to use it in combination with copper-containing sprays or dusts.

Bacthane L69. See Thuricide.

Benzene Hexachloride (BHC). This synthetic insecticide forms the basis of various commercial products used as dusts, sprays and aerosols designed to control a very wide range of insects, including aphids, lace bugs, caterpillars, leaf miners, moths, thrips, whiteflies and weevils. As a soil insecticide, it may be used to control wireworms, leather-jackets, flea beetles, Carrot rust fly and Cabbage maggot. It imparts an objectionable flavor to food crops. On these it is better to use the purified form of benzene hexachloride which is called lindane.

Calomel (mercurous chloride). This is commonly prepared as a dust containing 4-5 per cent calomel for use in controlling Cabbage maggot and Onion maggot. Unlike mercuric chloride, calomel is not dangerously poisonous.

Carbon Disulphide (carbon bisulphide). This is a nearly colorless liquid, very inflammable and giving off fumes toxic to humans if inhaled in quantity. It is used as a fumigant to control soil pests, injections with an injector tool being made at the rate of ½-1 oz. per sq. yd. It may also be used to exterminate ants by pouring a small quantity into a hole made in the nest and sealing it with soil at once.

Chlordane. This insecticide is effective against many pests, especially ants, grubs and other creatures that work in the soil, and thrips and leaf miners. It is sold as a 50 per cent wettable powder, a 5 per cent dust and in emulsified liquid form. Do not combine it with lime, lime-sulphur, Bordeaux mixture or nicotine.

Chlorobenzilate. This newly introduced chemical is effective in controlling most species of mites. It has good residual properties and is compatible with most insecticides and fungicides.

Cyanogas (calcium cyanide). This deadly poison is used for fumigating greenhouses, destroying woodchucks and other burrowing animals and for killing wasps. When using it, follow the manufacturers' directions implicitly. Take great care not to inhale the dust or the gas that is generated from it and to wash the hands thoroughly immediately after handling it. Do not use Cyanogas in greenhouses that are attached to any buildings in which people or animals live.

D-D Mixture. This soil fumigant gives good control of nematodes, wireworms, symphylids and other soil pests. It should be used only on ground that is free of crops, and is most effective on light, sandy soils. Place it in holes 6 in. deep and 18 in. apart at the rate of 1 oz. to 3 holes. Planting may be done 2 weeks after this treatment.

DDT. This is a synthetic insecticide of great value. It is relatively non-poisonous to humans and animals at horticultural strengths, is non-injurious to nearly all plants and is lasting in its effects. It is a contact and stomach poison that paralyzes the nervous systems of the insects it affects but it is somewhat gradual in action. It is prepared for use as dusts, sprays and aerosols.

DDT is very effective against codling moth and gives good control of many other insects, including some borers, caterpillars, beetles and grubs as well as leaf hoppers and thrips. The use of DDT tends to increase mites by killing their parasites. When it is used on any plants subject to infestations of mites, a miticide such as Aramite or Ovex should be added to the DDT.

Certain kinds of aphids are also very likely to increase in numbers following the application of DDT. Other insecticides, such as malathion, must be used to control aphids.

DDT is sold as a 50 per cent wettable powder and as dusts containing 3, 5 and 10 per cent DDT. The normal dilution is 2 tablespoonfuls of the 50 per cent wettable powder to 1 gallon of water. DDT should not be used with lime, lime-sulphur or other lime-containing compounds or with oil sprays.

Demeton (Systox), used as a soil drench, and absorbed through the roots, is effective against many insects and mites. It may harm Chrysanthemums.

Diazinon has powerful insecticidal and, possibly, miticidal properties.

Dieldrin. This synthetic is similar to aldrin but remains effective longer and kills more different pests. It is especially useful against ants, beetle grubs and other soil insects as well as chinch bugs, webworms, cutworms, sowbugs, pillbugs, thrips and many other pests. It kills young leaf miners inside the leaves.

Dimite or DMC. This miticide is especially kinds. It is not very poisonous to man or animals, but, if used too strong, it easily damages plants. Use it at the rate of 1 teaspoonful of emulsion to 1 gallon of water.

Heptachlor, similar to chlordane, controls the same pests as it and, in addition, Apple maggot, Plum curculio and European cornborer.

Kelthane. This is another new miticide especially effective against red spider mite and cyclamen mite. Use it at the rate of ½ lb. of the 25 per cent wettable powder in 50 gallons of water, or ½ pint of the 25 per cent emulsifiable solution in 50 gallons of water.

Lead Arsenate. This is a very powerful stomach poison used to control caterpillars and other chewing insects and to grub-proof lawns. As it is poisonous to humans, animals and bees, care is needed in handling and precision in timing the applications. Lead arsenate, or arsenate of lead as it is also called, may be bought in powder or paste form. Normal strengths of application are 4 oz. of powder or 8 oz. of paste to 10 gallons of water. Lead arsenate as an insecticide is now largely superseded by DDT, rotenone and benzene hexachloride. In certain cases it may still be preferred to DDT, because it does not bring about an increase in mites.

Lime-Sulphur. Although primarily a fungicide, this has insecticidal properties too. It is chiefly used as a dormant spray.

Lindane. This is a purified form of benzene hexachloride. Although its odor is much less objectionable than that of the latter, it is slightly malodorous and is likely to spoil the flavor of root crops such as Turnips and Carrots. Lindane controls a wide variety of pests but is not effective against leaf hoppers or mites. It should not be used with lime-sulphur, Bordeaux mixture or other alkaline materials. It is obtainable as 1-5 per cent dusts, as an emulsion and as a 25 per cent wettable powder. Use 1 tablespoonful of the latter to 1 gallon of water.

Malathion. This spray is less toxic to man than some others but still it should be used with care. It gives good control of aphids, borers, mealybugs, scales, whiteflies and many other insects. It is sold as a 50 per cent emulsion and a 25 per cent wettable powder, and is a constituent of many brand-name sprays and dusts. One teaspoonful of the 50 per cent emulsion in 1 gallon of water is the usual dilution. This may be doubled or quadrupled for scale insects.

Marlate. See Methoxychlor.

Metaldehyde. This is used in combination with calcium arsenate or chlordane in slug baits, and as a dust for controlling slugs.

Methoxychlor or Marlate. This insecticide is closely related to DDT but is much less toxic to warm-blooded animals and safer to use on Cucumbers, Melons, Squash and related plants and on Tomatoes. It is effective against the Mexican Bean beetle and other pests of vegetables. This insecticide may be obtained as 24 per cent and 50 per cent wettable powders and is used in various brand-name dusts.

Nicotine. This valuable insecticide kills insects, mites and some other pests on contact, and is therefore extremely useful in controlling sap-sucking pests. It is sold for dry application as a dust (2-4 per cent nicotine), and in liquid form, as Black Leaf 40, for dilution and use as a spray. The usual dilution is 1 teaspoonful to 1 gallon or 1 pint to 100 gallons. Soap at the rate of about 1 oz. to the gallon should be dissolved in the water to increase the wetting power of the spray.

Nicotine is volatile and short-lived in effect. Because it is poisonous to humans and animals, care should be exercised in storing and handling it.

Oil Sprays. These are chiefly mineral oils prepared so that they readily form an emulsion with water. Miscible (mixable) oils are used as dormant sprays and are obtainable under various trade names. Dormant sprays should be applied only to trees and shrubs that are dormant and leafless, never to specimens in active growth. Do not use them when the temperature is below 45 degrees or is likely to drop to 32 degrees or lower the night following. Never use them within 3-4 weeks of applying a spray containing sulphur, and do not make more than one application of a miscible oil spray in any one season.

Summer or white oil emulsions are safe to use as summer sprays and on house and greenhouse plants to control scales, mealybugs and other sucking insects. They are obtainable under various trade names and it is very important to follow the manufacturers' directions carefully. Never apply them in bright sunshine or when the temperature is above 85 degrees. Nicotine and rotenone may be combined with these oil sprays but not with most other insecticides and fungicides. Allow at least 3-4 weeks between an application of any spray or dust containing sulphur and an oil spray.

OMPA. See schradan.

Ovex. This miticide is effective against the eggs of mites, less so against the adults. It is sold as a 50 per cent powder and 5 per cent and 10 per cent dusts and is an ingredient of some brand-name insecticides. It is scarcely harmful to man or animals.

Paradichlorobenzine. This insecticide may be used to discourage soil pests such as wireworms, slugs, etc. Used at a rate of ¼-½ oz. per sq. yd., the powdered crystals are dropped in holes 9 in. deep and 9 in. apart and sealed with soil immediately. Paradichlorobenzine is also widely used as a soil fumigant for the Peach tree borer.

Parathion. This is available as a wettable powder and in aerosol form. It is effective in controlling aphids, spider mites, mealybugs, certain scale insects, thrips and other sucking insects and as a spray against some leaf nematodes. It is extremely poisonous to man and must be used with utmost protective precautions and strictly according to the directions of the manufacturer. For home gardens malathion is to be preferred.

Pyrethrum. This insecticide, derived from a kind of Chrysanthemum, is essentially harmless to man and warm-blooded animals but kills insects by contact and by acting as a stomach poison. It is valuable for controlling pests of vegetables. It should not be combined with lime, lime-sulphur or Bordeaux mixture and must be used immediately after it is mixed with water, otherwise it soon loses its effectiveness. It is an ingredient of many brand-name sprays and dusts.

Rotenone. This insecticide is derived from several tropical plants. It is non-poisonous to man and affects insects on contact and as a stomach poison. It is very useful for controlling insects on edible plants and is available as a spray or dust under many trade names. Rotenone kills fish. It is not compatible with alkaline materials.

Ryania. A South American plant produces this insecticide, effective in controlling European Corn borer and some other pests. It is not poisonous to man or warm-blooded animals.

Schradan (sold as OMPA) is used in the same way and for the same purposes as demeton.

Sevin (N-methyl-l-napthyl carbamate). This is a new carbamate insecticide effective against leaf-rollers, leaf-eating caterpillars, Japanese beetles, Mexican bean beetles and many other insects. It is used at the rate of 1 lb. of the 50 per cent wettable powder in 100 gallons of water, or 2 tablespoons in a gallon.

Sodium Selenate. This poison, when applied to the soil, is absorbed by plant roots and becomes distributed through their stems and leaves. It then poisons insects feeding on the sap, and leaf nematodes which live inside tissues.

Sodium selenate is highly poisonous. It should never be used on soil on which food crops are to be grown within four or five years.

Sulphur. In the form of fine dust this is sometimes used to control mites. It is also used as an ingredient of lime-sulphur as a dormant spray, and against scale insects, but its chief use is as a fungicide. See under Fungicides, below.

Systox. See demeton.

Thimet is a contact and systemic insecticide of particular value for treating seeds and seedlings.

Thiodan is extremely effective in controlling aphids on greenhouse Roses and Chrysanthemums.

Thuricide is sold under the name Bacthane L69. It is effective in controlling leaf-eating caterpillars.

Toxaphene (chorinated camphene) is a powerful contact and stomach pesticide effective against Cyclamen mite.

Vapam (sodium methyl dithiocarbamate) is a synthetic product that is used as a soil treatment to control nematodes and certain fungi and bacteria as well as weeds.

V-C 13. This phosphorus compound is effective against nematodes and may be used near living plants without harming them. The material is diluted and sprayed or sprinkled on the soil and then soaked in with water.

Warfarin is a synthetic product used in baits to kill rats and other rodents. It prevents clotting of the blood and thus favors hemorrhages.

FUNGICIDES

As used here, the term fungicides covers materials used to control diseases caused by bacteria as well as fungi. The function of a fungicide is either to destroy a parasitic fungus or bacterium or prevent its attack, without injuring the host plant. But fungi, bacteria and hosts are all plants, and the choice of a chemical that will control the parasites without injurying the hosts narrows the range considerably.

Until comparatively recently, simple fungicides based on copper, sulphur and mercury were those chiefly used. These are still of great importance but they are now supplemented by many newer forms of the same materials and also by other newer fungicides, many of synthetic origin. Before using any fungicide, read the label carefully and follow accurately the directions given.

The need for effective application of fungicides is quite as important as for insecticides. See Insecticides and Miticides, above. The following are the fungicides most widely used:

Acti-dione (cycloheximide). An antibiotic used to control mildew and other plant diseases.

Ammoniacal copper carbonate is sometimes used as a substitute for Bordeaux mixture. It has the advantage of not leaving a visible deposit on the foliage. Ammoniacal copper carbonate may be prepared by mixing 1 level teaspoon of copper carbonate with 2 teaspoons of household ammonia and adding 1 gallon of water.

Anti-damp. See oxyquinoline benzoate.

Arasan (tetramethyl-thiruam disulphide), or thiram, is sold as a seed disinfectant for the control of seed-borne diseases and damping-off disease. The same chemical is sold as Tersan for treating bulbs and tubers.

Bichloride of mercury (mercuric chloride, corrosive sublimate), a very poisonous chemical, is used to disinfect any seeds, corms, rhizomes, etc., which are or may be infected with certain diseases; to disinfect soil infected with crown rot disease; and as a fungicide on lawns (see Calomel). It is commonly used at a 1 to 1000 dilution which is obtained by dissolving it at the rate of one 7-grain tablet to 1 pint of water. Because of its corrosive action on metals, solutions of bichloride of mercury always should be prepared in a vessel made of glass or enamel. Note that this chemical is quite distinct from mercurous chloride (calomel), described below.

Bordeaux mixture is used to control many fungus diseases. It is available commercially in paste and powder forms, but home-made solutions are entirely satisfactory. To make: prepare two stock solutions, one of copper sulphate dissolved at the rate of 1 lb. per gallon of water in a wooden or enameled vessel, and the other of 1 lb. hydrated lime per gallon of water. To make up the mixture to a required strength, strain the lime solution through cheesecloth and add it to water, in the proportions described below, stir well and then add the copper sulphate solution, stirring thoroughly.

The standard solution for use as a general fungicide is that known as the 8-8-100 or 4-4-50 dilution. This consists of 1 part lime solution, 1 part copper sulphate solution, 12½ parts water. Use Bordeaux mixture within 24 hours after it has been prepared.

For many plants Bordeaux mixture of 4-4-100 dilution is effective. To prepare this, 1 part lime solution, 1 part copper sulphate solution and 25 parts of water are used.

For special purposes Bordeaux mixtures containing greater or lesser proportions of the lime solution than in the standard formulas given above, are used. Bordeaux mixture should not be mixed with benzene hexachloride, chlordane, dinitro compounds, dithiocarbamates, lime-sulphur and organic mercury fungicides.

Cadmium fungicides are those based on chemicals containing cadmium. See Puraturf 177 and Crag Turf Fungicide 531.

Calomel (mercurous chloride). This is chiefly used to control club root disease, certain diseases of Grass turf, and also for treating corms of Gladioli and the seeds of Celery. When used on Grass, two parts of calomel and one part of bichloride of mercury are mixed together and applied at the rate of 1½-3 oz. per 1,000 square feet. Five oz. of calomel in 1 gallon of water is correct for treating Gladioli corms, 1 oz. of calomel in 1 gallon of water for celery seed.

Captan (N-trichloromethylthio tetrahydrophthalimide) is an organic fungicide that is effective against many diseases, and is safe to use on fruits and vegetables. It is sold as Orthocide 406.

Carbon bisulphide is carbon disulphide.

Carbon disulphide (carbon bisulphide) is a highly inflammable, poisonous liquid which gives off a deadly inflammable vapor, heavier than air. It is used as a soil fumigant. For this purpose, holes 18 in. apart are punched into the soil and 1⅗ liquid oz. of carbon disulphide are injected into each. As this chemical is harmful to living plants, it should be used only on soil that is cleared of crop plants and ornamentals.

Chloropicrin (tear gas) is sold under the name of Larvacide and is used as a soil fumigant. It is injected into the soil with a special applicator to a depth of 6 in. and at the rate of about ½ teaspoon per injection, the injections being spaced 10 in. apart. Best results are had when the temperature is high, the temperature of the soil itself being over 60 degrees, and when the soil is moist. Immediately following treatment the soil should be smoothed and soaked to a depth 1-2 in. with water.

Copper-lime dust is a mixture of 80 per cent hydrated lime and 20 per cent monohydrated copper sulphate. It is used as a substitute for Bordeaux mixture. It should be applied when the foliage is moist.

Copper oxide is sold as Cuprocide, which see.

Copper sulphate. See Sulphate of copper.

Corrosive sublimate. See Bichloride of mercury.

Crag Turf Fungicide 531 (calcium-zinc-copper-cadmium-chromate) is a cadmium-containing fungicide effective against dollar spot and copper spot of turf Grasses.

Cuprocide (copper oxide) is used as a seed disinfectant and as a spray to check damping-off of seedlings after they show above ground.

Dithane D-14 (disodium ethylene-bisdithiocarbamate) is a liquid fungicide used in the control of Potato and Tomato late blight, botrytis disease and certain leaf spots. This fungicide is also known as nabam.

Dithane Z-78 (zinc ethylene bisdithiocarbamate) may be used as a 6-8 per cent dust or mixed with water at the rate of 1¼ to 2 lb. to 100 gallons. It is useful for controlling Azalea petal blight, black spot disease of Roses and downy mildews. This fungicide is also known as zineb.

Cyprex. See Dodene.

Dodene (Cyprex) is a fungicide used for controlling Apple scab, Cherry leaf spot and other foliage infections.

Ferbam (ferric dimethyl dithiocarbamate) is sold as Fermate, Ferradow and Karbam Black. It is very effective against black spot of Roses, Grape black rot and many other fungus diseases. It is used as a spray at the rate of 2½-3 oz. to 10 gallons of water and as a 7-10 per cent dust. Unlike sulphur, it is safe to use in hot weather. It should not be mixed with lime-sulphur, lime, fixed copper fungicides or Bordeaux mixture.

Fermate is ferbam. See above.

Ferradow is ferbam. See above.

Fixed Copper Compounds. These include chemicals offered as a variety of sprays and dusts containing copper that are often easier to use, are safer on some plants than Bordeaux mixture and leave less visible residues. They are used to control blights, leaf spots and mildews. Among fixed copper compounds are the following: Basicop, Bordow, COCS, Compound A, Coposil, Cuprocide, Cupro K, and Tennessee Tribasic. These are good substitutes for Bordeaux mixture in many cases, and leave less foliage discoloration. They should not be mixed with benzine hexachloride dithiocarbamates, lime-sulphur or organic mercury fungicides.

Folpet. This is identical with Phaltan, which see.

Formaldehyde is used as a soil fumigant and is available commercially as formalin, which see.

Formalin is a solution of about 37 per cent by weight of formaldehyde gas in water with a little methanol added. It is often called 40 per cent formalin and is used to control certain fungus diseases, especially those, such as damping-off, which infect soil. To disinfect soil, mix 1 part of formalin with 49 parts of water, pulverize the soil to a depth of 10-12 in., apply the diluted formalin at the rate of ½-1 gallon to each square foot. Then cover the soil with a tarpaulin, tar paper or other material that will prevent the escape of the gas and leave for 7-10 days. Afterward fork over the soil. Do not use formalin close to living plants.

If soil is to be treated for sowing seeds indoors, fill it into flats or pots, drench it with the formalin solution, cover to prevent the escape of gas for 24 hours, then drench the soil with plain water and sow the seeds. While they are being treated, do not leave the flats or pots of soil in a greenhouse containing plants. Fumes from the Formalin will kill or seriously damage living plants.

This 1 to 49 solution of formalin may be used to soak sand and other media in propagating benches and to spray over the entire insides of greenhouses that are cleared of plants, as a disinfecting measure. A 5 per cent solution of formalin (1 part formalin to 19 parts water) is useful for disinfecting tools, which if untreated may transmit disease organisms.

Karathane (dinitro capryl phenyl crotonate) is the same as Mildex, which see, below.

Karbam black is ferbam, which see.

Kromad is a commercial fungicide especially useful for controlling turf diseases.

Larvacide is chloropicrin, which see.

Lime-sulphur as a fungicide may be used as a dormant spray on Roses and some fruit trees at a 1-9 dilution and at a 1-15 dilution for the control of Peach leaf curl. At summer strength, 1-50 dilution, it controls leaf blight of Boxwood, but should not be used when temperatures exceed 85 degrees. Because contact with this material discolors some white paints, care should be taken to avoid spraying on surfaces that are painted white. Lime-sulphur should not be mixed with most other sprays.

Maneb (manganese ethylene-bisdithiocarbamate) is used as a spray to control certain leaf blights and fruit rots. It is sold under the commercial name of Manzate.

Manzate (manganese ethylene-bisdithiocarbamate) is maneb, which see.

Mercuric chloride is bichloride of mercury, which see.

Mercurous chloride is calomel, which see. Note that this is quite distinct from mercuric chloride.

Mersolite 8 is phenyl mercuric acetate, which see.

Mildex (dinitro capryl phenyl crotonate) is a material that effectively controls powdery mildews. It should be used, preferably, in the early stages of infection but not when temperatures above 85 degrees prevail. It should not be mixed with any form of sulphur or applied to plants that have been recently treated with sulphur. Follow the manufacturers' directions carefully. This chemical is also sold as Karathane.

Nabam is Dithane D-14, which see.

Oxyquinoline benzoate, sold as Anti-damp, is used to control damping-off disease.

Panogen Turf Spray (Methylmercury dicyandiamide) a powerful fungicide effective against diseases of cereals and other grasses.

Parzate (zinc ethylene-bisdithiocarbamate) is used to control Potato and Tomato late blight and Snapdragon rust. This chemical, also called zineb, is sold as Dithane Z-78, which see.

Phaltan (Trichloromethylphthalimide). This new fungicide gives good control of black spot and powdery mildew diseases of Roses. It is compatible with most insecticides and is used at the rate of 1½ tablespoons of the 75 per cent wettable powder in one gallon of water. This fungicide is also called folpet.

Phenyl mercuric acetate, an organic mercury compound sold as Mersolite 8 and as P.M.A.S., is used to control certain diseases of lawn Grasses and basal rot of Narcissus.

Phygon (dichloronaphthoquinone) is used as a seed protectant, and as a spray for Azalea petal blight, brown rot of stone fruits, Apple scab, black spot of Roses and many other diseases. Phygon XL contains magnesium sulphate, which checks a tendency of this fungicide to harm slightly the plants to which it is applied.

P.M.A.S. is phenyl mercuric acetate, which see.

Puratized Agricultural Spray is an effective phenylmercury type fungicide.

Puraturf 177 (phenyl amino cadmium lactate) is a cadmium fungicide that is particularly effective in controlling dollar spot disease and copper spot disease of lawn Grass.

Semesan (hydroxymercurichlorophenol) is an organic mercury preparation that is used to disinfect seeds and to treat certain diseases of lawn Grasses.

Spergon (tetrachlorobenzoquinone) is used as a seed disinfectant and bulb and tuber treatment and for the treatment of downy mildew of Cabbage.

Streptomycin. This antibiotic is used to control the bacterial disease fire blight and also in the control of crown gall. It is the active ingredient in Agrimycin, Agristrep and Phytomycin.

Sulphate of copper (copper sulphate) is used in the preparation of Bordeaux mixture and for eliminating algae in ponds and other bodies of water. See Algae, and Scum in Ponds, in alphabetical sequence in this Encyclopedia.

Sulphur. This is one of the most effective fungicides. It is available in several forms. Dusting sulphur consists of very fine particles, finer than those of flowers of sulphur. Flotation sulphur and micronized sulphurs are even finer than dusting sulphur. Wettable sulphur is prepared by mixing with sulphur dust other ingredients so that it will mix readily with water. Sulphur is of special value in controlling black spot of Roses, powdery mildews, rusts and many other diseases. It is used as an ingredient of lime-sulphur, which see, above. Sulphur should not be mixed with oil sprays, dinitro compounds or parathion.

Terraclor (pentachloro nitrobenzene) used as a soil drench is effective against many fungi.

Terramycin is an antibiotic effective against fire blight and certain other bacterial diseases.

Tersan (tetramethyl-thiruam disulphide). See Arasan.

Thiram (tetramethyl-thiruam disulphide) is sold under the names of Arasan and Tersan, which see.

Zerlate (zinc dimethyl-dithiocarbamate) is ziram and is also sold as Karbam White and Opalate White. It is effective in controlling anthracnose and early blight of Tomatoes and for anthracnose and downy mildew on Cucumbers, Melons and related plants.

Zineb (zinc ethylene-bisdithiocarbamate) is sold as Parzate and Dithane Z-78, which see.

Ziram (zinc dimethyl-dithiocarbamate) is sold as Zerlate, Karbam White and Opalate White. See Zerlate.